Tom McKennan
San Francisco 72

HOME
ORCHID
GROWING

Fourteen Genera of Orchids: Gold Medal Exhibit. (Courtesy of Lager and Hurrell)

REBECCA TYSON NORTHEN

HOME ORCHID GROWING

SECOND EDITION

D. VAN NOSTRAND COMPANY, INC.

PRINCETON, NEW JERSEY
TORONTO
LONDON
MELBOURNE

VAN NOSTRAND REGIONAL OFFICES: *New York, Chicago, San Francisco*
D. VAN NOSTRAND COMPANY, LTD., *London*
D. VAN NOSTRAND COMPANY, (Canada), LTD., *Toronto*
D. VAN NOSTRAND AUSTRALIA PTY. LTD., *Melbourne*

02684630

THIS BOOK IS FONDLY DEDICATED TO

HANK, BETTY, PHIL, AND TOM

Preface

Where once there were few orchid growers, now there are thousands; where once orchids were owned only by those who could afford an elaborate greenhouse and a trained grower, now there are little backyard greenhouses everywhere. Busy people of all ages, and from all walks of life, are finding relaxation and joy in their orchids.

Once a person has tried his hand with a few plants, his enthusiasm grows to unlimited proportions. He finds himself seeking more and more information. Even after becoming a successful grower, he will wish to learn about additional kinds and will find new problems facing him now and again.

This book is designed not only to give the beginner a start but to advance him through the years into every phase of orchid growing. More than that, it gives him, along with methods, a background in the functions and needs of the plants so that he will be able both to recognize problems and to solve them on the basis of his knowledge. It is sometimes thought that amateurs cannot be given scientific information lest it scare them away from their

project. But in this age when people insist on knowing the "why" behind everything they come in contact with, certainly orchid growers are entitled to every fact that can be of help to them.

Much has happened in the orchid world since the first edition of this book was published. We now have better insecticides, better means of controlling diseases, simpler systems for combating summer heat, an array of easier-to-use materials, and a better understanding of the plants themselves. New horizons in breeding hybrids have been opened up. Orchid growing, which has long been a fascinating hobby, is now more exciting than ever.

In order to bring to the reader the newest information, the revised edition has been almost entirely rewritten. Every section has been greatly expanded and new chapters have been added. Many more species are described and information on their hybrids has been added. The 250 illustrations more than double the number in the first edition, and include new how-to-do-it pictures, additional pictures on methods, diagnostic pictures of orchid diseases, and illustrations of many more kinds of orchids.

It is my hope that the revised edition will encourage many to venture into this rewarding hobby, and that it will be of help to all orchid lovers, both beginner and experienced.

A book is seldom the product of one mind alone. Not only do the experiences of others go into the actual making of the book, but they are absorbed by the author in the subtle forming of the background that comes before the book. In addition, there are the many whose writings have given me help and information, those who have communicated information to me by letter and through visits, and those who have so kindly loaned me pictures for publication. To all of these, too numerous to list, I extend my grateful appreciation.

R. T. N.

Laramie, Wyoming
March, 1961

Table of Contents

Illustrations

1 | *Orchids as a Hobby*

ORCHIDS are the most fascinatingly varied and beautiful of all flowers. There are close to 20,000 species, and new ones are being discovered every year. So different are they one from another that at first glance it is hard to believe they are related. Some are large and showy, others are almost microscopic; some have delicate coloring, others such bold colors and markings that one automatically compares them to tropical birds and animals; some are serenely simple in form, others are incredibly modified and complicated. It is as if nature, having invented the basic orchid theme, has, like a musician, played every conceivable variation on that theme. In fact, nature's imagination has gone far beyond the capabilities of human imagination.

Once you have grown a plant or two, you will find yourself under their spell. Call it magic, or just plain curiosity, it is legendary among orchid growers that one cannot stop with but a few. They are deeply satisfying plants. Even though the eventual reward is their flowers, there is joy in watching the new growths and roots, in seeing a plant that produced only one growth last year give rise to two this year with the promise of double the number of flowers. With the exception of a few whose flowers wink open and close in a day or two, most of them give flowers that last for weeks or months. The familiar corsage orchid, the Cattleya, stays fresh and perfect for two to six weeks, and Phalaenopsis can last from two to five months.

Growers who embark on the orchid adventure today are fortunate. They will not experience the trials and tribulations with which orchid growing was fraught in its early years, or even the problems that faced those of us who began fifteen to twenty years ago. Plants are readily available and relatively inexpensive, growing methods are better understood, and materials and equipment are scaled to the needs of the small grower. There are still problems, as there are with all kinds of plants, but anyone who has grown flowers for a hobby will understand that plants are not machines, and that successful growing requires care in learning their needs, judgment in handling them, and a good deal of common sense. You may have read that orchids are as easy to grow as African violets. Well, they are, but you do not grow them like African violets. Nor do you grow an African violet like a cactus. Orchids come somewhere in between.

To understand the fortunate situation in

1

Fig. 1 *Cattleya gigas,* the largest and most showy of the Cattleya species, typical of the large ruffled corsage orchid.

which you will find yourself, you must know a little about the phenomenal history of orchids and orchid growing. In the late 1700's and early 1800's, many expeditions were sent to explore Central and South America. The myriad of plants intrigued the horticulturalists of Europe, and botanical collectors eagerly searched out new forms and kinds. Among these were a wealth of orchids. The Europeans knew their native orchids, but were overwhelmed by the tremendous quantity and variety of those being sent from the tropics. A kind of horticultural and scientific madness ensued, as more and more kinds were discovered. Much money went into the expeditions, and collectors suffered physical hardship, even risk to life, in order to gain the prized plants. Competition was keen as the searchers scoured the lowlands, the river canyons, the jungles, and the high mountain areas. The collectors were quite jealous of their finds, and often kept locations secret, even falsifying their reports to throw other collectors off the track. Thus it was that sometimes the habitat of a certain kind of orchid was lost for years until later collectors rediscovered it.

The botanists whose job it was to study and classify the orchids had a monumental task, for orchids from the western hemisphere did not fit into the known genera. Orchids are peculiar in that kinds that look very different may actually belong to the same genus, and kinds that

look alike are not always closely related. Botanists today are still trying to straighten out the relationships. And the problems increased as orchids were found in the Pacific Islands, Asia, Africa, and Australia.

The people who first tried to grow these plants were faced with many difficulties. They found that they could not just put these strange plants in pots in ordinary soil. Nor could they grow them from seed in the usual manner. Their problems were multiplied by the fact that orchids come from widely different climates and temperature conditions. Some were found by waterfalls and streams, constantly bathed in spray and mists while some came from places boldly exposed to the drying sun. Some lived at low elevations where the temperatures were hot, others near the tops of mountains where the temperatures were cool day and night. Some perched on tree branches, and some grew on the ground in meadows and glades. Considering what we now know about the plants, it is a wonder any of them survived these early attempts to cultivate them. However, those growers who were successful fell into the same error as the early collectors, and jealously guarded their secrets. The wealthy people who could afford the traditional conservatory greenhouse did not do their own growing but hired trained growers to care for their orchids. The cloak of secrecy was kept drawn about orchid growing long into the twentieth century, except that the barrier was

Fig. 2 Cattleya Bow Bells 'Serene,' a fine modern white hybrid.

broken now and then by an occasional amateur willing to learn by trial and error. It was so generally believed that only the initiated could grow orchids that most novices gave up after a failure or two and others were afraid to try when there seemed so little chance that they would succeed.

Commercial orchid growing expanded tremendously between 1900 and 1920, and by this time the number of patient amateurs was also increasing. The demand put a great pressure on the supplies of wild plants. Unless one could obtain divisions of plants already in cultivation, the usual way to obtain more was by importation. The reason behind this was that it was so difficult to grow orchids from seed. Although a seed pod contains close to a million seed, and although growers had learned to make hybrid crosses, attempts to germinate the seed often resulted in complete failure or in the production of but a handful of seedlings. Ruthless stripping of the native plants, especially of Cattleyas, threatened their extinction in certain areas, and brought about eventual embargoes on their exportation.

A revolution in orchid growing was brought about by a discovery made by Professor Lewis Knudson of Cornell University in 1922. He was experimenting with the germination of various kinds of seed, including that of orchids. He found that orchid seed germinated readily in a glass flask containing an agar jelly to which chemical nutrients and sugar had been added. This medium is much like that on which bacterial cultures are grown. Orchid seed is tiny, as fine as dust, and contains little or no food for the developing embryo. The availability of the nutrients and sugar enabled the embryo to develop and grow. Dr. Knudson's discovery meant that instead of fifteen or twenty seedlings, thousands could be grown from one pod. It opened up a whole new world of possibilities to orchid lovers. Not only were they freed from the costly and wasteful importation of wild plants, but they could explore the promising field of hybridization. Orchid collecting still goes on, but for the purpose of obtaining the odd and unusual kinds, the "collector's items"

as we call them, and of finding new species. Amateurs often go orchid hunting on vacation trips, for the pleasure of seeing orchids in the wild and of bringing home the plants they have found themselves. Whether you can go collecting or not, you should give yourself the pleasure of growing some of the species brought in fresh from the jungle.

As do all revolutions, the one in orchid seed germination brought about an explosive period, which led to some mistakes as well as some wonderful results. One of the mistakes, which we can view with humor in the light of history, was an abortive attempt by some commercial growers to keep this discovery a secret too, so that they alone could capitalize on the seedling business. The results of such scientific discoveries are however free to all; and it wasn't long before growers everywhere, both amateur and commercial, were trying their hand with Dr. Knudson's new method. As soon as the amateur entered the picture, particularly the special breed of American amateur who will try anything and persist until he finds a way to success, there could no longer be any secrecy.

Out of pure exuberance, growers excitedly crossed any orchid with any other orchid, to see what beautiful or bizarre results might be obtained. Growers sold millions of seedlings on the naive assumption that any cross would embody the best qualities of its parents. Then the truth began to emerge—that not all crosses were good, that often all of the seedlings, or a large proportion of them, were actually inferior. Occasionally good things would emerge from some crosses, and many of these older hybrids proved invaluable as the basis for further hybridization. Although much time and effort was spent in raising plants that eventually had to be discarded, both by the growers and by the amateurs who bought them, much was learned.

Thoughtful growers began to slow down and study the problems more cautiously. They learned, for instance, that one fine flower when crossed with another equally fine might give good offspring, but that when crossed with a

Fig. 3 These are all orchids. Center, Phalaenopsis Grace Palm. Clockwise from the left side, *Pholidota imbricata, Oncidium ampliatum, Cycnoches aureum* (male flower), *Lycaste aromatica,* and *Oncidium papillio.*

4

different flower might not. Some flowers seemed to have the ability to transmit their best qualities, while others did not. Perhaps most valuable of the information gained during the explosive years was that not only could related species be crossed quite freely, but even related genera. Hybridizers are still exploring the thrilling possibilities thus offered. We can't say that orchid breeding is fully worked out even now, but the chance of obtaining good plants from seedlings is far better now than it used to be. Now, in exploring the possibilities of new hybrids, growers make the untried crosses in full knowledge that they must wait for the results before judging their worth. And buyers who purchase them as seedlings also know that they must wait to see what comes.

As the amateur growers increased in number, the demand for small prefabricated, inexpensive greenhouses was met by the greenhouse manufacturers, so that greenhouses of all shapes and sizes can be had at reasonable prices. Many amateurs who are handy with tools have built their own. Dealers now have an array of equipment for the small grower, as well as pre-mixed fertilizers and insecticides, and special types of potting materials.

And what are these orchids that have provoked such love and excitement for generations? They are the most highly specialized plants in their line of evolution, topping the lilies and irises. They grow wild all over the world, except in regions of perpetual snow and in parched deserts. You probably know Calypso and the moccasin flowers, most showy of our native North American orchids. However, the tropics offer the greatest profusion, and it is the tropical orchids that are sought for greenhouse collections and which are the progenitors of our present hybrids.

Among the kinds you most frequently see, and which are widely grown for corsages, are Cattleyas, whose showy flowers with their spectacular lips come in white and shades of lavender, pink, rose, yellow, bronze, and green; Cymbidiums, of more modest style than Cattleyas, but with a wide range of colors; Phalaenopsis, whose round white or pink flowers are serenely beautiful; and Cypripedium, the waxy ladyslipper, which can be delicately beautiful or boldly reptilian. Others, to mention but a few that are also the delight of growers, are Dendrobiums, Epidendrums, Oncidiums, Odontoglossums, and Vandas, all of which give sprays of charming, brightly colored flowers in varied designs and sizes.

Many orchids live in the tropical rain forests, at elevations of 3000 to 6000 feet. Among these are Cattleyas, Epidendrums, Oncidiums, and Odontoglossums. In these jungles vegetation is dense and competition for light is almost vicious. Plants grow so thickly that the jungles are really forests upon forests. Giant ferns and other vegetation completely cover the ground. Plants that need more light than they can get on the ground contrive in some manner to reach up above the undergrowth. Vines grow up the tree trunks and form a tangled network among the branches. Some trees whose seedlings would die on the ground send their seed to germinate on branches of other trees, and when a seedling is developed it sends roots down into the ground and eventually smothers the tree that gave it support. Light- and air-loving orchids would have been pushed out of existence long ago if they had not evolved some way to live above the stifling mass of undergrowth.

The whole top of a rain forest is an aerial garden. Orchids and some other kinds of plants have learned to cling to the trees. Sometimes the burden of plants grows so heavy that a thick branch may break under its weight. Plants that live on other plants are called "epiphytes," "epi" meaning above or on, and "phyte" meaning plant. The epiphytes obtain no nourishment from the plants on which they grow—they are not parasites. They merely grow where they can find a foothold and a collection of humus material consisting of dead leaves and bugs. Outside of the rain forests epiphytic orchids may be found growing on thatched roofs (often placed there by the natives), stone walls, fallen logs, or rocky cliffs.

The epiphytes have cleverly adapted their

Fig. 4 Rich in orchids, Panama is the southern limit of Central American and the northern limit of South American species. Altitudes from sea level to 12,000 feet offer habitats for a wide variety of genera. Upper, an agile native orchid collector (Courtesy of H. A. Dunn). Lower, an Epidendrum growing on a tree. (Courtesy of H. A. Dunn).

structure to their needs as air dwellers. Since they are cut off from a continuous supply of water, they must depend on catching rain and dew, and for this purpose their roots have a spongy coating that soaks up water. To withstand the period between rains their stems and leaves are thickened, like the stem of a cactus,

branches. Those that cannot resist drying quite so well, or which do better when shaded somewhat more, may live lower down on the tree, and some little miniature orchids often find protection among the roots and stems of a larger plant.

In addition to orchids which are epiphytic,

Fig. 5 The variety to be found among orchids is half of their charm. Gathered together here from this varied collection are Cattleya, Odontoglossum, Vanda, and Miltonia (Courtesy of Lord and Burnham).

for the storage of water. When such a plant is grown in a flower pot, the potting medium must be extremely porous to allow the roots plenty of air.

Many kinds of orchids may live on the same tree. Those that can resist drying most efficiently and which also require a lot of light live in the tops of the trees and on exposed

there are other kinds that live on the ground and are not equipped to resist drying. They are found in more open forests, in meadows, or along the banks of streams where the break in vegetation allows light to reach them. These are called terrestrials. The ground in which they grow is always fluffy with humus such as rotting wood or thick layers of dead leaves, so that even these, when grown in pots, must have an open, well drained compost.

Most amateurs start a collection with a few Cattleya plants, and add other kinds as they go along. Each kind has its own blooming season, so that even with a small collection it is possible to have a spread of flowers throughout the year. We always suggest beginning with mature plants, either species or hybrids. In the first place it is hard to wait years for flowers, so we think it is fun to get something that will bloom soon. Also the mature plants are better able to withstand changed conditions and are more likely to survive what mistakes you may make in learning to care for them. In growing a

robust and more demanding of light. Seedlings are priced according to their age—a flask containing a hundred plants sells for from fifteen to twenty-five dollars, just a few cents a plant. Community pot size are from seventy-five cents to a dollar and a half; and larger seedlings from two dollars on up. Seedlings about ready to bloom are often just as expensive as mature plants, and because their quality cannot be known until they bloom, we would rather buy several younger ones for the same money. Not every plant in a cross will be of equal quality, and we feel we increase our chances of obtaining some good ones by buying several of a cross.

Fig. 6 Lovely cluster-type hybrids are being made with many small waxy flowers to the stem. Left, Cattleya

Celia X Cattleya December Snow. Right, *Cattleya loddigesii* 'Stanley' × *Cattleya intermedia alba.*

mature plant, you learn to know the habits of the kind, how it makes its growths and roots, how the flowers develop, etc. After you have served an apprenticeship in this way, you are ready to try some seedlings, perhaps a few very young ones, just out of the flask, or some two- or three-year-olds.

Tiny seedlings just out of the flask are delicate, and even though they are about a year old, they are so small that they are put twenty-five to thirty in a community pot or small flat. Their growth for the next year is slow, still somewhat of a formative state, and some do not survive. They need to be shaded carefully and kept quite damp. During their third and fourth years they are moved from small single pots to increasingly larger ones, and become

The suspense of waiting for a new hybrid to bloom, or any plant new to your collection, is beyond description. Day by day you watch the buds grow larger, until one day you see that the tip of the bud is opening. Within a few hours the sepals and petals swing out and the lip starts to unfurl. You can almost see the flower parts move. It takes about twenty-four hours for the flower to open, but it is somewhat limp during this stage, and the colors are pale. As another twenty-four to forty-eight hours pass, the color intensifies, the flower becomes firm, its parts stretch open to their fullest, and finally its peak of perfection is reached. Here is one of nature's most artful creations, and it is yours to enjoy for days or weeks, and will repeat itself for years to come.

2 | *Basic Habits and Structure*

The charming array of shapes, sizes, and habits made by just a few different kinds of orchid plants adds to the fun of orchid growing, and keeps an amateur constantly adding new kinds to his collection. Also, it makes an orchid grower something of a marvel in the eyes of his friends.

■ GROWTH HABITS

There are two basic growth habits, or patterns of growth, among orchids. Essentially, one type makes a new growth (or lead) each year from the base of the preceding growth, and this new growth produces flowers, makes its own set of roots, and in turn gives rise to another new growth the following season. Such a plant consists of several stems arising from a creeping ground stem, or "rhizome." In the other type of growth pattern there is but one main upright stem that grows taller each year, adding new leaves to the top but not making any new growth from its base. It has no rhizome and forms no pseudobulb. Flowering stems and aerial roots come from between the leaves, following each other in succession up the stem year after year.

The names for these two growth habits are rather descriptive. The kind that makes new seasonal growths from a rhizome is called "sympodial" which freely translated means "feet together." The type that has but one main stem is called "monopodial," or "one-footed." There are far more sympodial than monopodial kinds, but each type contains some of our best loved orchids, so you will undoubtedly have both types in your collection.

When you first glance at a Cattleya plant you will be struck by how stiff and strong it is. The heavy, thickened stems and the thick, hard leaves may remind you of a cactus plant. Actually, there are some similarities, because both are built to withstand periods of dryness. The cactus has been reduced to a water-storing stem (its spines are its "leaves"), because it must subsist through long periods of drought. In the Cattleya and other orchids like it, the enlarged stem and thickened leaves are reservoirs for water and food. In addition, a heavy coating of wax protects the leaves. While in nature a Cattleya actually has to withstand only short periods of drying between rains or from one heavy night dew to the next; some other kinds live where there are definite seasons of dry weather. These orchids, including the Cattleya, have the capacity to go for weeks without water.

The thickened stems of sympodial orchids are called "pseudobulbs." Actually, the stem of the Cattleya is not as bulbous as is the stem of many other kinds in which it is truly spherical or pear shaped. The term pseudobulb is used to distinguish these fat stems from true bulbs because their structure is quite different. A true bulb, a lily for instance, is made up of scale-like leaves. An orchid pseudobulb is purely a stem, actually a jointed stem.

In the Cattleya the new growth, or "lead" as it is called, comes from a bud at the base of the growth made the preceding year. The bud swells, breaks through the dry covering scales, and elongates. It grows horizontally for an inch or so and then curves upward. The horizontal part becomes an extension of the rhizome or ground stem, and the upward growing part produces the new pseudobulb, leaves, and eventually the flowers. The new growth is covered with tight sheathing leaves that give it a criss-cross or braided look. When it is about three or four inches long the true leaf emerges from the tip of the growth. Some Cattleya species have a single leaf; others have two or three. As the growth continues the leaf expands, and within it you can see the "sheath," a thin green envelope that grows from the top of the pseudobulb and encloses the flower buds during the early part of their formation. It takes five or six months for the new growth to reach its full size, during which time it is soft and succulent. At the end of the growth period the pseudobulb becomes plump and the leaf also becomes thick and hard, a process called maturation or "hardening." Soon afterward the thin sheathing leaves dry to white tissue. Good light and proper care contribute to a good, hard plant and to flowers of good substance.

Flower buds in Cattleya are "initiated," that is, the flower parts are formed microscopically, at the tip of the pseudobulb; in some while the growth is developing, in others as the growth matures. But you may not be able to see the buds for some time. Some Cattleyas flower as soon as the growth is formed, in which case the bud expansion follows right along after the growth reaches its full size. Others wait for several months before the flower buds start to grow. At any rate, when the buds begin development, they appear as little dark shadows at the bottom of the sheath, enlarging slowly at first, and then growing more rapidly until they push out through the tip of the sheath. The growth from base to tip of the sheath takes about six weeks, and another three weeks or so are required before the buds reach full size and are ready to open. The species normally flower once a year, each in its own season, but many hybrids make new growths and flower two or three times a year.

After flowering, the cycle starts over again when this growth gives rise to a set of roots and new growth. Thus one growth follows another. A growth does not flower again (there are exceptions among some other kinds of orchids). The pseudobulbs and leaves remain green for a number of years, sometimes as long as six to eight years. On a plant that makes but one growth a year, you can tell the age of the oldest pseudobulb by counting back from the youngest growth. Eventually the older leaves die, and fall off, and finally the old pseudobulbs shrivel and die.

Each pseudobulb, with the portion of rhizome at its base, is essentially a plant in itself. Pseudobulbs divided singly from each other will give rise to new plants. But a plant started from a single pseudobulb is quite weak; its new growth is small, and it takes several years' growth to attain flowering size again. Therefore, divisions are usually made of clumps of pseudobulbs, at least three, preferably four. There is a bud at each joint of the rhizome, but not all of the buds become active and develop into new growths. This is one of nature's safety factors. When a plant is divided, the removal of the growing end stimulates the development of one or more dormant buds on the older part, so that division results in two active halves.

Sometimes two buds will develop simultaneously from the base of a single lead, giving rise to two new pseudobulbs from one. Each of these in turn will produce a new growth, so

many separate plants when divided. The habit of breaking extra leads is inherent in some plants, but is encouraged by good culture.

The roots of Cattleya and of all epiphytic

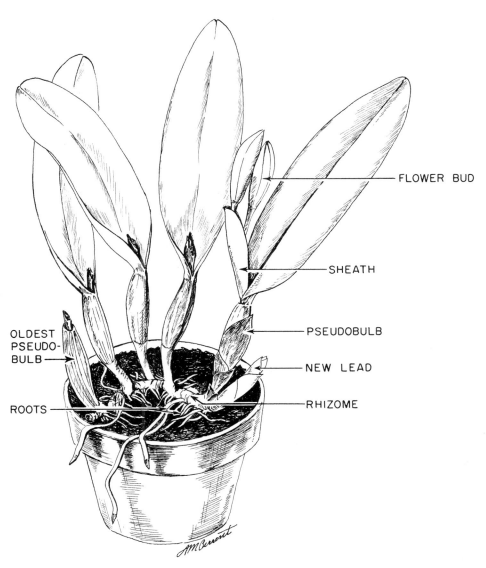

FLOWER BUD

SHEATH

PSEUDOBULB

OLDEST PSEUDO-BULB

NEW LEAD

RHIZOME

ROOTS

Fig. 7 Cattleya plant. Sympodial type of growth, with many stems arising from a creeping ground stem or rhizome. The new growth of the season, the "lead," comes from the base of the growth of the previous season.

that the plant becomes forked into two growing parts. Sometimes a bud farther back on an older pseudobulb will also start development, establishing still another line of growth. A plant with many leads is most desirable; it gives a greater number of flowers and yields

orchids are covered, except for the green tip, with a white, spongy coating called "velamen," which probably has several functions—to soak up water, to protect the inner root tissues, and to cling to surfaces to give the plant support. As the roots start to grow from the rhizome the green tip appears; then as the root elongates the velamen develops behind the green tip. The roots grow along in an exploratory manner, some penetrating the growing medium, others gliding across it to go down over the side of the pot. They cling tightly to any surface velop behind the tip. Older roots send out new branches each year.

Sympodial orchids that you will come to know, in addition to Cattleya, are: Epidendrum, whose plant forms run from those with fat round pseudobulbs to some with three-foot

Fig. 8 Vanda plant. Monopodial type of growth. A single upright stem grows taller year after year, adding new leaves at its tip. Aerial roots come from the stem between the leaves, as do the flower stems.

they meet, and those that do not meet with anything solid simply hang out in the air. This is their habit in nature, where they cling to the tree bark or hang down from the branch. The roots usually remain unbranched the first year, but if the growing tip is injured after the root has reached a fair length, branch roots will develop reed-like stems; Oncidium and Odontoglossum, whose pseudobulbs are compressed laterally almost to a knife edge; Dendrobium, another kind that has rather tall stems; and the Asian Cypripediums which do not form pseudobulbs at all. These last are terrestrial plants and do not withstand drying well.

The stately Vanda is a monopodial orchid. It has a single main stem and grows quite tall, adding several new leaves to its tip every year. The leaves grow close together, alternating on the right and left sides to give a beautifully symmetrical plant. The flower stems also alternate sides, coming from the axils of the leaves on the upper part of the plant. The huge aerial roots make their appearance farther down, splitting the base of the leaves as they force their way out from the stem. Each new root comes somewhat above the one made previously. The Vanda seems always to be making new leaves, but the roots occasionally undergo a period of dormancy. The tips cease growth and velamen covers the end. Then sometime later, the roots resume growth from the same tip. At the same time, branch roots grow along the length of the root.

The Vanda shown in the accompanying illustration is of the strap-leaf type, with rather broad, flat leaves. There are also kinds whose leaves are cylindrical, pencil shaped. You will come to know several other lovely monopodials. Phalaenopsis, which grows slowly, adds but one or two new, very large leaves a year. Its flower stems develop near the base of the plant, giving a tall, arching spray. Aerides grows quite like a Vanda and gives drooping sprays of the most delightful little flowers.

The monopodials listed above are all epiphytic, and can withstand some drying. Their leaves are thick, sometimes tough and leathery, and store some water. Perhaps also the main stem and the large roots are reservoirs.

■ FLOWER STRUCTURE

The orchid flower is built on a very simple pattern of three outer and three inner flower parts, albeit the often fanciful shapes these parts take make some flowers look quite complex. The outermost flower parts are the three sepals, which can be identified as they enclose the rest of the flower in the bud. Within these are three petals, one of which has been so modified that its appearance is entirely different from the other two and is therefore called by its own name, the "lip." The lip is not only shaped differently from the other petals, but it is embellished with its own markings of color and is often fantastically decorated with crests, horns, tails, or other protuberances. The lip is usually the most striking part of the flower, but there are some kinds in which the sepals or the petals are more elaborate.

The least conspicuous part of the flower is most diagnostic of an orchid, its hallmark. This is the column, a fleshy structure that sits in the center and consists of the fused reproductive parts. It adds charm to the flower, however, and if you take time to look at it you may decide that it is the most delightful part of all. Surely it is the most cleverly designed, both outwardly and from the point of view of function. It may be quite simply shaped, a white or pink or green cylinder, or it may look like a little figure, a doll, a bird, an insect, a face wearing goggles, or the neck of a swan. Often the column is decorated with wings, or a cap, or a fringed bonnet. At the tip of the column is

Fig. 9 Parts of the orchid flower, illustrated by a Cattleya.

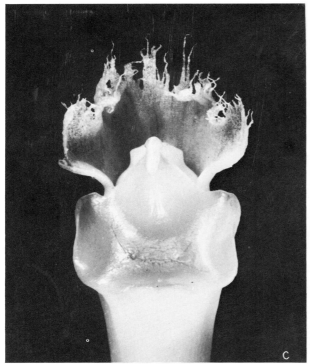

Fig. 10-A, A Cattleya column. At the very top is the anther cap, tipped up to show the fuzzy tails of the pollinia within. Below the anther, separated from it by the rostellum, is the stigma. B, a bee which has visited a Cattleya flower and bears on its back the four pollinia that became fastened to it as it crawled out from under the column. C, the column of *Trichopilia suavis*, decorated with a fringed bonnet. The "beak" of the column is the viscid disc. D, the column with the anther cap removed and the side sliced away to show the pollinia lying in the anther chamber. The pollinia are attached by a tail-like band, or "caudicle," to the viscid disc. The viscid disc will adhere to an insect touching it, and as the insect leaves it will bear the pollinia on its back.

the anther which bears the pollen, but instead of being dusty, the pollen grains are molded by wax into hard pellets. The pellets, called "pollinia," lie in a cavity covered by a hinged cap, where they look like a pair of eyes. Just below the anther, separated from it by a partition, is the female receptive organ, the "stigma," a shiny depression filled with extremely sticky fluid. The column arches out over the base of the lip.

By offering nectar to a visiting insect, the lip lures it into an ambush, for the column poised over the lip is equipped with a tricky device to fasten its pollen to the insect. The pollen-fastening mechanism is so designed that it applies the pollen to the insect as it *leaves*

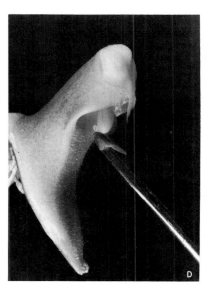
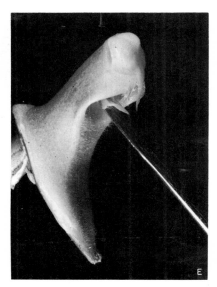
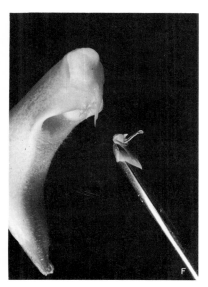

Fig. 11 Steps in pollination, as it would be performed by an insect.

A, a Vanda flower.

B, the column with flower parts removed. The swellings of the anther cap show the location of the pollinia within. Touch the under side of the "beak" and the viscid disc will stick to the needle.

C, the pollina attached to the needle.

D, put the needle bearing the pollinia into the stigmatic cavity.

E, touch the pollinia to the sticky fluid of the stigma.

F, pull out the needle. The pollinia will be left on the stigma, held so strongly by the sticky fluid that they are torn off of the caudicle.

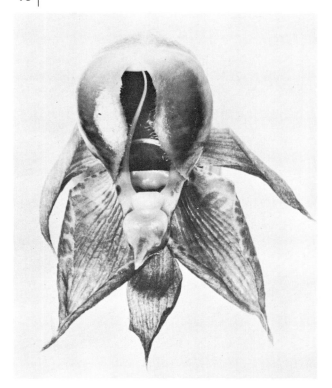

Fig. 12 A Catasetum flower. When a visiting insect touches the whip-shaped trigger within the hood-like lip, the pollinia fly up and become attached to it by means of the viscid disc.

that are accustomed to orchids think nothing of this, but the bees in this country are puzzled by the sudden burden they have acquired. Although we do not like to have bees in the greenhouse (because a pollinated flower quickly wilts and is therefore ruined), we have had a lot of fun watching an occasional bee that has happened to enter. The pollinia on its back are just like a load of suitcases, and they throw the bee off balance. Some are unable to fly, and spend their time helplessly crawling around over the plant. Others make attempts at wobbly flight. One may become well enough adjusted to visit another flower, whereupon, as it forces its way into the throat, the pollinia are caught in the viscid fluid of the stigma and are torn off the caudicles. The bee emerges from the second flower with the stubs of one

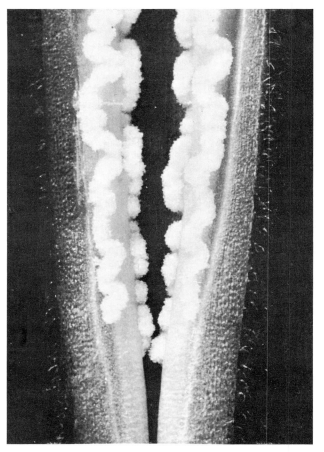

Fig. 13 Section through the ovary of a Cypripedium flower, showing the rows of ovules. When fertilized, each ovule becomes a seed.

the flower, causing it to carry the pollen off and deposit it on the next flower it visits, ensuring cross-pollination. Some kinds of orchids are pollinated by only a single kind of insect. It is fun to discover this mechanism in the column of any orchid you may have. In the Cattleya, the partition (rostellum) that separates the anther from the stigma bears a gland that secretes sticky fluid. The pollinia within the easily-tipped-up anther cap have fuzzy tails (caudicles) that lie just under its edge. In search of nectar an insect, usually a bee, has to crawl underneath the column, between it and the lip. As it backs out, it presses against the gland on the rostellum, ruptures it, and becomes smeared with "glue." At the same time, its movement tips up the anther cap and the fuzzy tails of the pollinia are caught in the glue. It flies away with one or two, sometimes all four, of the pollinia attached to its back.

I am sure that the South American bees

set of caudicles, bearing on top of them the new set of pollinia it has just acquired.

Some kinds of orchids have even more ingenious methods. Instead of having a gland on the rostellum, the pollinia are themselves attached to a little disc that is viscid on its under surface and hangs down like a beak from the end of the column. As an insect enters the flower it does not touch the sticky side of the disc. But as it backs out, or flies up from the lip, it hits the viscid surface, which instantly becomes stuck to the insect. So, as it flies off, it pulls the attached pollinia out of the anther and bears them off on its back to another flower. Try this yourself, with a needle or the tip of a pencil. Touch the under side of the beak and you can pull out the attached pair of pollinia, golden globules as shiny and beautifully shaped as jewels.

The Catasetum has a trigger within the hood-shaped lip which, when pressed by an insect, causes the pollinia to shoot out with some force. The viscid disc flies up and hits the insect, sticking to it instantly. If you imitate an insect, by touching the trigger with a pencil, you can actually feel the recoil as the pollinia shoot out and will have some difficulty scraping the fast-setting cement of the disc off the pencil.

When an orchid grower wishes to make a hybrid cross, he removes the pollinia from one flower and puts them on the stigma of another. He does not use the haphazard method of the insects, but carefully chooses which flowers to use as parents. Placing pollen on the stigma sets off a series of events leading to the fertilization of the eggs in the ovules contained in the ovary. The ovary is situated below the sepals, forming, for our utilitarian purposes, a "stem" to the flower. After pollination, the ovary swells, the ovules develop into seeds, and the ovary turns into a seed pod.

■ TEMPERATURE GROUPS

When the myriad climates to which orchids are native are put together and analyzed, it turns out that there are three basic temperature ranges into which most of the kinds can be fitted. Winter temperatures are kept somewhat cooler than summer temperatures, partly because we can control the winter temperatures whereas we have less control over the summer's, and partly because when artificial heat is used moderate temperatures give healthier plants and better flowers. The night temperature is critical; in fact, some kinds of orchids will not flower if the night temperature runs above a certain limit and others do poorly if it goes below a definite point. The three temperature groups that have been established are therefore based on *winter night* temperatures. Winter day temperatures are kept about ten degrees higher than those of the nights. Summer temperatures, particularly where the days become very hot, offer special problems that will be dealt with later on.

The three temperature groups are: "cool," with nights held between 50° and 55°; "intermediate," with nights of 55° to 60°; and "warm," with nights of 60° to 65°. A different group of plants is grown in each temperature range, except that if the temperature runs a little warmer or a little cooler in some spots in a greenhouse it may be possible to add plants from another temperature range. In choosing orchids to grow it is of utmost importance to learn first their temperature requirements and be sure that you can give each the range it needs. It is of no avail to put a "warm" orchid in a "cool" greenhouse, or vice versa.

The cool greenhouse (50° to 55°) is used widely throughout this country for many kinds of plants; in fact it is used for many of the florists' cut flower crops such as carnations, stock, snapdragons, and camellias. If you already grow some of these flowers, you can slip in a few cool orchids such as Cymbidiums and some Cypripediums. It is the most economical of the three ranges, since heating costs are lower. However, many orchids that demand cool conditions in the winter also prefer cool summers, so that in general the cool types are better grown in the cooler part of the United States. With special coolers and attention to keep environmental factors in balance, they may sometimes be grown in warmer climates.

The "intermediate" greenhouse (55° to 60°) accommodates by far the greatest number of kinds. It is often referred to as the "Cattleya house" because it is the range in which Cattleyas are usually grown. Along with the Cattleyas you can grow Epidendrum, Laelias, Oncidiums, Dendrobiums, Vandas, some species of Miltonia, Cypripedium, Odontoglossum, and a tremendous array of odd and unusual kinds called "botanical" orchids.

The "warm" greenhouse (60° to 65°) is used for kinds that do not do well with nights under 60°. These include Phalaenopsis, some Cypripediums, and others.

You may ask why, since the upper range of the intermediate and the lower range of the warm greenhouse meet at 60°, should there be a distinction between the two; why not grow everything at 60°? In running a greenhouse, it is almost impossible to keep the temperature at an exact point. There is always a fluctuation of a few degrees as the heat goes on or off. By keeping the air circulating we narrow the margin of fluctuation, but about five degrees of difference inevitably occurs. These five degrees can be critical for many kinds. If you run the temperature repeatedly below 60°, Phalaenopsis and some others will do nothing. If you run it repeatedly above 60°, you automatically eliminate many kinds that you otherwise could grow. While some people grow Cattleyas at 60° to 65°, problems often arise that are eliminated in the 55° to 60° range. In the intermediate range we feel that Cattleyas are stockier, flowering is more regular, and the flowers are of better substance and last longer. Since Cattleyas do so well at 55° to 60°, and since using this night temperature range allows you to grow so many other kinds, there is a real reason for adhering to it, and for separating it from the warmer 60° to 65° range.

Since Cattleyas are the most widely grown of all orchids and since most growers start with them, the conditions that suit Cattleyas and their method of culture have become a sort of base, or point of departure. For orchids that are to be treated exactly like Cattleyas (as to light and water in addition to temperature), it is customary to say "handle like Cattleyas," or "likes Cattleya conditions." Then, for those that vary a bit one way or another from the needs of Cattleya we say "Cattleya conditions except a bit more shade, or more frequent watering, etc." We shall therefore spend the longest time and give most space to Cattleya culture, and in this section you will find the basic rules for all orchid culture. When we take up other kinds, we will give their specific needs and tell you how to vary the basic rules for them.

3 | *Adult Cattleyas*

ADULT CATTLEYAS include plants just matured from the seedling stage and propagations made from older plants. The matured seedlings show a succession of leaf sizes from the small leaves up to the larger flowering lead. A propagation is a division of a plant. It may be made from the lead end of a plant—the youngest growth plus the two or three pseudobulbs just behind it, in which case it should flower on its next new growth—or it may consist of the older half of the plant. If these older pseudobulbs (or backbulbs as they are sometimes called) are plump and still have their leaves, the first new growth they make may flower. But if the pseudobulbs are shriveled and have lost their leaves, the first new growth may be quite small, and it may require another two years before a flowering size growth is produced. It is therefore preferable, in buying mature plants, to get those in flowering condition, unless you know that the backbulbs are from very good plants and that it would be worth waiting the several years for them to flower again. The plant should be vigorous and healthy. If it is a propagation it should show evidence, by cut flower stems on each pseudobulb, of having flowered regularly.

You can buy species or hybrids. There are two groups of species. One, the "labiata" group, has the wide frilled petals and lip with which most people are familiar, and its pseudobulbs bear a single leaf. The other, the "bi-foliate" group, has smaller, more waxy flowers, some with a spade-shaped or fiddle-shaped lip and a remarkable array of colors and markings. The species are usually quite inexpensive and dependable, and some offer exceptional interest to any collection. The hybrids are priced according to their quality. Those that come in the six-to-ten-dollar class (the price of most of the species) will be about average in quality. For your first plants it would be wise to buy in this price range. Later on, when you are sure of your growing ability, you will want to have some of superior quality, which you may buy as higher priced mature plants, or raise from seedlings that cost less. If you live near a professional orchid grower, you will benefit from picking out your plants in flower so that you know exactly what you are getting. However, this is possible for relatively few of us. Otherwise, send for catalogues of reputable dealers, and buy but a few plants at a time until you know with whom you like best to deal, and which growers furnish the best plants.

Cattleya flowers come in many sizes and a great range of colors. Orchid hybridizers for years were so intrigued by their ability to produce ever larger flowers that giant flowers became the vogue, and small ones, unless they had exceptional coloring or some other unusual quality, were rather looked down upon. Truly, some of the nine- and ten-inch Cattleyas are spectacular, and if their color and shape are good, they are very handsome. But many people had the feeling that something of grace and daintiness was lost in the giant size, and that the smaller flowers should be loved for their special appeal. Now the small flower has come into its own. More frequent crosses are being made using the delightful smaller species, which offer their waxy substance and unusual coloring along with more flowers to the stem. In between these and the giants come the six- and seven-inch flowers, the size liked best by the florists, which is just right for a glamorous corsage. It is large enough to make a marvelous showing either on the plant or when worn, and small enough to be in good taste on an evening gown or a suit.

In judging the quality of Cattleya flowers, regardless of the size, there are certain characteristics to look for. A strict point system is used in judging flowers for awards. The color must be pure and fresh. It may be dark or light, but never dull or muddy, and the color in the lip should be in harmony with, or make a pleasing contrast to, the rest of the flower. The flower should have an aristocratic, graceful bearing. Its parts should be generous according to its kind (in some of the species the parts are normally slender). In the large-flowered hybrids, we especially look for broad, straight sepals and broad, flat or gently curving petals that do not fold back on themselves, as well as a nicely ruffled lip that opens fully to show the markings in the throat. Good substance is important. The more turgid, waxy flowers are better looking, do not become floppy, and last longer. Fragrance is an added attraction. Most Cattleyas have a delightful, delicate perfume,

and in some the fragrance is so aromatic that it fills the house.

The plants may be shipped to you out of their pots. Many growers like to save shipping weight and packing difficulties by removing the plant from the pot and substituting a polyethlyene bag. You should have some pots of various sizes on hand in which to put these when they arrive. Plants are also shipped "bare root." Since most of the potting material has been shaken off these, you will have to furnish them with fresh potting material. If you prefer to receive them in their pots, inform the dealer. Perhaps your first plants should arrive this way, to give you a chance to get used to them before you tackle a repotting job.

Up until a few years ago, practically all orchids in this country were grown in osmunda fiber, the roots of the osmunda fern. Its fibers are tough and springy so that they give the roots plenty of air, yet in the process of decay it furnishes all the nutrients the plants really need. It is somewhat difficult to learn to use it properly, and potting with it is a slow process requiring a strong arm. Also, it has become scarce and rather expensive with increased demand. A number of other potting materials have been tried, and it has been proved that orchids will accept a variety of materials if they have the basic qualities of giving the plants a firm foothold, of not breaking down rapidly, and of furnishing good drainage and aeration. Out of the experiments to find new materials came the discovery that the chopped bark of various trees worked beautifully. Chopped bark has the advantage of being easier to use and less expensive than osmunda fiber. The choice of a potting material is now a matter of personal liking. Some growers still prefer osmunda fiber, others prefer bark. Some have switched from one to the other and back again, and some like one for certain kinds of plants and the other for different kinds. The plants you buy may come to you in one or the other. Growers in Hawaii introduced "hapuu," tree fern fiber which is similar to, but tougher than, osmunda fiber, and this is now quite widely used. Slabs of tree fern are useful for growing some of the "botanical" orchids. In Australia tan bark is much used, and in Europe polypodium and sphagnum moss are popular. Terrestrial orchids may come in a variety of mixed composts. In the section on potting, Chapter 5, we will tell you how to handle the various materials and how to transfer plants from one to another.

■ TEMPERATURE, HUMIDITY, AND LIGHT

Plants do not keep accounts, but if balance sheets were published for them, they would be quite similar to those you receive from the bank each month. If you spend more than you earn, you end up in debt. If you earn more than you spend, you have money left over for savings, and philosophically savings mean better living. The earning of plants is the food they make, and their spending is the food they use for energy. Their savings go into growth and flower production, with a reserve kept over toward launching the next season's growth.

During the day a plant carries on three activities, the making of food (sugar) for which light is necessary, the use of food (respiration, similar to our own use of food for energy), and growth. At night no food is made, but respiration and growth continue, drawing on the food made during the day.

Temperature regulates the rate of the plant's activities. Low temperature slows down the processes; rising temperature speeds them up, although not all at the same rate and not indefinitely. The reason behind what we call an optimal temperature range is that within this range the plant can carry on all of its life processes in a normal way, with no one activity out of balance with the rest.

The ideal night temperature chosen for a particular kind of orchid is the temperature at which growth and respiration are in good balance so that the plant makes good growth without using too much of its food reserve. For Cattleyas this is between 55° and 60°. At lower temperatures growth is slowed down; at higher temperatures there is a tendency for respiration to exceed growth and for the plants to become depleted.

With abundant light, food making increases as the temperature rises up to about 85°. The day temperature should ideally be about ten degrees higher than it is at night. In the winter and in cool weather, this is easy to maintain. Problems come with hot weather. The plant's activities remain in pretty good balance up to about 85°, but over this the equilibrium is upset. With higher temperatures there comes the danger of burning and finally death. Plants can tolerate 95° for a few hours, and 100° for shorter intervals, but when the temperature rises above this the situation rapidly becomes critical, for the lethal point is not far off.

There are ways to modify the greenhouse conditions with shading, ventilation, humidity, and air circulation, so that we can pretty well control the environment. We don't wait for extremes to arrive, we anticipate them, and we use the various means in coordination with each other throughout the year so as to give the plants a good balance of the various factors; a balance between day and night temperatures, between the amount of light and the day temperature, and between humidity and all the other factors.

Temperature. Winter for most of us means cold weather, but for some it is merely a cool season. In some regions winter brings dull skies, long periods when the sun shines but rarely; in others, winter is a season of bright sun. For these reasons no one set of rules can be made as to just what to do in what month. The basis must therefore be the needs of the plants themselves, and each grower must adjust his own conditions accordingly.

In the winter we can maintain what we consider the ideal temperature conditions for Cattleyas, 55° to 60° at night, and days of 65° to 72° degrees. On a dark day, or during a spell of dull weather, it is good to let the days hover between 65° and 68°. With the lessened amount of light the plants cannot make as much food as they can when the sun is shining, and a higher day temperature would cause them to use the food as fast as it is made. On a sunny day, however, let the temperature run up to 70° or 72°. We welcome the sun. In itself it helps to warm the greenhouse with a heat more natural than that produced artificially, and the good light allows the plants to make a generous amount of food. On these nice bright days, open the ventilators a crack to give the plants fresh air. We try always to maintain a buoyant atmosphere for orchids. The winter greenhouse tends to become a bit dank, and airing it out whenever you can gives the plants a lift and helps prevent disease. Always open the ventilators away from the direction of the wind.

Day and night, winter and summer, the air within the greenhouse should be kept in circulation. Circulation of the air keeps the temperature more uniform, preventing layering of hot and cold air or pockets of dead air. The air should be moved from one end to the other under the benches and returned up and over the plants. In a small greenhouse a single fan may do the job, blowing the under-bench air against the opposite end of the greenhouse, where it rises against the wall and naturally flows back toward the end where the fan is located. In a larger greenhouse it may help to have a second fan placed at the opposite end, pointing vertically to keep the air in circular motion. Nearly all makes of natural gas heaters come equipped with a fan. Often the wiring directions that come with the heater cause the fan to run only when the heat is on. The wiring should be changed to make the fan run constantly. If you have no fan in connection with the heating system, which would be the case with hot water heat, one can be installed separately. Not only is moving air a means of keeping a uniform temperature, but it is an important aid in disease prevention. Moving air does not hurt the plants as long as it is of the proper temperature and moisture content. Hot dry air blowing on them is harmful, as is a current of cold air.

More on heating systems will be given in Chapter 22, but we should say here that *artificial gas should never be used within a green-*

house, nor should gas that has any amount of artificial gas mixed with it, for it is fatal to orchids. Natural gas is safe to use, but even with this the heaters should be vented to carry out all fumes of combustion. These fumes contain constituents that are harmful to Cattleyas, causing what is known as "sepal wilt." (See Chapter 21.) Buds just ready to open are aged prematurely so that the buds may be blasted before opening or, if they open, the sepals are thin and tissue-like and the flower is ruined. Strong fumes can even injure the plants, aging them prematurely, so that they lose their older leaves before they normally should.

During an unusual cold spell it may not be possible to keep the greenhouse temperature quite up to normal. We experience this in Wyoming if the wind is blowing on a night when the outdoor temperature goes to minus 20°. A few nights of 50° or 45° will not harm Cattleyas, although it may retard their flowering somewhat. Some kinds that grow with Cattleyas may possibly drop their buds. Plants should be kept from contact with the cold glass, else they may have some leaves frozen. In England during World War II, fuel rationing forced growers to run their greenhouses at low temperatures, and although growth and flowering were poor, they were nevertheless able to keep their valuable plants. Heat may be conserved by tacking up sheets of polyethylene film on the inside of the greenhouse. Growers have reported that this works very well.

Problems with the heating system, power failure, etc. can bring on emergency conditions. We have no data on the length of time Cattleyas can stand freezing or near-freezing temperatures. We have had a number of near fatal experiences ourselves, and have learned of others which have been worse. It is not as bad for the temperature to dip to freezing for half an hour and then rise again as it is for the temperature to stay at freezing for a longer period. During a short interval perhaps only some leaf tips and flowers may be frozen, but during a longer interval freezing may progress to the whole plant. We will give the treatment and handling of frozen plants in the section on ailments. Two aids against such emergencies are the installation of a temperature alarm, which rings a bell in the house to warn you of a dangerous drop (or rise) in temperature, and having on hand some form of auxiliary heat.

Spring brings such changeable weather that you have to watch the greenhouse rather carefully. The sun is traveling more nearly overhead, and the days are becoming warmer. On a bright, warm day the greenhouse can heat up in a short time. For a comparable example, consider how hot a closed car becomes when it is parked in the sun. Shading is an important means of controlling day temperature. We shall go further into shading under "light," but the relation between light and temperature and humidity and temperature make it difficult to separate these three factors. As the days brighten, you can control midday heat for a while by opening the ventilators. The afternoon temperature drops quickly so be sure to close them by mid-afternoon. Automatic ventilator controls can be bought and might be necessary for those who have to be gone from home all day. Soon, however, you must apply a thin coat of shading to the glass to prevent the burning of the plants. This must be done by February in some areas. As spring advances a heavier coat will be needed. The aim is to keep the day temperatures between 70° and 80°, yet allow the plants enough light to get their season's growth off to a good start.

Summer brings the real problems in temperature control. We do not worry about summer nights. They will usually run somewhat higher than the winter nights, in fact, we simply have to accept what the outdoor night temperature brings. Cattleyas probably prefer a summer night temperature not exceeding 65°, but nights may go to 70° sometimes. There is always a contrast between day and night temperatures in the summer. The cooler night air brings the plants relief from the hot days. During hot weather we like to keep the ventilators open both day and night. It takes some time for the greenhouse to cool off—everything is

warm, the pots, the benches, etc. Open ventilators during the night bring about cooling earlier than would be the case if the greenhouse were closed up, and keep it cool during the early morning.

When you can keep the summer day temperatures under 85° you are doing the plants a favor. As the leaves absorb light they become warmer than the surrounding air. If the greenhouse air goes to 100°, the leaves are even hotter and a further rise in air temperature will take them dangerously close to the burning point. Thick-leaved Cattleyas and other kinds are more susceptible to burning than are some of the thinner-leaved kinds. Keep the fans running to circulate the cooler ground air, and step up the humidity to keep a current of moist air moving through and over the plants. Additional shading will be necessary, but try not to cut the light below the needs of the plants, about which more in a moment. Keep the ventilators open a few inches to let the heated air move out.

Evaporation of water into the air cools the

Fig. 14 An evaporative cooling unit. Aspen pads built into three sides are kept wet by means of a circulating pump and distributing tubes. A blower draws outside air in through the wet pads and forces it into the greenhouse. (Courtesy of International Metal Products Div., McGraw-Edison Company).

air and the surfaces from which it is being evaporated. Air blown through a mist of water or a wet pad becomes cooled in the process. An evaporative system of one sort or another is a great help in cooling a greenhouse as well as in supplying humidity. A unit cooler such as those built for home use is satisfactory for a small greenhouse. Aspen pads are incorporated in the walls of the unit and are kept wet by means of a circulating pump. Air is drawn through the wet pads by a blower which blows the damp cool air into the greenhouse. For most efficient cooling, the unit should be placed so that it draws air from outdoors. Another cooling arrangement is a "pad and fan," which can be operated in two ways. The pad, with a circulating water system (see Chapter 22 for details), is set in the wall of the greenhouse at one end, and a fan is installed to draw air through it. The fan may be an exhaust fan placed in the wall at the opposite end of the greenhouse, which pulls air through the pad and through the greenhouse and exhausts it at the other end. Or the fan may be placed directly in front of the pad so that it pulls air through the pad and pushes it through the greenhouse. A ventilator must be open at the opposite end to allow air to move out. Such evaporative cooling systems are capable of lowering greenhouse temperatures by as much as fifteen degrees.

Humidity. The older growers used to say that they could gauge humidity with "their noses." We like to be more specific, but you can sense when the atmosphere is right, or nearly so. When you walk into a greenhouse and it smells dry to you, when you can "smell the heat" as it were, chances are that the walks and ground are dry, and that the dry air will soon dessicate the plants if they are not quickly given some moisture. Or, if the air is stagnant and dense with moisture, oppressive to the point where you feel as if you must open the door for some relief, trouble of another kind is in store. But if, when you enter a greenhouse, you feel that you have opened the door on a spring morning, if the air is light and invigo-

rating, moving as if in a gentle breeze, and you smell the gentle, damp, earthy fragrance of the plants, then you know that the atmosphere is right for orchids.

Warm air can hold much more water vapor than cool air, and relative humidity, expressed as a percentage, indicates the amount of water actually held by the air compared to the amount it could hold at a given temperature. For instance, at noon of a day when the temperature is 80°, the air may actually be holding only 35% of the water it could hold, so the relative humidity is expressed as 35%. But in the cooler evening, if the temperature drops to 50°, without any change in the actual amount of water the air is now saturated, and the relative humidity becomes 100%. It is the temperature that determines whether the air can hold more or less water. Warm air therefore tends to attract water, to draw it from surfaces and from plants. You have seen garden plants wilt on a hot day when the warm air is drawing water from them faster than they can replace it by root action. And you have seen these same plants become turgid again in the evening when the cooler air allows them to replace the lost water.

Plants lose water through pores, or stomata, and it is through the stomata, also, that they take in carbon dioxide with which to make sugar. They lose water to the air faster when the relative humidity is low than when it is high. The thick-leaved Cattleyas do not wilt; but if the air is too dry for them over a period of time, they cannot replace it fast enough through the roots, and the plants become emaciated, the leaves become thinner, and the pseudobulbs shrivel. Flower stems may be weak, unable to hold the flowers up properly, and the flowers themselves may be of poor substance.

In the winter, with moderate greenhouse temperatures, a relative humidity of 40 to 60% creates a good moisture balance for the plants. It is helpful to have a humidity gauge in the greenhouse so that you can actually know what the relative humidity is at all times. If your climate is mild and naturally humid and artificial heat is needed only occasionally at night, you may not have to add much moisture to the greenhouse air. But in a dry climate or one where artificial heat is needed throughout the winter, the greenhouse air becomes very dry, and humidity must be added.

You can add moisture to the air by "damping down," wetting the walks and under-bench areas with the hose. With a fan in operation

front of the heater, so that the air blown by the fan picks up the moisture. We also damp down the floor on bright days when the sprayer does not furnish quite enough moisture. The number of mist sprayers could be increased, so that there are several at intervals under the benches.

Although the natural state of affairs is for the relative humidity to rise at night as the

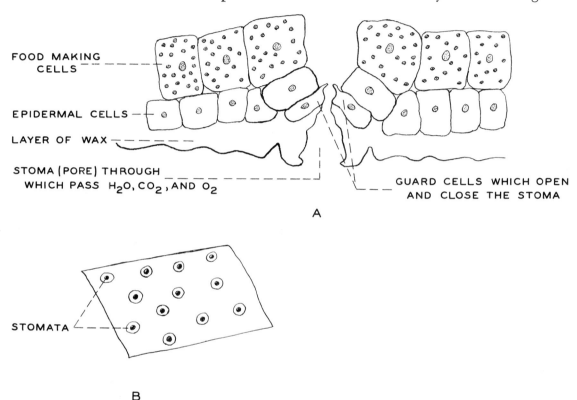

FOOD MAKING CELLS

EPIDERMAL CELLS

LAYER OF WAX

STOMA (PORE) THROUGH WHICH PASS H_2O, CO_2, AND O_2

GUARD CELLS WHICH OPEN AND CLOSE THE STOMA

A

STOMATA

B

Fig. 15 A, a section of a Cattleya leaf, showing the structure of a single stoma and the cells surrounding it. Note particularly the guard cells that regulate the opening and closing of the stoma, and the heavy layer of wax. B, a microscopic view of the under surface of a leaf showing how the stomata appear externally.

the air picks up and circulates the moisture. Damping down is the old, standard method; but it requires that someone be home to do it. Those who are gone from home all day or who object to getting their shoes wet may prefer to add a humidifier of some sort. Various types with various capacities are manufactured. These may be controlled by an electric humidistat, which turns the humidifier on or off according to the setting. A simple system, which we use, is a mist sprayer installed in

temperature drops, in the winter the air may become quite dry when the heat is running. A factor that contributes to this is condensation (or freezing) of moisture on the cold glass, taking it out of the air. When we were new at running a greenhouse, we did not realize that this was happening, and only learned it when plants began to show some dehydration. We then made it a practice to damp down the floor in the evening, and now let the sprayer in front of the heater run during

Fig. 16 Mist sprayer placed in front of heater so that blower moves moist air through the greenhouse. The heater is a gas-fired, vented, forced air type.

the night as well as in the daytime. One exception to this is that after we have watered the plants, and the ground and benches are thoroughly wetted, we turn off the sprayer until the next day, or until needed again.

Spraying the plants with a fine mist, often called "syringing," is a practice that was once used rather freely, but is now used with caution, especially in the winter. The need for it has been reduced by the more general use of humidifiers. When a current of sufficiently moist air is kept moving through the greenhouse, it is ordinarily not necessary to mist the plants directly. There are circumstances when it is helpful, such as when it is necessary to protect plants from drying, and in warm seasons to help cool them when the sun is hot. The plants can absorb some water through their leaves, and water on the foliage also creates a saturated atmosphere for the plant, preventing excessive evaporation from the plant tissues. Syringing is therefore advised for newly potted plants until their root systems are again functioning, for hanging plants that dry out faster than benched ones, for seedlings, and for kinds that are more moisture demanding than Cattleyas. In the winter, on a bright day, if the air is dry, a light syringing can be given to all the plants, Cattleyas included, but this should never be done on a dull day, or when it is chilly in the greenhouse, or when the humidity is already high enough. Syringing should always be an extremely fine mist, applied with just a quick swish of the sprayer over the plants. (See Figure 18.) Heavy syringing tends to wet the potting medium and may actually serve to keep it too wet.

Any syringing, or watering, should be done early enough in the day to allow the plants to dry off before night. This does not mean that the air or the potting medium should become dry, but simply that no water should be left standing on the plant parts. Fungal and bacterial spores can germinate only on wet surfaces. Water standing on the plants gives the spores a chance to germinate and infect the plants. Dry foliage and rhizomes discourage infection. Often a spreading infection in a greenhouse has been traceable to too frequent syringing. Crowding plants too close together on the bench also contributes to over-damp conditions. The air does not move as freely between the pots or through the plants as it does when they are well spaced. This is particularly important to watch in damp climates and where the winters are dull.

Signs of too much humidity or of stagnant, over-damp conditions are the appearance of brown watery spots on the leaves, little brown spots on the flowers, and blackened sheaths. A local spot of infection can be quickly treated, but if spotting becomes general throughout the greenhouse, the first thing to do is lower the humidity, dry off the plants, and increase the circulation of air. Sometimes water that has condensed on the glass drips onto the plants below, keeping the foliage or the potting medium too wet. If you can't cure the drip, move the plants. Diseases and their treatment will be taken up in a later chapter. We mentioned earlier that a relative humidity of forty to sixty per cent is good in the winter. We rather like a fluctuating humidity; 60% at night and for most of the day, but dropping to 40% sometime during the day. We feel that a brief period of lowered humidity—a short "drying off" time each day—contributes to the general health of the plants.

In spring and summer as the temperatures rise, it is necessary to open the ventilators more often to allow the heated air to move out. This, of course, lets some of the moisture escape. We have found that wide open ventilators do not reduce the temperature appreciably more than having them open only a few inches, and that the saving in humidity is worth the difference. If you have had the ventilators open all night you will not have to worry about opening them early in the morning, but if they have been closed, be sure to get out to open them before the greenhouse heats up.

Although it is a challenge to do so, the humidity should be stepped up in hot weather, so that it reaches 70% some of the time if possible. With rising and falling temperatures and the need to have the ventialtors open the humidity will fluctuate, but this is a healthy condition provided that the plants do not lose too much water during the heat of the day. Be sure that the current of air moving over the plants is moist enough to help them conserve water. Dry air in motion will only serve to hasten water loss. A vertical fan, in addition to the one running horizontally, is helpful in keeping the damp air moving upward. If your humidifier or evaporative cooler plus damping down does not supply enough moisture, a light, quick syringing by hand with a mist spray will help. This can be done several times a day in hot weather, provided you have the foliage dry by nightfall. In order to determine when the plants need misting, feel the leaves with your cheek. Your hands are usually cooler than your cheek, so the leaves may feel warm to your hand but cool to your cheek. When they feel hot, it is time to syringe them.

A good many of us, at one time or another, have tried overhead mist sprayers controlled automatically by a humidistat. We do not like to say that you should not use them, but we feel impelled to suggest that you try evaporative coolers, pad and fan arrangement, or under-bench sprayers plus fans first. There is a tendency for the overhead sprayers to run too long, and to keep the plants too wet. When you give a mist spray by hand just a quick swish is enough, not more than two or three seconds over any one group of plants. If the overhead sprayers could be controlled to run for as brief a time, they would be all right. A humidistat would have to be extremely sensitive, responding instantaneously, in order to turn off the sprayers within two or three seconds, and would have to be checked and possibly reconditioned frequently. There is as much as five minutes time lag in the response of some humidistats. A time switch is not to be relied upon because, unless you are there to turn it off on a rainy day, it will operate regardless of the weather.

Light. Good light is important at all times of the year. Gone are the days when Cattleyas were grown with heavy shade. When it was

discovered that Cattleyas made more flowers with bright light, the pendulum swung all the way in the other direction to where "all the light short of burning" became the slogan. This is a little too close for comfort and most of us prefer not to keep our plants under the constant threat of burning. Burned areas on the leaves and leaves in which chlorophyll has been destroyed cut down the efficiency of the plant. We strive to give them as much light as they need, anticipating from season to season what changes to make in the amount of shading, and keeping the light balanced with temperature and humidity.

The plants themselves show whether they are receiving the right amount of light. In good light the pseudobulbs are plump and hard, the leaves thick and firm, and the color is a medium to light green. Plants that give colored flowers may show red or purple pigment in the newly developing leads and often in the sheaths, and some leaves will retain a tinge of purple on their undersides. Plants that give pure white flowers do not show any of the purple pigment. Flowering is the final clue to light conditions; plants that flower well, giving flowers with strong stems and good substance, show that they have had enough light during the important period of growth and maturation, as well as during the time of flower bud development and the opening of the flowers.

Insufficient light leads to spindly growth that tends to be soft and succulent. The pseudobulbs do not round out well; the leaves may bend over at their juncture with the pseudobulb; and the plant may fail to flower. Growths that produce no sheaths, or sheaths and no buds, are called "blind" growths. (Don't write off such growths entirely, though. Sometimes flower buds come without a sheath, and a blind growth occasionally flowers later on.)

Too much light causes the loss of chlorophyll, the leaves becoming yellow or bronze and dry looking. Extremely strong light can burn the foliage. A burn first appears as a scorched area that later becomes dry and brown. It can be distinguished from a diseased spot by the fact that the latter remains soft and spreads if not arrested by treatment. Burning is actually a heat effect, produced when strong light raises the leaf temperature to the killing point.

These various signals are used to determine how much light to allow the plants at each season. It is not possible to bring all of the plants to the same shade of green, or to have them all make pseudobulbs of the same dimensions. Under the same light conditions, among plants standing side by side on the bench, one may have bulldog proportions and another be slim and dainty, one a light shade of green and another somewhat darker, depending on inherited differences, yet all may be doing well and all may flower eagerly. Watch their flowering and their new growths. When you have made all the adjustments that seem necessary for the plants in general, let well enough alone. If any one plant fails to flower, or if its new growths are smaller than the previous ones, you can suspect that this one needs more light. (We shall see later that watering and potting are other things to check.) Some individual plants may be more light demanding than their neighbors. Some of the hybrids between Cattleya and Laelia (Laeliocattleyas) are in this category. Find a brighter spot for them, stand them on an inverted pot or hang them above bench level where they will not be shaded by other plants.

It is helpful to have some measure of the amount of light to give Cattleyas. It has been found that they need, and can take, between 2000 and 4000 foot-candles, or about 20 to 30% of full sun. The lower levels may have to be used in the summer when the heat of the sun, added to the warmer air temperatures, would make the greenhouse too hot. The level may even have to be reduced a bit more in some areas, but try not to go below 1800 foot-candles. The higher level is possible in the winter when the sun is not as strong and the air is cooler. It is also possible to give more light in the summer when the air can be cooled by means of an evaporative cooler. Foot-candles can be measured by some photographic light meters, those which have an attachment with which foot-

Fig. 17 Burned spot caused by too intense light.

candles can be read directly, or a conversion table that translates the reading into foot-candles. If yours cannot be used, perhaps you can borrow one. The reading should be taken during the brightest part of the day, with the meter pointed directly toward the sun through the glass, making sure that you do not get any shadows from the framework of the greenhouse.

The usual method of shading a greenhouse is to apply a white shading compound to the glass itself. Such compounds can be obtained from a greenhouse supply company. Mixed according to directions, it is sprayed or painted on the glass to the desired thickness. There are also types of fixed shading, such as louvered-aluminum or wooden-slat shading, that can be fastened by sections to the outside of the greenhouse. And there are roller blinds that can be raised and lowered according to the weather, and various types of plastic netting. These are described more fully in Chapter 22.

In many regions in the winter, in order to give the plants enough light, the glass must be clear (unshaded), but in parts of the West it is necessary to keep a thin skim of shading through the winter. The bright fall sun can necessitate keeping some shade on the glass, but this is gradually thinned out by the weather. As winter approaches, watch the plants carefully. Don't let them burn by allowing the shading to become too thin during October and November. If it is necessary to do so, give the glass a thin coat of shading, perhaps only touching up the spots that have worn clear, or tack up cheesecloth where additional shading is needed. By the end of November or early December, judge whether to let the rest of the shading wash off. Perhaps you will have to scrub off the stubborn remnants. Only you can tell, by watching the signals from your plants, whether to let the glass become clear or to keep some shading on all winter.

Toward the end of winter, as the days lengthen and the sun becomes stronger, keep an eye on the plants for the time when shading must be applied again. During the first warm days you can regulate the temperature by ventilation and a mist spray at noon, thus giving them the advantage of increasing light to make up for the short, often dull days of winter. When you see leaves becoming yellow, it is time to put on some shading; since spring often bursts upon us without much warning, do it before the plants become burned.

Cattleyas do better if light is not increased too suddenly. Plants that have been grown "hard" (with good light) can take sudden changes better than soft plants, however. A few days or a week of dull weather will not soften plants enough to keep them from taking the usual clear weather that follows, unless the rain or snow has washed off needed shading. (*Watch this carefully.*) But six weeks to two months of continuous dark weather can make them susceptible to burning when the sun comes out, hence the warning to beware of the onset of bright spring weather following a dull winter.

Summer climates vary from the mild that allow around 3000 to 4000 foot-candles of light to the very hot where the light may have to be cut down to 2000 or below under extreme conditions. Do everything you can to cool the greenhouse so that you won't have to reduce the light too much. Spring and summer are the growing seasons for most kinds of orchids, and future flowering depends on their having sufficient light. More light can be allowed when the greenhouse air is cooled by an evaporative cooling system, and the small cost of installing such a system will be more than repaid by heathier plants and more flowers.

At one time growers hoped to develop a system whereby the greenhouse could be kept closed and unshaded, using brisk movement of nearly saturated air to cool the plants, with the intention of giving them full sun. There are very few places where this can be practiced fully. It is true that more light can be allowed with judicious use of moving air and humidity, but most growers have to use ventilation and shading as well. Fiberglass, a substitute for glass (see Chapter 22) has been experimented with for some years. It transmits 85% of outdoor light in a diffused manner, and with this it was again hoped that plants could be grown without any additional shading with the aid of an exhaust fan and humidity control. Some growers are apparently able to do so in areas of mild summers. However, it has been the experience of many that the approximately 7500 foot-candles transmitted by fiberglass is too much, and that shading must be used during much of the year. Incidentally, plants that have been grown in the usual 2000 to 4000 range must have the light increased gradually if you wish to experiment with higher light intensities. Terrific burning will occur if you move them directly into the 7500 foot-candle range which fiberglass gives in most areas or even into a much lesser increase of intensity. Cattleyas in nature do not have full sun. They are shaded by the moving foliage of the trees in which they grow, so that in our temperate zone, a zone of extremes, it seems logical to aim at some wise modification of outdoor light.

4 | *More on the Care of Adult Cattleyas*

■ WATERING

ALTHOUGH Cattleyas in nature receive almost a daily rain, in cultivation they rarely need a daily watering. In nature only a few of the roots are embedded in the shallow substratum, while the rest cling to the bark or hang out in the air. Hence the roots are freely aerated at all times and are subjected to drying between periods of precipitation. Orchids in pots have most of their roots confined in the osmunda fiber or bark which dries out relatively slowly since it is enclosed by the pot. The difference is comparable to that between the drying rate of a shirt hung on the line and one left crumpled in the laundry basket. The former dries in a few hours, the latter may stay damp for days. The roots in the pot receive a good wetting when the plant is watered, and then for some days can absorb all the water they need from contact with the damp potting medium.

Osmunda fiber and the various barks used for potting have been chosen purposely for their porous nature and water-holding capacity. They allow free drainage, excellent aeration, and at the same time hold water while allowing the interstices to be filled with air. With these media it is a temptation to water more frequently than necessary; it is difficult to realize that it is actually possible to overwater them. The secret is to be very observant, to check the fiber or the bark from day to day, and *not to water until you are sure it is needed*. Beginners are usually cautioned to "err on the dry side," because it is much easier to step up the frequency of watering if you haven't been watering quite enough than it is to recondition a plant whose roots have become rotten from too much water.

Fresh osmunda fiber holds water well from the start. If it is properly watered, it has a clean feel and remains firm even after two or three years of use. Each watering should be thorough. Run the hose around over the surface of the pot until the water runs out of the bottom. It is not good just to give the pot a dribble of water, for this does not soak it uniformly or wet it through. After a thorough watering, the fiber should be allowed to become almost dry before watering again. Feel the fiber, press it with your fingers, or force your fingers between the pot and the fiber. If it is at all springy, and if your fingers feel cool from it, it still has enough water for the plant. If the fiber is crisp and nonresilient, it is bone dry. Try to judge a point when the fiber is *approaching dryness*, just before it reaches the crisp state, to water again. If you let the fiber become bone dry it is difficult to get it thoroughly wet again, and this means that you will have to water it two or three times over at intervals of a few minutes, or else soak the pot in a bucket of water. When the fiber is slightly damp it will readily take up more water. Usually you can tell when it is ready for water by the weight of the pot; the nearly dry fiber is light, while damp fiber is heavier.

The barks, being in chunks, allow the water to run through very quickly, so you must be careful, again, to let the hose run in the pot long enough to insure getting the bark wet clear through. Bark of small size pieces, used for seedlings and plants with fine roots, and even the larger chunks of bark before they are well held by roots, are easy to wash out of the pot with a strong stream of water. Use a water breaker on the hose such as a "rose" or a Dramm "400," which breaks the water into gentle streams. After a thorough watering, watch the bark from day to day, and *do not water again as long as it is damp*. The surface bark may dry out before the rest, so you will have to dig down a bit to see what is going on within the pot. New bark does not hold water well at first. It takes a while for bacterial action to get going and for the process of breakdown to set in. Fresh bark therefore is not very absorbent and it may be necessary to water it every day or two for several months. After this period you will notice quite a difference in it; it stays damp much longer, and becomes a shade darker in color. When this stage is reached, it will not be necessary to water so often. Douglas fir bark takes longer to reach this point than white fir, as it is much harder in texture and sheds water more readily.

Frequency of watering, either of osmunda fiber or bark, depends on many things; so it is not possible to give an absolute watering schedule. Small pots dry out faster than large ones; drying is more rapid in warm weather than in cool; and of course dry air causes more rapid drying than damp air. Plastic pots hold water longer than clay ones. The condition and size of the plant in the pot also has much to do with the drying rate. A plant with many growths and an extensive root system will use water more rapidly than one with just a few pseudobulbs. Therefore a plant that has been in the pot for two or three years and is just about ready for division will use more water than one just becoming established after division. A big old plant that has a heavy aggregation of pseudobulbs and which is becoming root-bound is harder to water. It is necessary to run the hose around the rim of the pot and through the pseudobulbs for quite a time to be sure that enough soaks down in all parts to water it uniformly. To help in watering, it is a good idea to keep plants sorted as to size and condition. Plants in small pots that need frequent watering should be put together in one place, newly potted ones that need special care (see "potting") in another, and larger plants that should be watered less frequently in still another spot.

Seasonal differences in the frequency of watering are based on the actual use of water by the plant coupled with the effects of environmental conditions. Even though in nature the Cattleya species are not subjected to appreciable changes in either moisture or temperature, they have periods when their outward activity pauses. In our greenhouses, they have periods of activity when new roots and new growths are developing or flowers are being produced, and periods when, so far as we can see, no activity is going on. A species or a hybrid that flowers as soon as its new growth is formed makes a set of roots and then shows no further activity for several months until eventually new growth starts again. Another will make and mature its new growth and then rest for several months before producing flowers. But the plants are not inactive during these periods of rest. Internal changes are going on which, when the time is ripe, will trigger the start of new vegetative growth or the production of flowers. During a period of

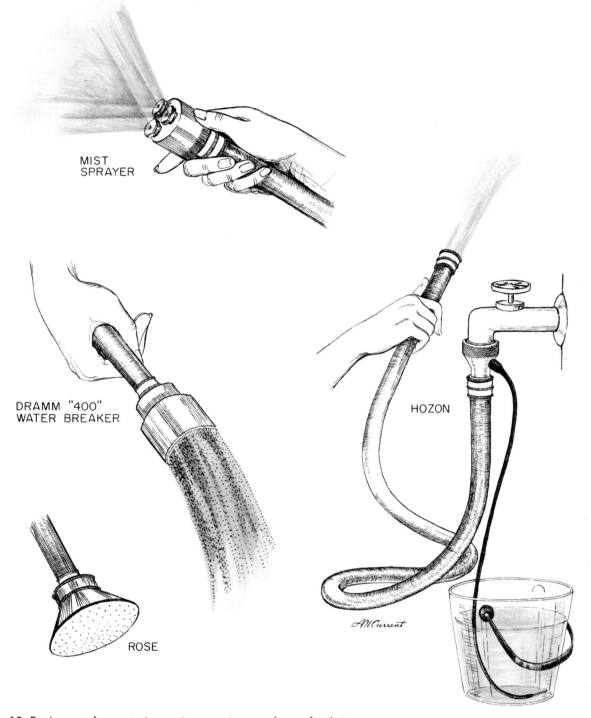

MIST
SPRAYER

DRAMM "400"
WATER BREAKER

ROSE

HOZON

Fig. 18 Equipment for watering, mist spraying, and fertilizing.

rest the plant's processes may be slowed down, but it is still making and using food, and still needs water for the job. There are a few species, especially of Laelias, which are crossed with Cattleyas, that require less water than Cattleyas when at rest. And these hybrids may need to become thoroughly dry between waterings in the winter. If Cattleyas and Cattleya hybrids are given water *according to how they use it* they maintain their schedules regularly.

During the winter, because of cooler temperatures and shorter days, the plants do not use water as fast as in the summer. Also, the cooler temperatures retard the rate at which the potting medium dries. It may not be necessary to water large plants in osmunda (pots of eight to ten inches or so) more often than once every two or three weeks, and those not quite so large (five- to seven-inch pots) once every week or ten days. The barks usually have to be watered somewhat more often than osmunda, especially the coarse grades. Eight- to ten-inch pots of bark may need watering every week or ten days, and the five- to seven-inch pots every four to seven days. The state of activity of the plant also determines how much water it uses, one that is not making active growth will not absorb water from the potting medium as rapidly as one that is doing so. It is well to take the chill off the water in the winter, to have a means of mixing some hot water with the cold to bring it to about fifty or fifty-five degrees.

In the summer the watering for all plants will have to be stepped up—for plants in osmunda to once a week or ten days and for those in bark to every three to six days, depending on the size. When it is necessary to syringe the plants with a mist spray, as during hot weather, be sure you do not actually water them at the same time. Frequent misting almost invariably dampens the surface of the potting medium, so don't be deceived by the surface condition but check the material within the pot.

Osmunda fiber that is watered too often gradually becomes soggy and has a sticky feel, and the air spaces become filled with water. Eventually it deteriorates into soft mush. Not only does the absence of air hinder the efficiency of the roots, but it allows the accumulation of toxic substances and promotes the growth of harmful bacteria and algae. This combination of conditions causes the roots to die. A potful of continually wet, soggy os-

munda is usually full of rotten roots. The growth of algae over the surface of the fiber and on the pots themselves is an indication of too much moisture. Mosses often appear. While these are not harmful to the plants, they may conceal the condition of the fiber and form a hiding place for slugs and insects.

Many of the same problems are met when bark is over-watered, although the aeration is not so much interfered with until the bark begins to break down. It first becomes quite dark in color, almost black, and the pieces may have a slippery feel to them. A plant in over-watered bark does not do well; its roots may become stunted and its growths gradually lose their vigor. Badly decomposed bark becomes compacted into a hard mass in the bottom of the pot.

Since over-watering contributes to the death or lack of vigor of the root system, it naturally follows that the plant itself cannot grow well. Water-logged roots can absorb neither water nor minerals for the use of the plant. The leaves become yellow, especially the older ones, new growths fail to flower and are smaller than the previous ones. A plant that has been over-watered for a short time can be assisted toward recovery if the potting medium is allowed to become thoroughly dried out and to remain dry for several weeks. The plant must then be put on a schedule of less frequent watering. One that has been over-watered for a long time and which shows decayed roots had better be repotted and be watered infrequently until new roots form. This is the way all newly potted Cattleyas are handled.

There is a second reason for watering plants so long that water runs out of the bottom of the pot. Salts gradually accumulate in osmunda fiber and in the pots themselves. When these salts become quite concentrated they can damage the roots. Flushing out the fiber at each watering helps maintain a proper balance of minerals. Fir bark itself does not accumulate salts but the pots may still do so, making flushing a good practice. Some water contains a good bit of dissolved minerals, so that even if you do not add fertilizer to it, it may contain enough to be accumulated by the potting medium or the pot. The addition of fertilizers to the water (see below) of course adds that much more to the salt content of the water, so that flushing out the pots with plain water at intervals between "feedings" is especially necessary with osmunda fiber, and wise with the barks.

■ QUALITY OF WATER

Most greenhouse growers, of orchids as well as other crops, are able to use their community water supply. Collecting rain water, which was once thought to be the best way to obtain water for orchids, is far too expensive and unreliable a method. Instances where the local water supply has not been suitable are few and far between, but they do exist. Visit other growers in your area. If the greenhousemen use the city water successfully, and if gardens and house plants do well with it, it will be all right for you to use it. Do not use water that has been softened by the addition of sodium, used in most home water softeners. The sodium replaces calcium and magnesium, two nutritional salts, and it in itself is toxic in the quantities that result. With too much sodium, plants start many growths that reach an inch or two in length and then cease to grow.

Cattleyas like a slightly acid medium, one of about pH 6.2. This refers to the pH of the potting medium itself. Tap water is often less acid than this, usually somewhat alkaline. Osmunda fiber and bark both seem to be able to maintain their normal pH even though the water used upon them is of a different pH. (Bark is fairly acid at first, but becomes less so after it is put into use.) We say they are self-conditioning. The numbers in the pH scale refer to the degree of acidity or alkalinity. The mid-point in the scale, pH 7, is neutral. Below pH 7 decreasing numbers refer to increasing acidity, and each number is ten times more acid than the preceding number. For example, pH 6 is moderately acid, pH 5 more acid, and pH 4 still more acid, and so on. Above pH 7,

the numbers refer to increasing alkalinity; pH 8 is moderately alkaline, pH 9 more alkaline (very alkaline as far as plants are concerned), and so on. Cattleyas have been grown successfully with water up to pH 8.

If your water is more alkaline than pH 8 you can rectify it rather easily by adding a little acid to it as you use it. We suggest doing it as you use it rather than attempting to keep a quantity acidified between waterings. Phosphoric acid is probably the best acid to use for this purpose, although hydrochloric acid is also good. It will not take much to do the job. You can use phosphoric acid full strength, but should obtain a one-tenth normal solution of hydrochloric acid rather than handle it full strength. First you must find out how much acid to add to your water. Measure a gallon of water in a clean container. Check its pH with hydrion paper, which is obtainable from most orchid supply houses. For measuring the acid, you should have a graduated cylinder marked in cubic centimeters (cc.). Let us say that you put 5 cc. of acid in the cylinder. Pour a very small amount into the gallon of water, stir thoroughly, and test with hydrion paper. If the acidity is not yet down to where you want it, add a little more, stir, and test again. Do this until the pH level you wish is reached. (It is not necessary to take it below pH 7.) Now write down the amount of acid it required to bring the one gallon of water to that level, and keep this information handy.

Perhaps the easiest method of acidification is to add the acid to the water by means of a Hozon siphon usually used for adding fertilizer to the water. This is a device that is screwed on between the faucet and the hose. It has a little side vent to which is attached a small tube that goes into a bucket of water. The force of water as it travels from the faucet through the hose siphons the water out of the bucket and adds it to the main stream of water, at the rate of one part from the bucket to sixteen parts of hose water. The solution in the bucket is therefore used in a concentration sixteen times as strong as you wish the final product to be. To acidify the water, measure the amount the bucket holds, and add sixteen times the amount of acid it would take to bring this quantity to the proper acidity. For instance, if it takes one cc. of acid to acidify one gallon of water, add 16 cc. for each gallon in the bucket. Before watering the plants, check the pH of the water delivered by the hose. There is also a jar-siphon mixer, called Hydromix, which can be used. The Hydromix holds enough solution to treat 25 gallons of water. Therefore you add to the jar enough acid to adjust 25 gallons of water.

Both the Hozon and the Hydromix require good water pressure to work accurately. If you have low water pressure, you might have to resort to a gravity tank or one with a pump. The former is a tank installed above bench level, with a hose through which the water will run by gravity. Determine the amount it holds, add the right amount of acid to bring it to the desired pH, stir thoroughly, and check the pH as the water comes through the hose. If you prefer a tank at floor level, a small pump can be used to deliver the water through the hose. Be sure to keep the tank clean, and if you do not mix the acid solution fresh each time, be sure to check the acidity frequently.

We should say here that if your water is far too acid, which is an almost unheard of situation, you can make it less acid by adding potassium hydroxide solution. The same method of measuring and testing with hydrion paper is used, this time to bring the water up in the pH scale from a lower level to something in the neighborhood of pH 6 or pH 7.

■ FERTILIZING

Osmunda fiber. Osmunda fiber gives the plants a balanced diet of minerals, and the plants will grow and flower without any added fertilizers. However, dilute applications of fertilizers will give them a boost and produce somewhat stockier growth and more and heavier flowers. You must be cautious about applying fertilizers to osmunda fiber, partly because only a slight supplement to the minerals already present is needed, and partly because over-feeding is a danger. Too much

feeding leads to soft growths that do not harden up properly and also tends to discourage flowering. The fertilizer should be one in which nitrogen (N), phosphorus (P), and potassium (K) are in equal proportions, a so-called 10-10-10 formula. There are many brands put out especially for orchids. These are obtainable from orchid supply houses, but any of the complete fertilizers on the market will do, provided that these three minerals are in equal proportions. A concentration of one-half teaspoon per gallon of water is as strong as you should use, and many growers feel that one-quarter teaspoon per gallon is sufficient. Use every third or fourth watering.

In order to put the extra minerals to use, plants in osmunda must be in active growth and have enough light to make sufficient amounts of carbohydrates to balance the minerals. Most Cattleyas make their new growth during the spring and summer, some starting as early as January, maturing the growths by July, and others starting later and maturing the growths in the fall. They should be fertilized only during this period of activity, and be given no fertilizer during the rest of the year. Some hybrids inherit the growth habit of one or another of their species ancestors, and should be fertilized accordingly. However, some hybrids are continually in a state of growth or flowering, often making two or more sets of growths a year, and starting new growths before the previous ones have matured. Such types can make use of some fertilizer through the winter, although because of the short days (fewer daylight hours) the concentration should be reduced to half, or the applications should be spaced farther apart.

Bark. Although the barks have been in use as growing media for a number of years, there is still not too much agreement on how often to fertilize, or what proportions of the minerals to use, or in what concentration. By analysis, the various barks differ somewhat in the amounts of available minerals, and all are lower in nitrogen than is osmunda fiber. Because of this basic lack most growers agree that at least nitrogen should be added to the bark. There are those who prefer to add nitrogen alone, those who like a 10-10-10 ratio, and those who like a fertilizer in which nitrogen is in greater amounts, such as a 30-10-10, a 50-10-10, or a 30-10-20 ratio. Staunch advocates of one or another formula are to be found wherever you go. Lack of absolute agreement on what is best is to be expected, because of differences in handling the plants, because of climatic differences in environment, and because of personal differences in what individuals look for in their plants. The barks are still fairly new. Orchids are slow to respond, and Cattleyas are not "heavy feeders." It is difficult to diagnose why plants may produce fewer flowers one year than another, and equally difficult to know just what brings about more flowers. Bumper crops may be as much due to a happier combination of environmental factors, such as fewer cloudy days, a cooler summer, etc., as due to whether you used a 10-10-10 or a 30-10-10 fertilizer formula, or whether you gave it at every watering or at every other watering.

If all this seems to leave some questions as to where you should start, remember that, fortunately, in general orchids will grow and thrive with a variety of fertilizers. An overabundance of nitrogen will usually encourage vegetative growth over flower production. In general, higher levels of fertilizer may be used when the plants are making vigorous growth and when light conditions are at their best, with the concentration reduced when the plants are less active and when the days are shorter or the weather cloudy. As a starting point, we suggest that you try the 30-10-10, or the 30-10-20 ratio, giving it in a concentration of one-half teaspoon to a gallon of water, at every other watering. This schedule may be kept up for plants in active growth during seasons of bright light. For plants that are resting, or during spells of dull weather, reduce the concentration to one-quarter teaspoon per gallon of water. If you happen to have on hand a quantity of 10-10-10 fertilizer but wish to give your plants a higher nitrogen value, you

can do so by mixing equal parts of ammonium nitrate and 10-10-10, then measuring the amount to use per gallon as above. Some growers like to furnish a continuous supply of nitrogen by incorporating a slow-dissolving material such as uramite (just a light sprinkling) in the potting material, and then using a 10-10-10 fertilizer on it.

If you are of an experimental nature, you might try fertilizing half of your plants at every watering and the other half at every second watering, or set up some other trial program, and compare the results. Some growers advocate a stronger concentration of fertilizer when plants are in active growth, one teaspoon to a gallon of water, and some like as high a nitrogen ratio as 50-10-10. If you wish to try this, perhaps you should do so on one group of plants before treating them all. It is better to start off in a moderate way and gain a good background for comparison than to start out with an extreme method.

The Hozon siphon mixer and the Hydromix jar make fertilizing easy. These are described above in the section dealing with acidifying water. In using the Hozon, you make the concentration sixteen times as strong as you wish the water in the hose to be. For a strength of one-half teaspoon per gallon this would be sixteen one-half teaspoons, or eight teaspoons, for each gallon the bucket holds. In the Hydromix jar you would put twenty-five times the amount of fertilizer needed for one gallon, since the Hydromix holds enough solution to treat twenty-five gallons of water. If the water pressure in your area is low, you might have to use a tank for fertilizing, also described above.

When you grow a mixed collection of orchids, you may have some that require more frequent fertilizing, such as Vandas and Dendrobiums, and you may have some plants in osmunda and some in bark. You may wish, on the same day, to give plain water to some and fertilizer to others, or you may wish just to syringe a few plants or to damp down the floor. We happen to use a Hozon for our fertilizing, and it is a nuisance always to have to take it off or put it on. So we leave it attached, and mix up a bucket of fertilizer. Then when we wish to use plain water we lift the tube out of the bucket, and when we wish to fertilize we put it in. When the Hozon tube is out, air is sent through the hose, which makes the water "buck" a little, but we tolerate this for the time it saves. Occasionally a little piece of dirt will plug up the side vent of the Hozon. Pull off the tube to dislodge it. If necessary, run a needle through the vent opening to clean it. Keep the bucket clean, scrubbing it once in a while to remove deposits.

■ CARE OF FLOWERING PLANTS

Flowering Cattleyas are treated in the same way as those not in flower. They are watered on the same schedule and are allowed the good light that brings the flowers to their fullest color and firmest substance. Perhaps in hot weather they might be given a bit more shade after they are fully open to help them last. Once the flowers mature, that is, after they have been open three or four days, the plant can be brought in the house to be enjoyed, and can be placed on a table or the mantel or wherever it can be shown off, for the flowers do not need light in order to keep well. If you bring a plant into the house before the flowers are open, keep it in a bright (but not too hot) window until they are fully open.

We used to try to move flowering plants in the greenhouse to an area set aside for them so as to avoid getting water or insecticides on them. Moving plants, especially large ones, is a chore often involving shifting several others to make room for one. Sometimes new growths are damaged, or buds broken off in the process. We have learned that water does not hurt the flowers provided they can dry off quickly. Some prepared fertilizers have a coloring material added (so that you can know whether the Hozon or the Hydromix is working properly); as this dries it will leave a deposit on the flowers, as will insecticides. Try to avoid splashing the flowers during watering, and avoid spraying them. But if some do become wet with these materials, rinse them off with a fine spray

of plain water before the materials have a chance to dry. Dust carried in by the wind may also be washed off.

It takes five to eight weeks for the buds to grow up to the tip of the sheath, depending on the individual plant. The length of time from the moment the buds break the tip of the sheath until they are open also varies. Some develop very quickly, requiring about a week, but most take two weeks or more. The flowers are not ready to cut until they have reached their fullest color and substance, at least two full days, sometimes four days, after the flowers open. Cattleya buds will not open in water, nor will flowers mature if they are cut too soon. The latter remain limp and green and soon wilt. After you have lived with your plants for a while, you come to know when the flowers have reached their prime, and how long it takes them. If you intend to use them for decoration or for corsages, or to sell them, it is important to avoid the disappointment of not having them last.

Cut flowers keep a long time in water, in a narrow necked vase so that the flower parts are not submerged. Their life can be lengthened by putting them in a cool place at night, or in a refrigerator at not lower than forty-five degrees. To keep a corsage, lay it on a little shredded wax paper in a polyethylene bag, close the bag tightly, and put it in the refrigerator. We learned some time ago that carnations can be kept for six to eight weeks after cutting when wrapped in polyethylene film and stored in a refrigerator or in a cool place, so we have tried this with orchids a few times. Usually some can be kept for longer than they would last on the plants, and can thus be saved for special occasions. Not all flowers will keep equally well. Those of heavy substance last better than thin ones, but the keeping qualities are sometimes a matter of individuality. They should be cut while in their prime, not necessarily during the first few days after opening, but not past the middle of their normal life. A fading flower or two can shorten the life of others stored with them. The flower stems are put in tubes, and they are then laid on shredded wax paper in a shallow box. The box is wrapped tightly in polyethylene film and stored at forty-five degrees. Among those we have tried, Phalaenopsis kept particularly well; but some Cattleyas kept for two weeks longer than they would have otherwise.

As plants come into bloom, watch to see that the buds are not cramped in the sheath or prevented from coming out through its top. Sometimes a sheath becomes dry before flowering time, or is too long in proportion to the length of the flower stems, or is too tough for the buds to force open. Except for those with a double sheath, you can see the buds by holding the plant against the light. If the stems become bent back on themselves, cut off the top of the sheath or open it with your fingers; otherwise the stems will become distorted and the flowers may not grow fully out of the sheath before they are ready to open. Watch to see that a sheath is not growing up under an adjacent leaf which would cause the buds to be injured or bent. You can slip one leaf behind another to allow room for the flowers, or tie back leaves that are in the way. If the group of flowers on a stem is too heavy for the stem, the stem may bend with their weight, in which case the stem should be staked so that the flowers will be held upright. Occasionally a flower has difficulty in opening; its parts may be very tightly clasped together. Let it alone for a couple of days to see whether it can open by itself, but if it doesn't you can ease the petals apart or unfold the rim of the lip with your fingers, or perhaps accomplish this by blowing into the flower.

The keeping qualities of the flowers are partly due to a protective covering of wax, but this is also an individual characteristic. In general, those of heavy substance last the longest, but some not particularly heavy can last for weeks. Good culture, of course, contributes to this. As the flowers fade they should be cut; when the last flower on a stem is removed, the stem and sheath should be cut off close to their base. Dying flowers in the greenhouse are something of a hazard. They give off ethylene gas, which can cause sepal wilt in flowers just ready to open. Two or three fading flowers will not produce enough to harm others, but a large number of them may do so. Also, old flowers are susceptible to spotting by the botrytis fungus; and once this fungus is on the increase in the greenhouse, fresh flowers may become infected. Whenever such spots make an appearance, remove the flower at once. Thrips, red spiders, and aphids are enemies. Thrips chew the surface tissues leaving little silvery or brown scars. Red spiders and aphids puncture the tissues, leaving small wounds surrounded by a transparent halo. The control for these is given in the chapter on pests. "Honey" is secreted at the tips of the sepals and also at their juncture with the stem. This is a pleasant sweet-tasting substance. When the flowers are growing close together, sometimes a bit of this honey becomes smeared on an adjacent flower part and a transparent streak results. Wash it off with a touch of water and the streak will disappear.

Keep a record on the label of each plant as to the flowering time, the number and quality of the flowers, and how long they last. When your greenhouse becomes crowded, you will wish to dispose of some plants in favor of better ones, or ones which flower at a different time of the year. Don't discard a plant on the basis of its first flowering, unless the flowers are exceedingly poor on a well-grown plant. If they are nicely shaped, but small or poorly colored, see if better culture won't bring them along to be larger or brighter. A plant that consistently gives poor flowers is, of course, not worth keeping, nor is one that refuses to flower in spite of good culture. Sometimes a recalcitrant plant can be encouraged to flower by giving it better light, or a slightly warmer or cooler night temperature. It is worth a bit of experimenting to find out. However, often we find ourselves giving our best locations and our most earnest care to a plant that performs poorly, when it would be better to discard it in favor of a more rewarding plant. The value of keeping records

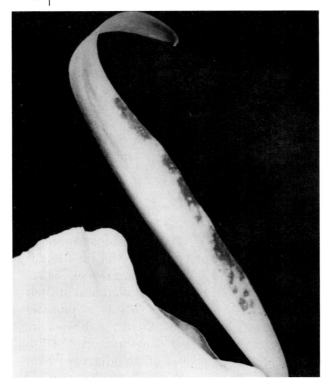

Fig. 19 Left, closeup of flower damaged by red spiders.   Right, a flower ruined by slugs.

is proved when you have an opportunity to trade plants with a friend, or to sell some, or when you wish to make room for new plants by culling out poor ones.

■ GENERAL SUGGESTIONS

When a plant is making new leads, help it to maintain a nice upright position by staking the leads as they develop. Some leads will assume a good position by themselves, but others may lean out too far. Newly developing growths are quite soft and easy to break, so be gentle. You can't do much until a lead is about half grown, and then you can begin to train it. Place a stake (steel) in the center of the pot or use a clip-on stake. Usually one stake is sufficient for a medium-sized plant. Using soft string, make a turn around the stake, then bring the string out and around the lead and back to the stake to be tied. You can snug in a young lead by placing the string fairly close to its base, where it is strong, to bring the main curve closer to the plant. When this lead is more fully grown, replace the string with

another placed at the juncture between the pseudobulb and leaf. Never constrict a stem by looping the string around it; always tie the leads with a "sling" of string. A plant with many leads becomes a challenge to keep staked. Don't try to pull all the leads in close to the stake; just give them a good position and leave room between them for flower buds to emerge without crowding.

Keep the pots free from weeds. Oxalis is a particular pest, because it shoots its seed as the pods become ripe, thus insuring a new crop as soon as you have pulled out one. It is best to get oxalis plants out while they are tiny. The barks are free from weed seeds, and osmunda can be treated before being put into use.

As the sheathing leaves that surround the pseudobulbs become dry and start to fall away from the stem, they may be removed. They come off more completely when they are wet. Do not peel the still green ones from the young pseudobulbs. When you have finished weeding, cutting old flowers etc., gather up all trash and remove it from the greenhouse.

Whenever you are in the greenhouse, working or just looking, you may discover something that needs attention—crowded flower buds, a new lead that needs tying, a few weeds to be removed, bugs on some flower buds, a light burn, or a disease spot. Don't forget to look over the plants in the back row; they sometimes become neglected. A regular program of spraying for insects should be established as a preventive measure to keep insect populations under control. Keep a little hand sprayer ready in between times, in case you find a few aphids, red spiders, or other pests on flower buds. And if you find a plant with a few suspicious spots, treat it with a little fungicide right away. See Chapter 21 for disease and pest control.

Two frequent pests are slugs and snails. The former are easier to control than the latter, but both are killed by preparations containing metaldehyde. Do not use an arsenic preparation on orchids. Chewed leaves and flowers, as well as root tips, are evidence of slugs, and you often see a slug lying along a stem or a newly developing lead. Regular treatment with a "slugicide" will keep them under control. More difficult to control are the snails, a very small flat-coiled kind, the largest of which reach about three-sixteenths of an inch in size. They remain in the potting medium for the most part, wreaking destruction on the new root tips; but occasionally they will be seen on the rhizome or the developing young growths. When you see new root tips badly chewed off, and do not find slugs, you can suspect that snails are present. It doesn't take many to keep the new root tips whittled off as fast as they form. The metaldehyde preparations should be used repeatedly. Metaldehyde has some residual action, but it does not necessarily get all the individuals or all the eggs. The treatment must therefore be repeated every few weeks, and then at intervals of three or four months. Where a bad infestation is found, we remove the plant from the pot, take off all the potting medium, pick off all the snails we can find, wash the bare roots with the hose, and dust the roots and the base of the plant thoroughly with metaldehyde powder before putting it in fresh medium.

Occasionally a plant is found whose roots just simply stop growing. Perhaps the plant was overwatered unwittingly at some time, possibly by drip from the roof. Perhaps the bark is moldy. Various kinds of mold can invade the bark. There is a slippery feeling kind, a slime mold. There is also a granular, dry-looking mold. And there is a cobwebby kind. Sometimes the bark smells moldy without your being able to see anything. In all these cases, it is well to remove all the old bark, wash off the bare roots with the hose, and put the plant in fresh bark. We do not know whether the molds actually do any harm, whether they are the cause of cessation of root growth, but plants seem to recover nicely when repotted.

As you go along the bench watering the plants, glance back from plant to plant to see whether the water drains rapidly through the pot. Once in a while fine material becomes washed out of the bark into the bottom and clogs up the drainage hole. With your fingers or a screw driver, push up the crock over the hole to let the water run out. Then flush out the pot thoroughly to remove the material that was clogging the drainage. If this doesn't remedy the situation, remove the plant from the pot to see what was causing the trouble.

Sometimes a grower is disappointed in the flowering of a plant which he bought while in bloom, and from which he expected a duplication of the flowers he saw. Changed conditions can alter the quality of flowers. A plant that gave brightly colored flowers under good light may give paler ones with less sun. An unusually hot summer, or a dull chilly fall can cause poorer blooming than usual. You will find this so from year to year with your own plants, so if it happens to one you have recently bought, see whether improved conditions won't remedy the situation.

5 | *Potting Mature Cattleyas*

In the preceding chapters we gave methods for culture with osmunda fiber and bark. In this chapter we shall tell how to pot with both. Many of you will have to make a decision as to which medium to use. When bark was first put on the market it was shredded and packaged unscreened. Since then it has been found that the bark gives better results when it is screened to remove the fine material. Not only that, but growers now prefer a coarser type, chopped instead of shredded, and this is available in an assortment of grades ranging from small size pieces for seedlings on up to large sizes for mature plants.

Many growers who are accustomed to osmunda fiber and like it have not changed to bark. Some have tried bark and gone back to osmunda fiber. But more and more people are using bark with great satisfaction. I have come to like it so well that I should like to suggest that you give it a good try. Osmunda fiber is still invaluable for certain things. Little botanicals fresh from the jungle seem to get off to a better start in it. For such plants as Cycnoches which has tall heavy pseudobulbs we find it gives a better foothold. I now have nearly all of my plants in bark, both fir and Douglas fir, as well as some in osmunda fiber, some in the newly produced shredded whole crown osmunda, and some in tree fern mixed with bark. You would be pressed to find any significant differences among them as to their size, number of leads, and number and quality of flowers. In other words, all will do equally well provided each is handled properly. Growers are now successful with bark for kinds such as Cymbidium and Cypripedium, which have formerly been grown either in osmunda fiber or a mixed compost. The ease of handling bark, especially in moving a plant from bark to bark, is its most desirable feature. By dampening a pan of bark, I can pot two or three plants whenever I find some that are just ready, or whenever I have a spare half hour. When the time comes for a major potting job, I can do half a benchful of plants in the time it used to take to do ten or a dozen in osmunda fiber —and with far less effort. Shredded tree fern and its mixture with bark are as easy to use as bark.

I might mention here that bark is now doing everything that it was once hoped gravel culture would do. This method is described in the chapter on mineral nutrition. Gravel culture still has its fans, however. It had its start with experimental work on plant nutrition, where an inert medium was used (such as gravel or Haydite) and all of the nutrient chemicals were supplied in solution. Many who were at first enthusiastic about it for orchids gave it up because of problems in keeping the necessary chemical salts in exact balance. The barks do not present the same problems and are easier to handle in this matter.

Most of the potting will be done in the spring, since this is the time when most plants start their growth. Those that make new roots as early as January and February can be potted then, and those that do not start new growth until May or June can be potted at that time. Plants make their best growth during spring and summer, and it is well to put them in fresh medium in time to take advantage of the good growing weather. Individual plants that start new growth at some other time of the year may have to be potted accordingly. We do not like to shift a plant that has finished its active growth phase and is going into a rest period. Disturbing it at such a time will force it to sit for months without an active root system.

A plant needs to be repotted (1) when it has outgrown its pot and (2) when the potting material is no longer in good condition. The first is easier to judge, but the second is more important from the point of view of the immediate health of the plant.

Outgrown pot. As a plant adds successive leads these come closer to the edge of the pot. Soon the leads will grow out over the edge, and the new roots will travel down the outside to wind around the pot or go along the bench. It does no harm for one lead to extend beyond the edge, provided it maintains a nice upright position, or can be tied up straight. In fact, if the potting material is in good condition, it does no actual harm to the plant if two successive leads grow out of the pot. Roots hanging in mid-air seem to remain healthy, but they are subject to injury when the plant is moved, and if they cling to the bench they

will, of course, have to be broken off eventually. A plant should not be allowed to grow for too long a period in this manner, for subsequent leads will grow downward, flower stems will stick out horizontally, and the shape of the flowers may be impaired. It must be confessed that almost all growers have a few plants that do not get repotted when they should be. Especially is this true with plants in osmunda, with which potting is a time-consuming job. Once the plants are in bark, moving them on is easier, although even so, when one has many plants and little time, or when family emergencies prevent attending to the plants at the right time, some are inevitably skipped. As long as the medium is good, and care is given to watering and fertilizing, the plants will survive in good condition.

Condition of the medium. Osmunda fiber and bark will remain in good condition for varying lengths of time, depending on how they are watered and on the relative humidity of the environment. They break down more rapidly when they are watered to excess or kept in a very humid atmosphere. Two years may be as long as either will be good under these conditions. When moderately watered, or in a dry climate, or in a greenhouse where the relative humidity is kept only moderately high, they will last for three, possibly four years. Thus plants can be left longer in the same medium under the latter conditions, provided that they are doing well and still fit their pots.

How can you tell when either osmunda fiber or bark is not in good condition? Osmunda fiber becomes soft and spongy to the touch, and if you take a plant out of the pot you will find that the fibers have disintegrated into a soft mush. In such a pot you often find good roots only in the upper half or third of the pot where they are able to get more air and remain somewhat more dry than in the wet mush toward the bottom. Or you may find no good roots at all. Somewhat the same situation exists when bark has broken down. The lower half will have disintegrated more thoroughly than the upper half, and the broken down material will have compacted into a solid mass. Here again, you may find good roots only in the upper part. In order to find out how the potting medium holds up for you, check a plant or two after a year and a half. If the medium is deteriorating, you will know that you have been keeping it too wet and should therefore cut down on the frequency of watering. Possibly, also, you have been keeping the relative humidity too high.

■ TIME TO REPOT

Best time. The best time, in fact, the ideal time, to repot a plant is just before it starts the new roots of the season, or just as these roots begin to show. The new roots come from the base of the recently matured lead. Their first sign is little swellings underneath the curved basal section (rhizome) of the lead. The bright green root tips then push out through the brown covering of the rhizome. The root tips are very tender and are easily broken. By the time they have reached a length of half an inch it is difficult to repot a plant without injuring them. When a root tip is broken, the root ceases to grow

from that point. Older roots will form branch roots behind the tip if the tip is broken, but the very new ones may simply stop growing for the season. At the time the new roots make their appearance, the older roots undergo a wave of activity that causes them to branch, and you can then see new root tips all through the medium. There is a real advantage in potting a plant just when this activity starts so as to let the new roots and branch roots grow into fresh medium.

Next best time to repot. If the new roots develop before you can take care of a plant, wait until they have grown to a length of five or six inches rather than to risk breaking them. They are then old enough to form branch roots themselves. The older roots are still actively branching and if any of them are injured in the potting process they will form additional branches. Potting a plant at this time interrupts its growth for a few weeks, necessitating a period of recovery, and is therefore not as ideal a time as that given above. But it does offer a second chance to take care of plants you miss when the roots are first starting. Some species and hybrids habitually form new roots

Fig. 20 Left, new roots too long to be handled without damage. Better to pot just as roots are starting or else wait until they are five or six inches long and capable

of branching. Right, plant that was potted just as new roots were starting, allowing them to grow immediately into fresh medium.

just when the flower buds are developing in the sheath. To prevent any setback to the flowers, such plants can be handled at this "next best" time.

A hybrid that flowers two or more times a year will probably start growth cycles at various times of the year. Some may start a new set of growths before the last have flowered. Try to repot such plants during the spring or summer, catching them when they are forming a new set of roots.

Problem plants. An occasional plant may show signs of deterioration while its neighbors are in perfectly good health. If there is not a disease involved (See chapter 21), the cause is almost certain to be root loss, for which two possible reasons are overwatering and snail damage. More and more we have found the latter to be the cause of what seemed a mysterious cessation of root activity, with the roots still alive but blunted and crooked. The snails may have done their work and moved on to another plant, so that none, or perhaps only one or two, can be found. Since the roots are already inactive, whether from overwatering or damage by snails, and since you have the plant out of the pot, you might as well put it in fresh medium. This is particularly easy when the plant is in bark. Often a plant will make a remarkable recovery. Sections of roots that are still alive sometimes respond quite quickly with branch roots. An interesting phenomenon takes place when a plant with absolutely no roots starts a new lead. Ordinarily roots are formed only by a mature lead, but when no roots are present to support the young developing lead, it will often start its own set when it is still very small, barely an inch or two in length. The first new growths from plants that have been badly set back because of root loss may not be large enough to flower. But at least you will have rescued them from a bad situation and put them on the road to recovery.

■ HOW AND WHEN TO DIVIDE PLANTS

Each pseudobulb with its basal part, that is, its section of rhizome, is poten-

tially an individual plant. It makes its own set of roots, and gives rise to new leads from buds at the joints of the rhizome. If a plant is cut up into individual pseudobulbs, however, the new growths from them will be very small, almost like those of young seedlings. It will take several years for a one-bulb division to become a flowering plant. A new growth, if it is to be of flowering size, requires the support of several pseudobulbs behind it. For this reason, divisions are made of groups of connected pseudobulbs, at least four in a clump if possible.

Not all of the buds along the joints of the rhizome will develop into leads. Many remain dormant throughout the life of the plant, a sort of safety factor. The buds most likely to grow into new leads are the two located, one on each side, at the juncture of the pseudobulb

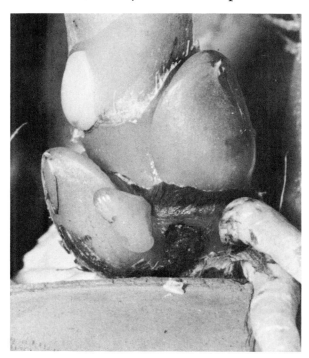

Fig. 21 Nature's safety factor. Base of a lead with covering tissues removed to show the buds, one at each joint. Usually one or two buds become activated and will develop into leads. Here two have enlarged and are growing. The small buds will remain dormant, possibly to develop later on when the plant is divided. If the leads should suffer a catastrophe, one or the other of the dormant buds will become active. Note, also, roots growing from base of lead.

Fig. 22 Two leads developing from buds situated as in Fig. 21.

with the rhizome. Sometimes a plant activates only one bud at a time from the base of each recently matured lead. This we call a one-lead plant. It grows along in a straight line, its pseudobulbs marching across the surface of the potting medium in single file. Sometimes, after giving rise to but one lead a year, a plant will break two buds, causing a fork in its growth line, each of which then continues to give a new lead each year—a two-lead plant. If one of the forks breaks two buds concurrently, the plant will then have three growing ends. Some individuals grow so lustily that they break two buds from almost every pseudobulb, and quickly develop into plants with six, eight, ten, or more leads.

The decision of whether to divide a plant depends partly on its habit, and partly on its size. A plant that consistently gives but one lead a year should definitely be divided when it has made enough pseudobulbs to give two strong divisions. This would be when seven or eight pseudobulbs had been formed, allowing for a lead division of four pseudobulbs and a backbulb division of three or four. Removing the growing end will stimulate one of the dormant buds on the back part to develop, so that you will have two plants to give flowers instead of one. The lead division should flower on its next growth; the backbulb division, being not quite so vigorous, may take two years to flower. Interestingly enough, an occasional plant keeps the habit of giving but one lead

a year from the time it is a seedling until it is divided. The stimulus of division may cause two or three buds to break simultaneously on one or the other half, so that from that time

Fig. 23-A A plant that is growing in two distinct lines. Each half has two or more leads. This plant should be divided in the center, and probably each half kept intact. B, a plant with several leads on the front half. Divisions should consist of the front half, to be carried on intact, and a back half, which will probably give several new growths. C, a compact plant with five leads in a seven-inch pot. Such plants give many flowers in little space.

onward that division becomes a plant with several leads.

A plant with two or more leads may not require a pot any larger than a one-lead plant, and for the same amount of space will give you double or treble the number of flowers. So if you have a plant with several leads, that is compact and growing in an orderly fashion, it would probably pay not to divide it. Such a plant can be moved along into a larger pot, perhaps removing only the backbulbs, and may become a very fine specimen. It is more thrilling to have a huge plant covered with flowers than to have several small ones with a few flowers each. Eventually, a plant becomes too large to handle conveniently, and then will have to be divided. You will have the choice of breaking it up into a number of smaller plants and waiting while some of these regain specimen size, or of making two or three large divisions.

The accompanying diagrams, Figure 24, give some types and suggestions. A shows a one-lead plant that should be divided. B shows a plant with two leads that also should be divided. The plant is growing in two definite lines, but each line has produced only one lead since the original break that caused it to fork. Dividing it may stimulate it to make more leads at a time. Each growth line can be separated at the point where it forked from the original part of the plant. The group of backbulbs can be potted if they are still plump and have some leaves, or be discarded if they are no longer vigorous. You will probably want to keep them if the plant is valuable, and in time they will make a third flowering plant.

C shows a two-lead plant that is not ready for division, but from which the backbulbs can be removed. Make the cut just behind the pseudobulb that gave rise to the two leads, so that they remain connected. The backbulbs are probably more vigorous in this plant than they are in A and B because they are younger. D shows a three-lead plant that should be divided in the same manner as the two-lead plant just described, keeping the three leads together and removing the backbulbs.

E shows a plant that has branched and re-branched, offering an opportunity either to keep it as a unit, removing just the backbulbs, or of making two or three divisions. The dotted lines show where it might be cut to make three plants, the solid line where it should be cut to make two divisions. F shows a similar plant that has made even more leads, each growing end making two leads a year. This plant surely should be kept as a unit as long as possible, for it is a beautifully symmetrical specimen.

Diagrams cannot possibly include all of the shapes your plants can take. Some will make all of their growth forward, producing a plant heavy with leads on one side of the pot and practically nothing on the other side. Then there are those whose many leads cross over each other, or force each other up in the air, offering a real challenge when it comes to dividing them. Each plant has to be dealt with according to its own needs. You can make a neater plant in some cases by removing one or two crowded leads with their connected pseudobulbs, leaving the rest of the plant intact. Also, a plant may send one lead over the edge, keeping the others neatly within the pot. The overhanging section can be clipped off and potted separately, leaving the rest of the plant undisturbed for another year or so.

■ POTTING IN BARK

There are a number of different kinds of bark on the market. In order to save on costs, growers are experimenting with the kinds available in their localities, and in the future some of these may prove to be as usable as those we now know. At present fir bark is the most popular and widely used. This is composed largely of white fir (*Abies concolor*), with some red fir (*Abies magnifica*) occasionally mixed with it. These come from California and are essentially alike as far as characteristics are concerned. Second in use is Douglas fir (*Pseudotsuga menziesii*, also known as *P. taxifolia*), from the Pacific Northwest. Its bark is hard and very solid and at first more resistant to water, but eventually it cannot be told from the others. Third in popularity is pine bark,

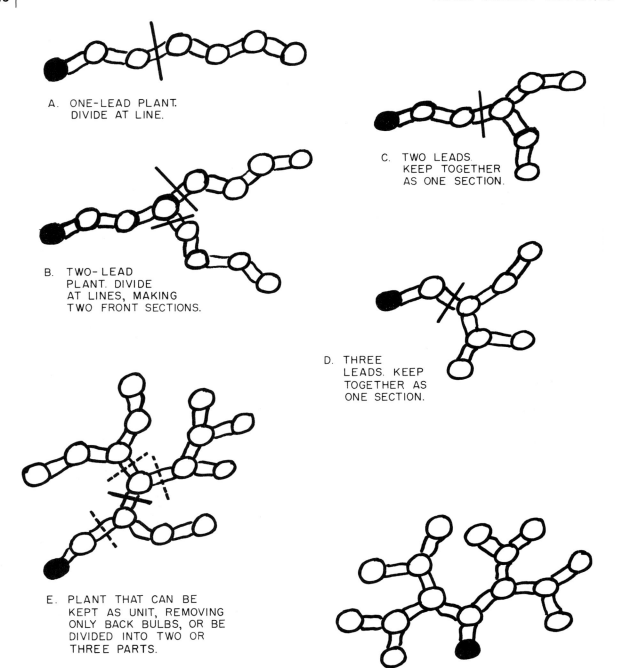

A. ONE-LEAD PLANT.
DIVIDE AT LINE.

B. TWO-LEAD
PLANT. DIVIDE
AT LINES, MAKING
TWO FRONT SECTIONS.

C. TWO LEADS.
KEEP TOGETHER
AS ONE SECTION.

D. THREE
LEADS. KEEP
TOGETHER AS
ONE SECTION.

E. PLANT THAT CAN BE
KEPT AS UNIT, REMOVING
ONLY BACK BULBS, OR BE
DIVIDED INTO TWO OR
THREE PARTS.

F. PLANT THAT SHOULD BE
KEPT AS A UNIT.

Fig. 24 Diagrams showing how to divide plants. In each one the oldest pseudobulb is shown as solid black.

the common southern yellow pine, used successfully by many growers in the southeastern section of the country. In New England, yellow birch is being used experimentally, and this and other hardwood barks may prove successful.

The barks are sold in various grades, screened of fine material. There are fine grades for seedlings, and the sizes range on up through a medium grade in which the chunks are between one-quarter and three-quarters of an inch, to a very coarse grade that runs as large as one and one-half inch. In a dry climate where watering has to be more frequent, the medium grades are satisfactory, and in a damp climate a coarser grade is probably best. However, you can choose the grade according to your own liking.

Many growers who use bark have tried plastic pots with some success. In a dry climate, or a greenhouse where the relative humidity is usually low, plastic pots allow the bark to remain damp somewhat longer, and watering does not have to be as frequent. A new transparent plastic pot allows you to see the condition of the roots. Whereas we would not recommend plastic pots for osmunda fiber, bark seems to allow good enough aeration to permit their use with it. Their value is greatest for small plants or small divisions, which would have to be watered quite frequently. Their usefulness diminishes with larger sizes where the surface area of the medium is greater. The standard clay pot is still the most widely used. We like them in the regular height up to about seven inches in diameter, and in the three-quarter height in larger diameters.

Choose a pot that will accommodate about two years' growth. For a plant that makes one lead a year, or one set of leads, judge the size needed by the distance between the pseudobulbs, estimating how much larger the plant will be with two years' growth added. For a plant that makes two or more sets of growths a year, the pot will have to be relatively larger. Ordinarily, a plant of four pseudobulbs that makes one growth a year will require a six-inch pot. A two- or three-lead plant that makes two or three growths a year should go into a seven or eight inch pot. If you are familiar with the discussions that have gone on during the period of trial and error in the use of bark, you will have heard that, "You may over-pot in bark," and "You must use larger pots with bark." This has caused some confusion and

should perhaps be explained. Many growers got so much better growth in bark that they found their plants were outgrowing their pots sooner in bark than they did in osmunda. Especially was this true where there had been a tendency to overwater in osmunda, a tendency that was almost automatically relieved when the plants were put in the more open, more rapidly drying bark. When using osmunda, growers are cautioned not to put a small plant in a large pot because the osmunda stays wet longer in the center where the roots of the small plant are concentrated. Bark is not as dangerous in this respect. However, putting a plant in a larger pot than it needs is purely a waste of material and space, and a plant will do no better in an oversize pot than in one more fitted to its size. You must therefore judge the size of the pots according to your own observations of how the plants do for you. If they outgrow their pots before the two years is up, next time use a larger size.

The pots should be clean. Wash old pots in plain water and rinse them. Soak new clay pots in water before use. Put several pieces of broken pot (crock) in the bottom of clay pots to keep the bark or the fine material from settling and blocking drainage. At the time of writing, plastic pots have three small drainage holes, which become blocked quite easily. Therefore, either use more crock or enlarge the holes with a hot soldering iron.

We like to dampen the bark before using it. It seems to make it easier to settle in the pot and around the roots. Also, wetting it through with the hose removes some of the dusty material, a small amount of which still remains even though the bark has been screened. You will see in a moment that we like to let newly potted plants remain fairly dry for a few weeks. For this reason, some growers use the bark dry, just as it comes from the bag. However, the bark does not stay wet very long from the original dampening; in fact, it is pretty dry by the next day, so that dampening it before use does not interfere with keeping the plants dry after potting. Try both ways and see which you like.

To remove a plant for repotting, first soak it in a bucket of water to loosen the roots that cling to the pot. It can then usually be knocked out of the pot quite easily. With your fingers work loose the roots clinging to the outside, then turn the pot upside down and, holding the plant with one hand, tap the rim on the bench. The plant should drop down into your hand. If it does not come out this way, run a knife around inside the pot to separate the roots that cling stubbornly to it. You may also have to do this with the roots on the outside.

Much of the old bark will fall away as you shake the plant a bit and gently move the roots apart. Run the hose through the roots to remove as much of the remaining bark as will come free, but do not try to pull away those pieces that cling tenaciously to the roots. Look for evidence of slug and snail injury. Decayed roots should be cut back to healthy tissue, or removed entirely if completely rotted. The healthy roots need not be cut back if their shape and length will allow them to be put into the new pot without being broken. Roots that have grown on the surface can be left on the surface. Any that have grown outside of the pot, and which would be broken in repotting should be trimmed back to a stub of three or four inches in length. Cut off any shrivelled pseudobulbs (backbulbs) by severing the rhizome.

Pull off the old tissue-like scale leaves that cover the pseudobulbs. Do not remove the coverings from the rhizome unless they are particularly dry and loose, lest you injure dormant buds. Leave the covering on the young pseudobulbs. As you clean off the old tissue, look for scale insects which have a habit of hiding under it. The young scale insect is free-moving, and crawls around until it finds a sheltered spot, where it then settles down, sticks its proboscis into the plant tissues, covers itself with a dome of hard material, and remains permanently. Eggs are laid under the shell, and as the young hatch, they move out and find a new location. Clusters of scales with whitish or brownish shells may be found in protected places, along the grooves and joints of the pseudobulbs and at the juncture of leaf and pseudobulb. We do not see as much scale as we used to. In fact, it rarely occurs in greenhouses that are regularly sprayed with DDT or Malathion. But it can occur, especially on old plants that you may have acquired from neglected collections. If you find scale, scrub it off with a soft toothbrush dipped in a DDT solution, and then dip the whole plant in the same solution. If you do not find scale, it is not necessary to scrub or dip the plant.

Decide whether to divide the plant, and how best to do it, and cut through the rhizome with a sharp knife. To prevent carrying disease from one plant to another, the knife should be wiped and then dipped in seventy per cent alcohol or in boiling water, or should be flamed before it is used on another plant. Put a label on each division. If snail and slug damage is present, dust the roots with metaldehyde powder or dip them in a metaldehyde solution. You are now ready to pot. Follow the steps in Figure 25.

Put a handful of bark in the bottom of the pot over the crock. With one hand hold the plant in the pot so that the rhizome comes about half an inch below the rim and the back end touches one side, giving room at the other end for new growths. With the other hand pour handfuls of bark in around the roots, filling it among them with your fingers. When the pot is about two-thirds full, thump the pot on the bench to settle the bark, still holding the plant in position with one hand. Then add more bark up to the rim, thump the pot again to settle it, and then with your fingers or the blunt end of a potting stick press the bark down firmly around the inside edge of the pot. The rhizome should lie in a trench on the surface, with the bark lapping up against its sides and the upper surface exposed.

If the plant does not have many roots to hold it down in the bark, a piece of stiff wire cut a little longer than the inside diameter of the pot can be placed across the rhizome and its ends wedged against the sides of the pot. Clip a stake to the side of the pot and tie the pseudobulbs to it.

Fig. 25 Potting in Bark. A, A one-lead plant that will be divided. Growth has reached the edge of the pot. New roots are just starting at base of lead. B, Remove plant from pot. Cut through rhizome to make a "lead" division of four pseudobulbs. C, The plant divided. Ease the sections apart. Trim back any roots broken in the process and cut off any dead roots. Shake off most of old bark. D, The pot has been prepared with several pieces of crock in the bottom and enough bark to hold the plant at the right level. Place the plant in the pot with the older end against one side. Scoop bark into the pot, thumping at intervals to settle it. E, Fill the pot, thump again, and press the bark down around the edges with your thumbs for extra firming. Note that the thizome is in a trench on the surface, with bark lying against its sides and the top part exposed. Level of bark is one-half inch below rim. F, attach a stake to the rim to give plant rigid support. (There are several types made for use with bark.) G, Tie each pseudobulb to the stake. Use a "sling" of string, making the tie at the stake.

■ MOVING PLANTS FROM OSMUNDA FIBER TO BARK

For moving plants from osmunda fiber to bark there are two methods in use. Some growers like to leave a chunk of fiber under the front end of the plant, their reasons being, first, to give something to help anchor the plant in the bark, and second, to leave the roots of the younger part somewhat undisturbed. Other growers, including myself, prefer to remove practically all of the osmunda fiber. It does not hurt to leave a few shreds clinging to roots here and there, if by so doing you can prevent breaking the roots, but a large chunk of fiber holds water longer than the surrounding bark and creates a "wet spot" in the pot. If the plants are repotted when new roots are just forming, or when the roots are actively branching, as we described on page 44, the plants will become reestablished rapidly. To give the plants an anchor, stakes are made which clip to the pot and furnish a rigid support, eliminating the need for a chunk of fiber for this purpose. We feel that plants will do better from the start in plain bark than in bark with a center of osmunda fiber.

It is quite a job to remove osmunda fiber. Proceed slowly, pulling away the back part and the core, and then easing the roots apart to remove other sections. It is inevitable that many roots should be broken, but remember that their stubs will form branch roots. If a root and its system of branches can be saved by not picking off every last shred of fiber, leave these bits attached. When you have finished removing the fiber, run the hose through the roots to wash out any accumulation of broken down fiber. Then trim off any decayed roots, and cut back broken roots to an intact stub. Now follow all of the steps given above for potting in bark.

■ POTTING IN OSMUNDA FIBER

Remove the plant from the pot as described above and follow the steps in Figure 26. Remove the fiber from the core and from the back part. Study the plant to see whether to divide it, and where to make the cuts. Now ease apart the sections of the plant. Try to leave a firm chunk of fiber under each growing end, with as many roots intact as possible. Remove the rest of the old fiber from each part. Cut off any decayed roots, and cut back any healthy ones (except those in the solid ball) to a four-inch stub. Remove the old tissue from the pseudobulbs, and treat for scale or slug and snail injury if these are found.

Prepare the fresh osmunda fiber by soaking it in water, wringing it out thoroughly and letting it drain until it is just damp, no longer dripping. With a hatchet, chop the pieces into chunks about three inches wide. Fill a clay pot to about one quarter its depth with crock, and lay a piece of fiber over the crock.

Now take the plant in your hand and place chunks of fiber under the rhizome and between the root stubs to re-form a good ball. Set the plant with its ball of fiber in the pot, pressing the back end of the plant tightly against the back of the pot. With one hand squeezing the ball of fiber against the pot, push in additional chunks at the front end and at the sides, between the fiber that is already in place and the side of the pot. The chunks should be inserted vertically. Do not build up layers of fiber on top of each other, but instead add them as you would add books at the end of an already crowded bookshelf. Osmunda fiber requires pressure from the sides to hold it in place. When you have put as much fiber in the pot as you can with your hands, lay a chunk on its side on the rim of the pot and force it in with a potting stick, pushing one edge down into the pot to bring it vertically alongside the rest, and always manuvering the potting stick down and toward the center of the pot. Do not let the rhizome of the plant hump up. If it does this, pull out one or two pieces of fiber, settle it down, and start again. The rhizome should lie in a groove on the surface of the fiber, with its lower surface in the fiber and its upper surface exposed. Mature plants should be potted "hard," that is, the fiber should have about the consistency of sod. If you can easily push your fingers between the pot and the fiber, it is not hard enough. Add more chunks of fiber to

Fig. 26. Potting in Osmunda Fiber. A, a two-lead plant to be divided. B, after removing the oldest few backbulbs, the plant is divided where it forked into two leads. C, the front divisions. Each must be trimmed up. D, prepare the osmunda by chopping it into chunks. E, a division ready for potting. Roots have been trimmed back so that stubs remain in a solid ball of fiber. F, the pot has been prepared by filling it onefourth full of crock, and adding enough fiber to hold the plant at the desired level. Set the division in place, with the older end at the side of the pot. Place a large notched chunk of fiber under the lead. G, press the fiber back with your hands and insert additional pieces, vertically, until no more can be put in by hand. H, work in more fiber with a potting stick. Place a chunk on the edge of the pot, catch it in the middle with the stick, and force the stick down and toward the center of the pot. Continue until the fiber is uniformly hard. I, stake and tie the plant.

tighten it up. Drive a steel stake into the center of the pot, and tie the plant to it.

■ POTTING WITH SHREDDED WHOLE CROWN OSMUNDA AND TREE FERN

Shredded whole crown osmunda has been offered as a competitor to bark to ease potting. It consists of the tough crown and stem, chopped so that the fibers average about two inches in length. Tree fern fiber is chopped in the same way, but is somewhat more wiry. Both can be used for Cattleyas and other kinds of orchids, and the plants do very well in them. The plant is prepared as for potting in osmunda. The chopped whole crown, or chopped tree fern, is then poured into the pot like bark, and is tamped down until it is firm. Plants in these materials must be watered and cared for like those in regular osmunda fiber, with special care not to overwater. Removing chopped osmunda crown or tree fern from a plant that is to be repotted is not as easy as removing bark. For those who prefer osmunda fiber, however, using the chopped whole crown does eliminate some of the drudgery of potting. The same holds true for tree fern.

■ POTTING WITH TREE FERN-BARK MIX

A mixture of one part medium grade shredded tree fern to two parts bark makes a good mix for most orchids. It holds water a bit longer than bark and has its open quality. The mixture is handled like bark except that it needs more tamping while potting and less frequent watering.

■ CARE AFTER POTTING

Roots that are bruised or broken in the potting process, and even those not visibly damaged, are subject to rotting if they are kept wet. They heal nicely if they are allowed to dry out and remain dry for several weeks. For this reason we let the potting medium go without water until we see the new roots developing. The barks dry more quickly than osmunda fiber, but the latter, even though it is damp when used, will dry in a few days.

During the period of root recovery it is necessary to protect the plants from water loss through the leaves and pseudobulbs. We give them a little extra shade and a light mist spray twice a day on bright days. Just swish the sprayer over the plants, to dampen the pseudobulbs and leaves. A bit of the spray will also dampen the rhizome and the merest surface of the potting medium. This will encourage new roots to form. As the root tips become visible throughout the medium, give light waterings for a while, not enough to soak clear through, and then as the roots develop further increase the depth of the watering. When the roots are growing vigorously, remove the extra shade and put the plants on a regular watering and fertilizing schedule.

Since osmunda fiber holds water well from the start, plants in new fiber should not be watered any more often than plants that have been in it for some time. It takes the barks longer to begin holding water. Douglas fir is especially resistant. After the period of recovery, plants in new bark will therefore have to be watered more frequently for the first few months than they will from then on. Watch them closely, water when necessary to keep the bark damp, and then lengthen the interval between waterings when you see that the bark remains damp for longer periods.

■ SPECIAL NOTES

Sometimes after it has first been wetted, osmunda fiber develops a little fuzzy white mold. This is not dangerous to the plants. It disappears as the fiber dries out and does not come back. We do not know what it is —nor does it always appear. Just ignore it.

A few growers have advocated soaking the bark in a fertilizer solution several hours before using it. Either ammonium nitrate or a complete fertilizer may be used. Since the roots are inactive for a while and since the bark is kept dry, this will not immediately benefit the plants. However, when you do begin to water, the developing roots can then absorb the nutrients. A system that is perhaps more beneficial to newly potted plants is foliar feeding—

adding a fertilizer (one half teaspoon per gallon) to the water with which you mist the foliage. This, also, can be either ammonium nitrate or a complete fertilizer. The leaves will take up some of the chemicals and the plants will thus receive a little boost until their roots are again active.

Backbulbs can be encouraged to start new growth by being enclosed in a polyethylene bag. Put some damp bark in the bag, set the backbulbs on it, and close the bag tightly with a rubber band. In time a bud may start growth. When this new lead has roots well started, remove from the bag and pot as you would any division.

6 | The Cattleya Species

MANY wonderful things have been discovered by accident, and it was an accident that introduced the first Cattleya plants to European botanists. The story goes that in 1818 a Mr. Swainson was collecting mosses and lichens in Brazil, and gathered some heavy, thick-leaved plants to tie around some of his collections for shipment to England. When this material arrived, William Cattley, an eminent horticulturalist, realized that the odd plants were something unusual and rescued them from oblivion. The first of these plants bloomed in 1824, and was studied by Dr. Lindley, a renowned botanist, who found it to be of a genus entirely new to science. Lindley described the plant and gave the new genus the name Cattleya, after its happy possessor. The founding specimen he named *Cattleya labiata autumnalis,* because of its beautiful lip and its habit of flowering in the autumn.

For many years these were the only *Cattleya labiata* in Europe, for no one could rediscover its native habitat. It seems odd that this was so, for many other Cattleyas were discovered in the following decades, *Cattleya mossiae* in 1838, *Cattleya gigas* in 1848 or '49, *Cattleya trianaei* in 1856, and so on. No great

numbers were imported and many plants did not survive the long voyage. The Cattleyas were highly prized by horticulturalists and brought high prices from wealthy collectors, but their future in the commercial market was not realized until 1891. In that year a tremendous number of *Cattleya labiata* were found, and their purchase by two different companies, one English and one Belgian, caused quite a stir in orchid circles. There ensued a heated argument as to whether these were indeed the true *Cattleya labiata autumnalis,* each company hoping that it alone held the prize. Finally it was established that all of them were the real *labiata*. Possession of so many of the same species caused the price to drop from about $20 to about $1 per plant.

That was the beginning of the great demand for Cattleyas for the commercial market. Improved steamship travel sent a stream of collectors to South America who sent back hundreds of thousands of Cattleya plants to importers in their various countries. These were sold at auction to commercial growers, horticulturalists, and amateur growers.

As the kinds of Cattleya were discovered one after another, in great profusion, and were classified by the botanists of the time, many were found to be so similar to *C. labiata* as to be considered varieties of that species rather than as separate species. These varieties of *C. labiata* are the ones with which the public early became entranced because of their large, showy flowers, and they have occupied the center of attention ever since. For convenience and brevity, it has become customary to treat them as separate species, but *C. mossiae* was named *C. labiata*, variety *mossiae*, *C. trianaei* was named *C. labiata*, variety *trianaei*, and so on for the rest of this group, *C. dowiana, C. eldorado, C. gaskelliana, C. lawrenceana, C. lueddemanniana, C. mendelii, C. percivaliana, C. rex, C. schroederae, C. warneri, C. warscewiczii* (called *C. gigas* more commonly). These and two other species, *C. luteola* and *C. maxima*, which are similar, are together referred to as the "labiata" group. They all bear a single leaf to the pseudobulb, and for this reason are sometimes also called the "unifoliate" group.

The other group of Cattleyas is called the "bifoliate" group because its stems bear two, sometimes three, leaves. They are distinctive and delightful, quite different from the labiata type, and are rapidly coming into their own both from the point of view of popularity and for use in hybridization. Their flowers are usually smaller, with more slender parts, but many are very waxy and some produce their flowers in clusters of from five to twenty to a stem. The lip is small, often pointed, and may be kidney shaped or fiddle-shaped, having a break between the side lobes sometimes referred to as a "spade" lip. They exhibit a fantastic array of colors and markings—yellow, green, yellow-green, brownish green, brown, orange, red-orange, white, bluish white, and tones of pink and pink-magenta that are often very brilliant. Many are spotted with brown or purple. The lip is often in complete contrast to the rest of the flower; for instance, *C. bicolor* is brownish green with a bright pink lip. With the interest now tending toward smaller flowers, these little species offer their individual charms both to the collector and to the hybridist. In crossing them with the larger labiata types, growers combine the characteristics of many smaller flowers to the stem, distinctive coloring, unusual shapes, and heavy substance with the fuller, rounder form of the labiata type.

Except for a few which retain their popularity, the species of the labiata group are found less often now in amateur collections than in former years, when they once formed the bulk of Cattleyas available both to amateur and commercial growers. The more luxurious hybrids, with their wider range of colors, have almost entirely supplanted them. However, good specimens of species have a real value, the very best of them being almost unobtainable because they are retained by the hybridists and by collectors who prize them. The value of the species to the amateur lies in their dependability for flowering times, and in the interest they have as the types that have gone into the making of the hybrids. Even though one may love his hybrids, he will know them better if he is familiar with some of their progenitors. If you have a good plant of any of the species, keep it.

The species of the bifoliate group, on the other hand, are becoming rapidly better known, and amateurs are eagerly adding them to their collections. This is a reflection of the widespread interest in the odd and unusual kinds of orchids. It also shows that the present-day amateur has come of age—he does not feel that he must have just the huge and the showy, although they have great attraction, but that he places value on the particular qualities each kind, large or small, has to offer. As a matter of fact, a single plant with many bright little flowers creates just as much of a show as one that gives larger flowers, and a tiny, dwarf plant holds its own by sheer contrast. Lovely things are coming from hybridization with the smaller flowers, but do save the species while you enjoy the hybrids.

I should like to translate for you a bit from an old book, "Les Cattleya" by Léon Duval, a French orchid grower, 1907. "It is no more just to establish comparisons or classes of beauty among certain Cattleya than it would be to compare certain works of art; let us leave to beautiful plants their own special qualities, which command our admiration for these same qualities, and not establish a royalty among the Cattleya. . . ."

■ **THE SPECIES**

The Cattleyas are all epiphytic, growing naturally on trees and rocks. Their stems vary in height from two inches to three feet; in some they are club-shaped and in others cane-like. They have from one to three thick, hard leaves, borne at the top of the stem, and the stem is clothed with thin sheathing leaves that dry after the first season. The flower parts are free and spreading, the sepals similar, the petals broader than the sepals. The lip has three parts—two side lobes that fold up around the column and a middle lobe that is spreading. In some the side lobes are quite distinct from the middle lobe, and are often more fleshy, especially among members of the bifoliate group. In others the side lobes are continuous with the middle lobe, as in the labiata group.

Fig. 27 *Cattleya labiata,* the species upon which the genus was founded, has played many important roles in orchid culture.

The column is plain, not decorated with wings, and bears four pollinia, two in each of the two sacs in the anther. Most of the species are delightfully fragrant.

The Labiata Group

Cattleya dowiana. This variety of labiata is a beautiful nankeen yellow with a large purple lip lined with gold. It has contributed its yellow color to many hybrids. The flowers are between six and seven inches across; from two to six occur on a stem. It was discovered in Costa Rica in 1848 by a Polish gardener, Warscewicz. However, the specimens that he sent to Europe arrived in poor condition, and it was not until 1864 that good specimens were obtained by Mr. Arce and purchased by Messrs. Veitch and Sons, English horticulturalists, who flowered it for the first time. The species was named for Captain Dow, whose ship carried many an orchid hunter and many a cargo of orchid plants. It is the most celebrated of Costa Rican orchids, but is quite rare now, having been nearly cleared out by collectors.

Cattleya dowiana variety *aurea.* This species occurs in Colombia, entirely separated from the *C. dowiana* of Costa Rica. The flowers are a deeper yellow and the lip is more copiously marked with gold. It is a large plant, similar in every way to *Cattleya dowiana.* Its period of vegetative growth is from May to September, and flowering follows immediately in September and October. It rests during the winter. The species is used a great deal in hybridization.

Cattleya eldorado. Pale rosy-lilac with slender petals. The lip of this flower is the same color but marked with a central orange blotch surrounded by white and purple. It is a variety of labiata, but not well known, which was discovered in Brazil in 1866. It flowers in late summer and fall.

Cattleya gaskelliana. These large, fragrant, handsome flowers are six to seven inches across. The sepals and petals are usually purple-violet, suffused with white, occasionally marked with a median band of white. The lip is generous in proportions, and the tube is the same color as the petals. The front lobe of the lip is deep violet with a pale border, the throat streaked with yellow and marked on each side by a spot of yellowish white. French growers used to call this species *"Cattleya chou"* (Cattleya cabbage) because it is so easy to grow. It is a variety of labiata and is still quite popularly grown by amateurs. Vegetative growth starts in about April and flowering follows immediately, from July to September, after which it rests during the winter. The species occurs in Venezuela and Brazil, where it grows on rocks at elevations from five hundred to three thousand feet. It was introduced into England from Venezuela in 1884 or '85 and was named for a Mr. Gaskell of Woolton. There is a white variety, *alba*, and one that has white petals and sepals with the front lobe of the lip crimson.

Cattleya gigas. This species should be correctly called *Cattleya warscewiczii*, but the name *gigas* is commonly used and will be found in lists and catalogues. It was discovered in 1848 or '49 in Colombia by the same man who found *Cattleya dowiana*. This is the largest flowered of all the Cattleyas, the blooms being seven to nine inches in diameter and most showy. The petals and sepals are rosy-lilac, and the huge, rich red-violet lip is marked with two brilliant yellow eyes. The edge of the lip is ruffled and has a pale border. *C. gigas* is one of the most popular of the labiata group. It should be watered sparsely during fall and early winter, and then as usual from time new growths start. It likes a bright airy location. See illustration page 2. The species flowers from late May to September. The earlier blooming plants start their new growth in January, while those that will bloom later on wait to begin new growth until about March. Flowering follows as soon as the growth is formed. The resting period is from October to January. The white variety, Firmin Lambeau, is very valuable.

Cattleya labiata. These beautifully proportioned flowers, of wonderful texture, are a rich, vibrant rose, almost luminous in quality. The dainty lip is modest in size, with the throat more open than tube-like. The front lobe of the lip is ruffled, deep red-violet with darker lines which run through two orange spots into the yellow throat. The flowers keep a long time. The flowering time of *labiata* and its hybrids can be controlled by manipulation of daylength and temperature. *Cattleya labiata* starts its growth in March or April, and flowers without pause in the fall, from October through November. The flower buds are produced in a double sheath, one sheath within the other. The period of rest is from the end of flowering to the start of new growth in late winter. Among the many color variations are a white form, var. *alba*, and one which has white petals and sepals with a crimson lip, var. *Cooksoniae*. This native of Brazil was discovered in 1818. See picture on page 58.

Cattleya lawrenceana. A small flowered species, not well known, has reddish-brown pseudobulbs. The flowers are four to five inches across with five to eight in a cluster. The petals are rather slender, and the lip small and tube-like. The color varies from pale rosy-purple to white, and the front lobe of the lip is purple with a maroon blotch. The species occurs in British Guiana, where it was discovered about 1882. It grows actively during the summer and remains through the winter with the sheaths formed, to flower in the spring.

Cattleya lueddemanniana, also called *Cattleya speciosissima*. This species closely resembles *Cattleya labiata*. The flowers are rose-purple, suffused with white, the front lobe of the lip is amethyst-purple, and lines of this color extend into the throat between two yellow blotches. It is one of the few whose handling is rather tricky. The clue to its behavior is probably that it grows natively under such a variety of conditions that the plants show more individual differences than are found in most species. It grows actively from spring to fall, and can flower anytime from April to September. Its period of lessened activity is November to February. The species occurs in Venezuela, where it was discovered in 1850. It was named by Professor Reichenbach for Mr. Lueddeman, for many years his chief gardener and a well-

Fig. 28. A wedding bouquet made with flowers of *Cattleya gigas* 'Firmin Lambeau', a rare white variety of this species. (Courtesy of B. O. Bracey and Co.).

known horticulturalist. There is a white form, var. *alba.*

Cattleya luteola. These charming little yellow flowers are only two inches across with petals about the same width as the sepals, and a small tubular lip that is yellow or whitish, often streaked with purple. The pseudobulbs are two to three inches tall and leaves three to four inches long. The species occurs in Brazil, where it was discovered in 1853. It flowers in early winter.

Cattleya maxima. The flowers, though large and nicely colored, have slender parts and lack compactness. Sepals and petals are lilac or pale rose, the front lobe of the lip is ruffled, pale rose or a deeper shade, with a central stripe of yellow from which radiate darker lines, and a pale border. The plant is not grown much now, though it was once very popular. It occurs in Ecuador and Peru and flowers in the fall.

Cattleya mendelii. One of the most distinct of the labiata group, this species has large delicately colored flowers, seven to eight inches across. The sepals and petals are whitish or pale rose, and the lip is generous in size with the outer lobe very much ruffled and marked with a clean-cut patch of purple. The throat is yellow, more or less streaked with crimson. It is easy to grow, and much loved by amateurs. Its native habitat is Colombia, where it was discovered in 1870, and named for Samuel Mendel, an English orchid lover. In habit it is similar to *Cattleya mossiae* (below). The species grows from June through September, and waits through the winter after the sheaths are formed to bloom in April and May.

Cattleya mossiae. Once called the Easter orchid, this beautiful species rivals *Cattleya gigas* in richness of coloring. Its spring flowering season gave it great value for Easter and Mother's Day. It is rosy-lilac in color, with wide, beautifully ruffled petals. The lip is as wide as or wider than the petals, the broad front lobe frilled, mottled with violet-purple, with a pale border. The throat is yellow, striped with purple. It was discovered in 1836 in Venezuela, where it grows in large quantities, and flowered for the first time in the col-

lection of a Mr. Moss, after whose wife it was named. It was collected so ruthlessly that it was threatened with extinction, and the Venezuelan government had to place a temporary embargo on its export to give it a chance to reproduce. There is wide variation in this species including some that are thin and poorly shaped, but a good specimen is very pretty. There are many magnificent named varieties, among them several whites of which the best known is var. *Wageneri,* white with a yellow spot on the lip. The species grows during the summer and early fall, and waits through the winter with its sheaths formed to flower in April and May. Some individuals flower as late as August.

Cattleya percivaliana. This is one of the smaller flowered of the labiata group, but a lovely orchid. The richly colored flowers are four to five inches across, varying from light to deep rose, and are nicely proportioned. The dainty, rather short lip has a pale, exquisitely frilled border surrounding a deep maroon center. The throat is orange, variegated with deep violet. It flowers at Christmas time. The species, which occurs in Venezuela, was introduced in 1882 to England by Sander. It is named after Mr. R. Percival, an English orchid grower. There is great variation in the species from good to poor quality. Growth may start in January, without any rest after flowering, or it may wait to begin new growth in April or May. Sheaths are formed by the end of the summer, but the flower buds wait until October

Fig. 29 *Cattleya mossiae.*

to begin development and mature in December.

Cattleya rex. These large cream white to pale yellow flowers are attractive but seldom grown. The lip is of good size, the throat yellow veined with purple, the front lobe crimson lightly veined, with a white, ruffled border. The species occurs in the Peruvian Andes. Growth starts in April, and the plants flower in September, after which they rest during the winter.

Cattleya schroederae. Lovely fragrant flowers are entirely pale rose faintly suffused with white, except that the lip has yellow or deep rose in the throat. It was originally designated a variety of *Cattleya trianaei*, and therefore belongs in the labiata group. However, it is much more ruffled than *Cattleya trianaei* and has a later blooming season, rivaling *Cattleya mossiae*. It is another of the handsome Colombian orchids, discovered in 1885 or '86, and named for Baroness Schroeder, wife of a famous orchid grower. The plant grows from May through September, and then, like *C. mossiae*, waits through the winter with the sheaths formed. The flower buds start to develop about the first of January, and open from March to May. The flowers mature more slowly than those of some other species, and should not be cut until they have been open four or five days. There are many named varieties, a white form and several near-white ones.

Cattleya trianaei. The flowers of this species are a little more plain, the petals and lip a little less ruffled than others of the labiata group, but they are still lovely, and a handsome specimen ranks with the best of the Cattleyas. The sepals and petals are pale pinkish-lavender. The lip is a little narrower than the petals, but sometimes equals their width. The front

Fig. 30 *Cattleya trianaei.*

lobe is usually purple, but is often a brilliant crimson hardly rivaled among the Cattleyas. The pale border of the lip varies in width, being fairly wide in some and hardly discernible in others. The throat is yellow, faintly streaked with deeper yellow. The average size of the flower is about six to seven inches. It is a species in which there is a great variation in coloring. *Cattleya trianaei* is a native of Colombia, where it was discovered in 1856 by the celebrated traveler, J. Linden. The species was named for José Triana, a well-known botanist of Bogota, who died in Paris. The blooming season extends from late December through March, with the largest number flowering in January. New growth starts a short time after flowering, in about March or April, and continues until August, at which time the sheaths are completely formed. The flower buds wait until October to begin developing. Among the varieties is a white form.

Cattleya warneri. A lovely member of the labiata group, this species is similar to *Cattleya labiata,* but with larger flowers. The sepals and petals are rose-lilac, the front lobe of the lip is heavily ruffled and bright purple. The throat is yellow-orange, streaked with white or pale violet. Growth starts in February and the flowers develop as soon as the sheaths are formed, opening during May and June. Its period of lessened activity is during the winter. The species occurs in South Brazil where it was discovered in 1859. There is a lovely white form, var. *alba,* that has a yellow throat.

The Bifoliate Group

Cattleya aclandiae. Greenish-yellow flowers are barred and spotted with chocolate brown, with a bright rose-purple lip. The short fleshy side lobes curve up beside the column, and the spreading middle lobe is fleshy in the center and kidney-shaped. The extremely broad rosy column is a decorative attribute of the flower. The plants are dwarf, the little two-inch stems spaced rather widely on the creeping rhizome. Each stem bears a pair of small rounded leaves. The four-inch flower is start-

lingly large for the size of the plant. The species, which was discovered in Brazil in 1839, blooms in June and July.

Cattleya amethystoglossa. Daintily colored, attractive flowers, three and one-half to five inches across, grow five to 8 in a cluster. Sepals and petals are white suffused with rose-purple, and spotted with amethyst. The lip has small, erect side lobes, and a broad, rounded middle lobe that is violet-purple marked with radiating ridges of papillae. The plants are very tall, with pseudobulbs reaching three feet, and bearing two leaves six to twelve inches long. The plant, discovered in Brazil in 1862, flowers in midsummer.

Cattleya aurantiaca. Small bright red-orange flowers, borne in a somewhat drooping cluster, make this a popular species. It has been included in the genus Epidendrum, and you may find it listed as such. Some forms have flowers larger than the usual inch-and-a-half diameter. Native to Guatemala and surrounding countries, it flowers in late winter and early spring.

Cattleya bicolor. This remarkable flower is olive-green tinged with copperish brown, with a bright crimson tongue-like lip that has no side lobes and leaves the column completely exposed. The pseudobulbs are tall and jointed, one to three feet high, bearing two leaves four to six inches long. This species has been used in hybridization with Cattleyas of the labiata group. It was discovered in Brazil in 1837. It usually blooms in the fall, sometimes in the spring as well, giving four to six very waxy flowers to a stem. See illustration page 78.

Cattleya bowringiana. A strong growing plant that sometimes produces as many as twenty flowers on a stem and is often used in hybridization with members of the labiata group. The flowers are small, less than three inches across, the sepals and petals rose-purple. The lip is similar to that of the labiata type, deep purple with white in the throat. It grows on rocks and rubble near streams in British Honduras, and needs a little more water than most Cattleyas. The species grows during the spring and summer, flowers in October and

November, and has a short mid-winter rest. It was discovered in 1884.

Cattleya citrina. This attractive and unusual plant has the habit of growing with its head hanging down. The flowers are spicily fragrant, yellow except for the white border of the tubular lip. The sepals and petals enfold the lip giving the flower the appearance of an upside down tulip. The bloom lasts a long time in perfection. The pseudobulbs are egg-shaped and bear two or three grayish leaves four to seven inches long. The plant should be grown in a basket suspended in a tilted position to allow the growths to hang over the edge. Discovered in Mexico in the 17th century by the Jesuit, Hernandez, it was not until 1859 that any large number of plants reached Europe. It flowers in late spring and early summer, and likes a cool spot in the Cattleya house.

Cattleya deckeri. Similar to *C. skinneri* and *C. bowringiana,* this species was once thought to be a variety of the former but is now accepted as a distinct species. The three-inch flowers are rose-purple and the lip is without the white patch in the throat. It occurs in Mexico, Guatemala, Costa Rica, and Panama and flowers in the fall.

Cattleya dolosa. This is a charming dwarf species from Brazil. The flowers are very waxy, four inches across, rose-magenta, with the front lobe of the lip amethyst-purple marked with yellow. The little side lobes of the lip are erect. It resembles *Cattleya walkeriana,* of which it was once thought to be a variety, but produces its flowers from the top of the pseudobulb. The species is rather rare.

Cattleya forbesii. These pale yellow-green flowers are three to four inches across. The paler lip is small and yellow, the side lobes forming a tube, the inside of which is streaked with red, while the roundish front lobe has a bright yellow center marked with purple. The species was discovered in South Brazil in 1823. It flowers in mid-summer and rests during the winter.

Cattleya granulosa. This species is well worth growing because of its striking flowers which are olive-green, sometimes yellowish brown, spotted with crimson-purple or red, occurring five to nine in a cluster. The white side lobes of the lip form a tube that is yellow or rose inside, while the long spear-shaped middle lobe is marked with crimson papillae. The flowers are very waxy, the lip so stiff as to appear to be carved out of wood. The flowers, which appear in the summer, last a long time. The plant is now being used in hybridization. The species occurs in Guatemala and Brazil; it was discovered in the latter country in 1840.

Cattleya guttata. These beautiful yellow-green flowers are spotted with deep purple. The lip has small white side lobes, and a spreading middle lobe that is amethyst-purple marked with papillae. The pseudobulbs reach thirty inches in height, and bear two leaves five to nine inches long. The flowers are three to four inches across, five to ten in a cluster. Discovered in South Brazil in 1827 its flowering season is from summer to fall. The plant is frequently used in hybridization. There is a form that has a pure white lip. *C. elatior* and *C. leopoldii,* once considered distinct species, are now felt to be varieties of *C. guttata.*

Cattleya harrisoniana. A popularly grown and attractive species, its flowers are bright rose-lilac, four to four and one-half inches across. The long side lobes of the lip are bordered with yellow, and the small middle lobe, spreading from a deep notch, is yellow shading to purple. The lip has a centrally located orange disk which has several thickened corrugations. The plant is twelve to fifteen inches tall, the flowers are borne in clusters of two to five. It is now being used in hybridization quite frequently. The blooming season is summer to fall and the flowers last a long time. The species is native to Brazil.

Cattleya intermedia. Charming, delicately colored flowers make this a most desirable species. The four to five inch flowers vary from pale rose to milky white and are sometimes dotted with amethyst. The lip has smooth side lobes that enfold the column in a long tube, while the spreading middle lobe is ruffled and of a rich amethyst color. The slender pseudobulbs are about eighteen inches tall, and bear

Fig. 31 *Cattleya harrisoniana,* typical of bifoliate species with its slender stems and paired leaves. (Courtesy of Rod McLellan Co.)

Fig. 32 *Cattleya guttata*. (Courtesy of Rod McLellan Co.)

Fig. 33 *Cattleya forbesii*. (Courtesy of Jones and Scully, Inc.)

two or three leaves. The flowers occur in a cluster of four to five. This is another of the species now being used in hybridization. It occurs in South Brazil where it was discovered in 1824. The flowers appear through the summer. There is a white form.

Cattleya intermedia variety *Aquinii*. This very rare form perhaps merits species standing as *Cattleya aquinii*. The petals are broad, somewhat ruffled, and carry the coloring of the lip, having the tips deeply marked with rich amethyst. This characteristic is contributed to some of the hybrids made with *C. intermedia* var. *Aquinii* as one parent.

Cattleya loddigesii. One of the most common orchids of Brazil, this species grows in a variety of locations. It is a small plant, about a foot high, with slender pseudobulbs that bear leaves four to five inches long. The species *C. harrisoniana* has been considered a variety of this species, but *C. loddigesii* differs in that it lacks the corrugations in the lip and has somewhat smaller, more delicately colored flowers. The flowers are waxy, and from two to five are produced on a stem. This, and the pure white form 'Stanley,' are used in hybridization. It oc-

curs in Brazil where it was discovered quite early and given a place in the genus Cattleya in 1824. The flowers, which appear in late summer, last several weeks.

Cattleya nobilior. This species produces its flowering growth from the base of the pseudobulb, as does *C. walkeriana* which it resembles,

Fig. 34 *Cattleya intermedia*. (Courtesy of Jones and Scully, Inc.)

and of which it may be a variety. The purple-lilac flowers are very fragrant, three to four and one-half inches across, but only one or two grow on a stem. The lip is fleshy, the side lobes entirely enfolding the column; the middle lobe is broad and yellow. It occurs in Brazil.

Cattleya pachecoi. Rather recently discovered, this species resembles *C. aurantiaca*, with flowers two and one-half to three inches across, six to ten on a stem, lemon-yellow with a buff to light yellow lip. The lip does not have distinct side lobes, but is rather tubular with the outer portion slightly expanded, and a disk with three slightly raised central veins. The plant occurs in Guatemala.

Cattleya schilleriana. These rather large, striking flowers are four to five inches across, olive-green tinted with brown and spotted with black-purple. The side lobes of the lip are white externally, marked with purple inside, while the middle lobe is kidney-shaped, crimson, with a white margin and streaks of white. It was discovered in Brazil in 1857, and flowers from June to September. A small plant, it somewhat resembles *C. aclandiae*, and is suspected of being a natural hybrid between that and *C. guttata.* It is rather rare.

Cattleya skinneri. Called the "Flower of San Sebastian" in its native Costa Rica, this plant is used by the natives to decorate their altars and the roofs of their houses. The flowers are three and one-half to five inches across, entirely rose-purple except for white in the throat. Five to ten grow on a stem. They have a sparkling, almost crystalline texture which gives them a radiant quality. They are not of heavy substance, but keep a long time. The lip is similar in character to the labiata type, but somewhat more tubular. This is a popular species and widely grown. Discovered in Guatemala in 1836, it occurs from Mexico to Panama. The flowers appear in late winter or spring. There is a pure white form.

Cattleya velutina. The tawny-yellow flowers, spotted with maroon-purple, make this a striking species. The small side lobes of the lip are white, streaked with purple inside, while the middle lobe is white marked with a yellow

spot and radiating purple lines at its base. It blooms in late summer and is fragrant. The plant is native to Brazil.

Cattleya violacea. These very lovely fragrant, bright rose-purple flowers are four to five inches across. The lip is fleshy, deep purple-violet, with triangular side lobes that expose the column, and a rounded, ruffled front lobe marked with a patch of yellow streaked with purple. The plant occurs at rather low altitudes in the northern part of South America, where the temperature is quite hot. It can be adapted to the usual Cattleya temperatures but needs a warm place in the greenhouse and rather more water. The flowers appear through the summer.

Cattleya walkeriana. A dwarf species whose stocky little pseudobulbs bear single leaves, the flowers are three to five inches in diameter. They are delightfully fragrant, rose-lilac in color, with a jaunty little fleshy lip. The front lobe of the lip is triangular, spreading out from under the tip of the column, yellow and purple, veined with a brighter shade of purple. The pink side lobes turn up around the column like flaring wings of a collar, leaving the column exposed. This species produces its flowers on a stem that arises from the base of the pseudobulb instead of at is top. It is a native of west-

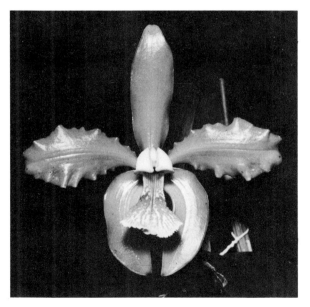

Fig. 35 *Cattleya granulosa.* (Courtesy of Jones and Scully, Inc.)

Fig. 36 *Cattleya walkeriana.* (Courtesy of H. F. Loomis)

ern Brazil, where there are definite wet and dry seasons. Discovered in 1839, and brought to Europe for the first time in 1848. Its flowering season is irregular, extending from fall to spring, and the flowers last for six weeks. The plants require much less water during their period of rest.

■ NATURAL HYBRIDS

The ease with which the species within a genus will cross with each other, and even with the species of related genera, is one of the remarkable features of the orchids. Because this is true it is to be expected that natural hybrids would occur in areas where related kinds grow together. That they do occur has led to some confusion in identification. Kinds which were at first thought to be species have later been found to be hybrids, and occasionally one that was thought to be a hybrid has been given the status of a species. Some of

the natural crosses have been repeated in cultivation, thus proving their origin.

Cattleya hardyana. Found in Colombia, this is a hybrid between *C. dowiana* var. *aurea* and *C. gigas.* The flowers are large, bright rose-purple. The richly colored lip resembles the lip of *C. dowiana* var. *aurea* but has the two yellow eyes of *C. gigas.* This natural hybrid has been repeated in cultivation. The man-made hybrid C. Hardyana is one of the best known of the older hybrids and has been used as a parent in a long line of subsequent hybrids.

Cattleya guatemalensis. This hybrid between *Cattleya skinneri* and *C. aurantiaca,* has pale rose-purple flowers. The lip has side lobes that are pale orange on the outside, and a middle lobe of purple with a red-spotted orange-yellow disk. Some plants give flowers that resemble the *skinneri* parent and others have flowers that are more like the *aurantiaca* parent. There is sometimes an orange tone to the flowers when they first open. It blooms in late spring and summer and is found in Guatemala.

Cattleya victoria-reginae. This plant grows with *C. labiata* and *C. guttata* var. *Leopoldii,* and is probably a hybrid between the two. Its pseudobulbs are tall like those of the latter and bear one or two leaves. The flowers are attractive, intermediate between the two species in size, and have the three lobed lip of the *guttata* parent, although the middle lobe is broadened by the influence of the *labiata* parent. The sepals are purple tinged with yellow, the petals purple; both are veined with red. This Brazilian plant, which was discovered in Pernambuco in 1891, is quite rare.

A few other natural hybrids have been found, and are sometimes described as species. They are rarely seen at present, and some may not be known in collections.

7 | *Control of Flowering in Cattleyas*

THE Cattleya species come from areas where the length of the days reaches neither of the extremes of short or long days that exist in our latitudes, and where the temperature changes from season to season are small. Yet the small changes in daylength and temperature are apparently critical for their flowering in their native habitats. These species exhibit their sensitivity to daylength and temperature in various ways when grown in our country. Our greater seasonal differences in daylength are imposed upon their inherent flowering habits, and the temperatures we maintain in our greenhouses may influence their response to the length of days.

Important to the understanding of their flowering habits is a knowledge of when and under what conditions flower buds are "initiated," and what conditions bring about the subsequent growth of the flower buds. Initiation of flower buds means the laying down of the flower parts in microscopic size by the meristematic tissue at the tip of the pseudobulb. The buds are not visible in the sheath at this time, in fact, in some species several months elapse between the initiation of the buds and the time they can be seen growing in

the sheath. Since our daylength is constantly changing from shorter to longer, or longer to shorter, each species has to find a specific daylength compatible with its inherent habit and the stage of development of its pseudobulbs for the initiation of flower buds. The daylength that prevails during the period which follows initiation, and the temperatures of the season or in the greenhouse, may or may not be condusive to their further development. Thus after initiating their buds, some species can develop them immediately, while others must wait for several months after initiation for the proper set of conditions to occur that will cause these buds to resume growth. *With Cattleyas (and other orchids as well) we must deal with two sets of conditions, one that causes initiation of buds and another that brings them into active growth.* Once the buds have been put into active growth so that they are elongating rapidly, they will continue to grow regardless of the length of the days.

The sensitivity to daylength of many garden and house plants, and control of their flowering by manipulation of daylength, has been known for many years. Plants, such as chrysanthemum and aster, initiate flower buds and develop them immediately following initiation. The conditions that bring about initiation also bring about flowering. Thus when we speak of daylength in connection with their flowering, we mean the daylength necessary for the whole process from bud formation to the opening of flowers. Among the plants of house and garden are "short-day" plants, which initiate buds and produce flowers when the days are less than 13 hours long (some require days less than 12 hours, and a few respond on a 14-hour day); "long-day" plants, which initiate flower buds and produce flowers when the days are longer than 13 or 14 hours, and "day neutral" plants which flower regardless of the daylength. Chrysanthemums and asters are typical short day plants. They can be brought into flower at any time of the year by controlling the length of day—by giving them long days by means of electric lights until it is desired to have them start the flowering process, and then short days to bring about bud formation and blooming. Calceolaria and scabiosa are examples of long day plants. Their flowering can be brought about in mid-winter by giving them artificially lengthened days. Night temperature can alter the flowering of many kinds. For instance, foxglove does not flower when grown continually with night temperatures of 55° to 60°; it will flower only after a period of nights of 40° to 50°. Stocks flower during the winter at a night temperature of 50° but not at 60°. Temperature can even change the response of plants to daylength. Poinsettia will flower with short days when grown at night temperatures of 63° to 64°, but becomes a long day plant with nights of 55°.

Comparison of a few Cattleya species on which work has been done will illustrate the role of both daylength and temperature on their bud initiation and flowering. The following table gives the normal dates of flower bud initiation at Ithaca, New York, as discovered by Gavino Rotor from microscopic studies of the tips of pseudobulbs. The plants were growing in normal seasonal daylengths and temperatures. These species and some other kinds of orchids were then grown experimentally under continuously short and continuously long days, at continuous night temperatures of 55° and 65°, and compared to groups grown normally. The short days were held at 9 hours in length by covering the plants with black cloth when the normal daylength exceeded this, and long days were kept at 16 hours by using artificial lighting.

Normal dates of bud initiation under greenhouse conditions in Ithaca, New York*

	1949	1950
Cattleya gaskelliana .		March 1
C. labiata	June 25	June 25
C. percivaliana . .	September 3	September 1
C. trianaei	September 3	September 15
C. mossiae	November 15	November 1

When *Cattleya gigas* (similar to *C. gaskelliana* in above table) is grown with a night temperature of 55° and normal daylength, it initiates its buds during the short days of late February and early March. The daylength of the following weeks is conducive to the further development of the buds, and they grow rapidly and come into flower before the pseudobulb is fully mature. The buds are thus initiated and begin development during the short days of spring. If instead of 55° nights, *C. gigas* is grown continuously with nights of 65°, it will not flower. If the plants are grown with continuous 16-hour days and either 55° or 65° nights they generally fail to flower. From the point of view of both flower bud initiation and triggering the buds into growth, *C. gigas* is a short day plant. Even though it completes its flowering during the long days of June and July, the significant day-length is that which causes the buds to begin growing up in the sheath. Once the buds have started this growth they will continue regardless of the daylength.

Cattleya trianaei normally initiates its flower buds in mid-September when the days are short, and waits until the even shorter days of November to start the buds growing up in the sheath. Temperature is not critical in its case, for it will initiate and develop its flowers

* Bulletin #885, Cornell University Agricultural Experiment Station, "Daylength and Temperature in Relation to Growth and Flowering of Orchids" by Gavino B. Rotor, Jr.

with either 55° or 65° nights. The daylength is critical, however, for flowering is entirely prevented by continuous days of 16 hours at either night temperature. *C. trianaei* is, therefore, another short day plant.

C. mossiae initiates its buds during the short days about November 1, at a night temperature of 55°, and waits through December and part of January to start the buds growing up in the sheath. Continuous long days entirely prevent flowering. In work done on *C. mossiae*, it appeared that this species would initiate some buds with 65° nights and short days, but the flowering was delayed and spread erratically over a number of months. Experience in growing *C. mossiae* has shown that its best and most reliable flowering comes when it has at least two months of short days with nights of 55° to initiate the buds and start them growing in the sheath. Here, therefore, is another short day species.

Cattleya labiata, under normal seasonal conditions, initiates flower buds during the longest days of the year, close to June 21. The long days and warm nights that usually prevail through the summer prevent these buds from going ahead and developing, and this species waits until the shorter days and cooler nights of fall to resume growth of the buds and bring them into bloom. Experiments with *C. labiata* turned up some remarkable inter-relationships between temperature and daylength. When it was grown with continuous long days and nights of 65°, it was entirely prevented from blooming (although we would expect from the above information that flower buds had been initiated). Grown with continuous long days but with nights of 55°, some plants flowered, though not all. A night temperature of 55° is apparently capable of somewhat offsetting the influence of long days. Grown with continuous short days and 65° nights, about half the plants flowered; and better flowering was had with short days and 55° nights. As a matter of interest, when we sort out this data we find the following to be true: (1) as far as flower bud initiation is concerned, *C. labiata* is day neutral, for it initiates buds with either

long or short days, regardless of night temperature: (2) at a 55° night temperature it is day neutral for it can both initiate and develop flower buds at this temperature with either daylength; (3) with 65° nights it is a short day plant as far as growth of the buds and blooming is concerned; (4) the only combination that entirely prevents the growth of the buds and therefore prevents flowering is long days plus 65° nights; (5) growth of the flower buds resulting in flowering requires either 55° nights, or short days, or both.

Not enough work has been done on other species of Cattleya. We can only speculate about the habits of those not actually studied. But if we were to speculate on the basis of what we know of those that have been described here and from the flowering times of others, we might guess that the kinds that flower in winter, spring, and early summer are all short-day plants. Where fall flowering is concerned, we would not know whether the plants follow the habits of *C. labiata,* or whether they have a pattern of their own. There are many Cattleya species, some quite unfamiliar and little grown. We do not know what any of these would show themselves capable of under experimental conditions. So far, the only patterns discovered among the Cattleyas are "short day" and "day neutral."

Hybrids inherit their growth and flowering patterns from their ancestors. Some members of a cross may inherit the pattern of one of the species in their makeup, others that of a different species. There are hybrids, however, that make several growths a year, and flower whenever a growth matures. We have a cross in which a number of flowering patterns appear. There are individual plants that always flower in the spring, others always in the fall, and still others always in the winter. There are some that flower regularly twice a year, both in the spring and in the fall. All of these we would call short-day plants. In this same cross there are some individuals that flower three or four times a year, and which, through a period of several years have hit nearly every month in the year. We have not studied their actual bud initiation, but we feel it would be safe to say that these individuals are day neutral.

Control of flowering has been worked out very exactly for *C. labiata* and its hybrids. *C. labiata* contributes its habits of bud initiation and flower development to its progeny. The more labiata there is in a hybrid, or the more recently it has been introduced into the strain, the more exactly can its flowering be controlled. The flowering of these hybrids can be timed for any date one wishes. Flowering has been prevented experimentally for as long as two years, and the plants then brought into flower. Hybridists have created crosses especially for the control of flowering, and greater success will be had in using them. This does not mean that you should not try control on any labiata hybrids you may have.

Essentially, the method of control is to give the plants long days and a night temperature of 65° to withhold flowering until it is desired to have the buds start to grow up in the sheath, and then to give them the short days that will bring about blooming. It has been found that complete control is had by starting the long-day, 65° night treatment in June. You might wonder why it must be begun so early, since these plants normally do not flower until fall. As a group, the labiata hybrids flower from September through November. Without studying each plant individually, there is no way of knowing exactly when the flower buds start to grow up in the sheath. If exact control is desired, it is best to keep the night temperature at 65° by means of thermostatically controlled heating, otherwise a cool spell of weather might trigger some plants into starting the flower buds up in the sheath, thus bringing them into bloom ahead of the date you wish. Also, since the days begin to shorten after June 21 and we do not know just what the critical daylength is for the start of flower bud growth, the days are held to 16 hours by means of electric lights from this date. It takes about two months, more or less (you would have to time this for your own plants), for the flower buds

to grow up in the sheath and be ready to open, so the long days and 65° nights are continued until about two months before the crop of flowers is desired. Day temperature during the long-day treatment is run ten degrees higher, around 75°. Suppose you wish to have the flowers for the Christmas holidays. The long-day treatment is continued until the middle of October, at which time the plants are allowed to have the normally short days of the season. The night temperature can now be dropped to the usual 55° to 60° range, although the buds will come along a little faster if 65° nights are continued. If you wish to have the flowers for Easter, you continue the long-day treatment until approximately two months before Easter, and then give short days. However, if you wish the flowers for June, the time for starting short days is April first. Because the days are becoming longer at this time, you will have to shorten the daylight hours by covering the plants with black cloth from five o'clock in the evening to eight o'clock in the morning. The accompanying drawings show both lighting and darkening techniques.

For merely prolonging the daylight hours, the light intensity does not have to be high. The lights should be of the incandescent or Mazda type, which gives a good bit of the red portion of the spectrum known to be necessary for flowering. Forty-to-sixty-watt bulbs, placed in reflectors two to three feet above the plants and at intervals of about eight feet, will be sufficient to withhold flowering. They are turned on at sundown and kept on long enough to give a total of 16 hours of light. In a greenhouse where other plants are grown you must be careful to enclose the group of plants being lighted so as not to affect the flowering of other things. During the period of high night temperatures and long days, the plants should be given regular applications of fertilizer, and they must have as good sunlight during the day as possible, short of burning. Watering should be watched carefully to conform to what the plants actually need, so that they become neither dehydrated nor too soft.

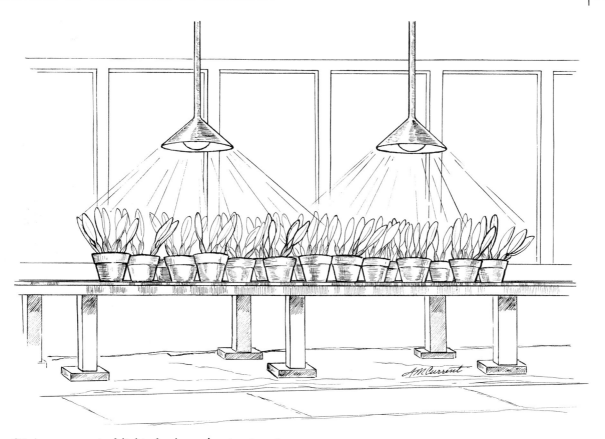

Fig. 37 Arrangement of lights for long day treatment.

For shortening the days artificially, it is necessary to build a framework over which black cloth can be drawn every night, and the cloth must be light proof.

From the time the buds show in the sheath, the length of time to bloom can be somewhat regulated by temperature. If the night temperature is 50° or 55°, the flowers will take about two weeks longer to develop than when it is held to 65°. If the night temperature is pushed to 70°, development time can be reduced further. This can be useful if for some reason you find that you are going to miss the date for which you have planned. If the buds are farther along than they should be at a certain time, you can hold them back a week or two by dropping the night temperature. We do not advocate a 70° night temperature for anything but an emergency, but if it is a matter of meeting a certain date or losing the

income from a crop of flowers, it would be worth raising the nights to 70° for the short time necessary to gain flowers a week or two earlier.

A number of growers are producing two sets of flowers a year from the labiata hybrids. They have found that by using higher light intensities to prolong the days they can stimulate plant growth so much that the year's cycle can be telescoped into six months. They use bulbs of 100-150 watts, spaced about six feet apart and two to three feet above the plants. They maintain nights of 65° and days of 80° to 85°. Extremely good air circulation is necessary because of the heat from the lights. Careful attention must also be given to the humidity, watering, and fertilizing. The long-day treatment is given from June to the middle of October, and the naturally short days from then on will bring on the flowers for the

Fig. 38 Black cloth for short day treatment. The cloth is arranged on a framework, so that it can be pulled over the plants to cut out the light, or drawn back to allow light.

Christmas holidays. As soon as the flowers are cut, or by the first of January, the plants are put under long days again. The long days and 65° nights speed up the growth that normally starts at this time of the year. About the first of April, the plants are given short days, and the flowers are ready to cut by June. As soon as this crop is cut, the long day treatment is started again, the plants now start another new growth, and the flowers can again be timed for Christmas.

It is a problem for an amateur with one greenhouse and a mixed collection of orchids to do much with control of flowering. Keeping a high night temperature for much of the fall and winter to control *C. labiata* hybrids, prevents many other kinds from flowering. Many amateurs have experienced difficulty in pre-venting light leaks when giving the long-day treatment, and if enough light reaches other plants it may prevent the flowering of some of them. To attempt the control of more than one kind of Cattleya presents additional problems. If you are giving labiata hybrids long days and 65° nights, and then must give mossiae hybrids short days and 55° nights, you can see how the troubles would multiply. About the only way an amateur can do much with controlling flowering is to have two greenhouses, one maintained at fifty-five degrees and the other at sixty-five degrees at night. In each greenhouse there can be lights installed and a framework for cloth. Groups of plants would then be moved from one situation to another as their schedule demanded. In the 55° house you could grow a few of the intermediate kinds of orchids, and in the 65° house perhaps a few of the warm kinds, so as to have more variety than just two or three types of Cattleya hybrids.

We cannot give you much in the way of schedules for types other than the labiata hybrids. Most commercial growers have found it easier to handle just these, since they comprise a wonderful array of richly-colored flowers and can be managed so exactly. But if you have a large number of plants that flower regularly in the winter or spring, you might use what has been given earlier in this section as a basis for some experiments. It seems to be difficult to do much about controlling the kinds which, like *C. gigas*, start their growth in the winter and bloom on this young growth in early summer. At best they can be speeded a bit into flowering by extending the normal daylength in gradual stages, starting after the buds are well up in the sheath. Midwinter blooming kinds can (if they are amenable to the treatment) be brought into bloom early, say for Christmas, by giving them short days starting in September. Timing of these must include a period for bud initiation which means a few weeks longer than the usual two month period. These mid-winter blooming kinds are usually prevented from flowering by long days, so to delay their flowering until spring necessitates giving them long days until about three months before you wish to have

them in bloom. Kinds that make up their growth in the fall and do not flower until spring, do not offer much chance of control. The short days of November and December do not normally trigger the flower buds into growth at that time, yet many of them require this period of short days and 55° nights in order to bloom at all. Their flowering can be brought about a little earlier than usual, say for Easter rather than in June, by giving the plants long days and 65° nights *after* the buds are well up in the sheath.

Remember that kinds other than labiata hybrids have not been much worked with. We do not know just what influence the various species have on their hybrids. Hybrids of complicated ancestry may have six or a dozen species in their makeup, often more. The fact that a certain hybrid has *C. mossiae* in it does not mean that it will behave like *C. mossiae*. As a matter of fact, it may behave more like some other ancestor whose habits have not been studied. We do know that most of the Cattleya species and hybrids grow well and flower faithfully with the normal daylengths of the seasons and with a night temperature range of 55° to 60°. An amateur who has a mixed collection of Cattleyas and other kinds can have something in bloom most of the time by choosing plants for their natural flowering period.

8 | *Hybrids*

I̲ɴ 1852 orchids were still new to Europeans. People were busy just learning to know and grow them. The possibilities of hybridization were apparently unthought of until a surgeon saw how it could be done and suggested it to an orchid grower. The surgeon was a Dr. Harris of Exeter, and the grower, Mr. J. Dominy, foreman of the firm of Veitch and Sons. In 1852 with Dr. Harris' help, Mr. Dominy performed the first hand pollination, and in 1856 the first hybrid orchid flowered, Calanthe Dominii (*Calanthe masuca* × *Calanthe furcata*). Mr. Dominy worked for twenty years, and produced about twenty-five hybrids, among them, in 1863, the first bi-generic hybrid, Laeliocattleya Exoniensis (*Cattleya mossiae* × *Laelia crispa*).

The exciting note injected into orchid growing by Dr. Harris had a powerful reaction. The best of the newly produced hybrids created a sensation at exhibitions. Old orchid books are full of glowing accounts of the new marvels, and predict wonderful things to come. Mr. Dominy worked alone in the field for most of the twenty years, for it was not until 1871 that a hybrid was produced by someone else. No one at that time could have foreseen the future extent of hybridization during the next seventy-five years. In 1890 there were 200 crosses registered. Now there are thousands upon thousands, and the number grows each year.

A large proportion of the best hybrids have been made by experienced growers, but amateurs have had a hand in hybridization, too. Success on both sides was largely a matter of chance, and indeed still is. Curiosity plus the desire to create something unusual prompted nearly everyone to cross whatever orchids he had at hand, in the hope that he would achieve some striking result. Many of the crosses made between hybrids of doubtful quality have not been wise, and have only cluttered the lists. Crosses between species have always been valuable for the tremendous amount of knowledge they have given us, and crosses between genera have contributed even more. All such crosses are the result of the burning curiosity possessed by human beings—the desire to see "what would happen if—." The early growers tried all sorts of things. During the first fifty years of hybridization, from 1856 to 1906, crosses were made in many genera, including Cattleya, Calanthe, Dendrobium, Aerides,

Cypripedium, Cymbidium, Lycaste, Zygopetalum, Miltonia, Odontoglossum, Stanhopea, Vanda, Epidendrum, Laelia, Phaius, and many others. At least fourteen bi-and tri-generic hybrids were created, including combinations between genera of the Cattleya tribe, as well as such things as Odontioda and Odontonia. Considering the difficulties with germinating seed, this is a phenomenal record, for the crosses numbered over 1500. Of these some 750 were in Cypripedium (Paphiopedilum) alone, the most difficult of all genera.

The nature of orchids themselves, being slow to mature and flower, necessitated accurate records, lest the parentage of seedlings be forgotten. The great interest in hybrids led to the registration of crosses, not only to insure credit to the first person to think of a cross, but to save others from repeating what had already been tried. The fortunate result of these factors has been the development of an orchid genealogy as accurate and complete as any family history in existence.

It early became the custom to give a hybrid a name of its own. At first this was done to honor the creator of a hybrid or someone who had achieved fame in the orchid world. The system gives us a handy way to identify the complicated hybrids that exist today. It would be impossible to call an orchid by the names of a dozen or more ancestors. It is even awkward to give the immediate parentage of a plant every time we want to speak of it. For instance, how much more simple it is to say Cattleya Hardyana, than to say *Cattleya dowiana, aurea* by *Cattleya gigas.* Nowadays growers are pressed to find names that have not already been used. Hybrids are named after the gods of ancient mythology, the letters of the Greek alphabet, presidents, generals, opera stars, and the grower's own relatives and friends.

Once a name has been given to a cross, it stands for any repetition of that cross. For instance, Cattleya Fabia is *Cattleya dowiana* × *Cattleya labiata,* and every time those two species are mated the offspring must be called Cattleya Fabia. Cattleya Fabia × Cattleya Hardyana produced Cattleya Princess Royal, while the mating of the white forms produced Cattleya Princess Royal, alba. Knowing the name of any hybrid enables you to trace its ancestry back to the species involved in all the branches of its "family tree."

For this purpose, Sander's *Complete List of Orchid Hybrids* is indispensable. One large volume covers crosses up to 1946 (price $25.00), and three addenda, each covering a three year period, bring the listings up through 1954. Addenda I and II are $4.50 each, and Addendum III is $6.00. All are obtainable through the American Orchid Society, Inc. These lists are straightforward and simple. They include the name of the hybrid, the names of its parents, the date of registration and the name of the person who registered the cross. Each volume consists of two tables. Table I enables you to look up a hybrid by its name and gives you its parentage. Table II lists under each species and hybrid the species and hybrids with which it has been crossed and the resulting hybrid names. These volumes are a monument to Mr. Fred K. Sander, of Sanders (St. Albans) Ltd., England, who devoted over fifty years of loving work to their compilation, all done without remuneration except for the gratitude of orchid growers all over the world. David F. Sander is continuing the work. New volumes will give all of the information in an ingenious one-table form, beginning with a set of two volumes containing hybrids from 1946 through 1960, priced at $22.50. Registration of hybrids is conducted by the Royal Horticultural society.

Primary crosses, crosses between two species, are likely to yield plants that are intermediate between the parents, and more or less uniform. But crosses between two hybrids are more complicated and show great variety among the offspring. A hybrid is made up of factors inherited from each of its parents and, when two hybrids are mated, these factors recombine in many ways. The offspring will show various combinations of the characteristics of the parent plants, as well as combinations reminiscent of many of the types found

in their ancestry. For an interesting series showing this see Chapter 15. The same thing happens when a hybrid is self-pollinated, for its inherited characteristics also recombine to give a number of different kinds of offspring.

During the earlier years of hybridization it seemed sufficient to know the names of the two species or hybrids crossed to make a certain hybrid. Through the years it has become obvious that certain individual plants have been better parents than others, and that some have been more consistent in transmitting their characteristics to their offspring. Often it is not a question of superiority but rather of distinctive characteristics obtained from certain individuals. It has become important to know exactly what individual plants have been used as parents. To mark an outstanding plant it is given a varietal name, a name added to the hybrid name and set in single quotes, for example Cattleya Bow Bells 'Serene.' (See Chapter 11.) Thus this plant is set apart from other members of the cross, and the varietal name is carried with it and all of its divisions, which together form a "clone." It would be very helpful if hybrid lists could contain all sorts of information about each plant in question, its color, the colors in the resulting offspring, and its chromosome number. However, such information is available in the records concerning the plants, and it is then possible, given the varietal name, to obtain what else is needed. The more recent Sander's lists do in-

Fig. 39 Modification of characteristics of two species parents in their primary hybrid. Upper, *Cattleya bicolor,* a bifoliate species which has slender sepals and petals and a lip without side lobes. Center, *Cattleya dowiana,* a member of the labiata group, with broad petals and a broad lip with the sides rolled over the column. Lower, Cattleya Iris, *Cattleya bicolor* × *Cattleya dowiana.* The lip, though wider and more ruffled than in C. *bicolor,* is still not as wide as in C. *dowiana,* and is still tongue shaped as in C. *bicolor.* The side lobes of the lip have been reduced to a merest trace at the very base of the lip. (*Cattleya dowiana* courtesy H. A. Dunn and H. Griffin)

Fig. 40 Two plants from the same seed pod, showing possible variation from good to poor in the same cross. Both have the same lip pattern, but one has inherited large size and fairly good shape, while the other has inherited small size and less good shape.

clude the varietal names, where these have been established.

We have seen that once a name has been given to a cross, that name stands for any repetition of the cross. Here we must explain lest some difficulties in understanding lead to confusion. Let's say that a certain cross proves to be so successful that there is more demand for seedlings than there are seedlings available. The originator of the cross may *remake* the cross, using the *identical parents* again. Another grower, who has *divisions of these same parents*, may also *remake* the cross. However, a grower who has other plants from the same hybrid groups, different individuals from those used in the original cross, will not get the same results by crossing them. It is true

that the resulting seedlings will have the same hybrid name, and if his plants are superior his cross may be better, but the offspring will exhibit quite a different array of characteristics. Let's say that there is a hybrid named Cattleya Alpha which has progeny ranging in color from pink to green, and one named Cattleya Beta that ranges from pale lavender to dark purple. A cross between a green Alpha and a pale Beta will be quite different from a cross between a pink Alpha and a dark purple Beta. Or let's say that in a cross which we shall call Cattleya Delta one individual occurs that is tetraploid, having double the normal number of chromosomes. Crosses in which this tetraploid Delta is used as a parent will be different from crosses in which other Deltas, diploid plants, function as parents. One can readily see the need for distinguishing individual plants used in hybridization.

The results of a cross cannot be known until a fair percentage of the seedlings flower. The fact that the parent plants are handsome does not necessarily mean that their offspring will be equally good. If the seedlings are good, however, the grower will be encouraged to use their parents again in other combinations. Proving the merit of parent plants is a long job, for they must be tried in a number of crosses, not just one. Failure in one cross may not mean that the same plants will fail when combined with other individuals. Again, the need for records and for identification of plants used as parents can be clearly seen. How disappointing it would be for a cross to turn out exceptionally well and then not to know which plants produced this cross! Equally sad is a situation, which has often occurred, in which divisions of valuable plants have been lost because of the lack of proper labeling. In the field of hybridization it is not enough to guess or think that a certain plant is a division of a particularly famous one. If a grower is going to represent his seedlings as offspring of certain famous parents, he must know beyond all doubt that this is so. If a buyer is desirous of obtaining a division of a certain plant, he must be given the assurance that the plant he receives is in fact that plant.

How do such differences among individuals occur? How are characteristics carried from parent to offspring? How is it that a characteristic that occurs in one generation may not show up in the next, but may instead be exhibited in a later generation? It is the purpose of this chapter to show, by highly simplified examples, the basic workings of inheritance. These basic principles will not cover all of the complications that arise in the passing on of traits from one generation to another, but will give a glimpse into the general methods by which this takes place. When you have read through the "A B Cs" of inheritance in this chapter, you will be better able to understand things that you can see in your own plants, and you will appreciate the work of the cyto-geneticists who are now studying inheritance in orchids. Compared to what is known of genetics of the fruit fly, we know as yet very little about the genetics of orchids. The problem is complicated by the thousands of kinds of orchids, by the fact that transmission of characters in different genera may be accomplished in different ways, and by the length of time from seed to flower.

In order to have handy in this chapter information about the genera with which Cattleyas are crossed we shall give descriptions of Laelia, Brassavola, and Sophronitis. Cattleya species were described in Chapter 6, and other members of this tribe will be given in Chapter 13. Something of inheritance in other genera will be given in chapters dealing with those kinds later on.

Genera Used in Hybridization with Cattleya

Laelia

Laelias are the most nearly like Cattleyas in appearance, differing from them in structure by having eight pollinia, while the latter have four. Their similarity has given rise to some disagreement among botanists as to whether certain of them should be classed as Cattleyas or as Laelias. Their special contribution to hybrids is their brilliant coloring, which includes yellow, coppery-bronze, scarlet, and red-orange, as well as deep tones of violet. Their flower parts are slender, and with a few exceptions, the flowers are small. The object in hybridization is to combine the Laelia coloring with the better Cattleya shape.

The genus consists of about thirty species occurring in Mexico, Guatemala, and South Brazil; none of the species is common to both regions. They are found on rocks and trees, often at quite high altitudes. Their culture is the same as for Cattleyas, with care to shift plants that do not thrive to warmer or cooler spots until the right conditions are found. Some may do well suspended from the roof of the

Sophrolaeliocattleya Anzac, Orchidhurst Variety. (Courtesy of Clint McDade and Sons)

Cattleya Bow Bells. (Courtesy of Clint McDade and Sons)

greenhouse for maximum light. They need quite thorough drying between waterings.

There is great variety among the species as to height of plants, shape of pseudobulbs, and other characteristics. They are usually divided into four groups. There are a few with the labiata type of lip, but most of them have a markedly three-lobed lip. Some bear one leaf to a pseudobulb and some vary in the number of leaves. The more useful ones have been chosen for description.

Group I. Pseudobulbs rounded or egg-shaped

Laelia albida. These small, fragrant flowers are two inches in diameter, pure white except for a yellow streak down the lip and crimson dots at its base. The lip has small, erect side lobes and a rounded middle lobe. The species occurs in Mexico and flowers through the fall and winter. It is popular in collections.

Laelia anceps. The species is the most commonly grown. Two to four showy, rose-purple flowers, four inches in diameter, are borne on a long jointed stem, one to one-and-one-half feet high. Sepals and petals have a green line on the back. The side lobes of the lip fold up over the column. The front lobe curves downward and is deep purple, with a thickened yellow keel down the center terminating in three ridges. The species occurs in Mexico, flowers in December and January, is popular in collections, grown somewhat commercially, and is occasionally used in hybridization.

Laelia autumnalis. Similar to *L. anceps,* but lacking the green line on the sepals and petals, this species has five to six flowers on a stem one-and-a-half to two feet long. It occurs in Mexico, flowers in the fall, and is quite popular in collections.

Laelia flava. Bright, pure yellow flowers, two to two-and-a-half inches in diameter, are borne in groups of four to eight on a stem a foot high. The lip has blunt side lobes and a ruffled middle lobe with four elevated ridges down the center. It occurs in Brazil, flowers in the fall, and is valuable in hybridization.

Group II. Pseudobulbs short and stem-like, consisting of several internodes

Laelia pumila. This pretty, dwarf species has several lovely varieties. The single, large, drooping flower is rose-purple. The lip has squarish side lobes and a short, curling, ruffled middle lobe. It is yellow in the throat and deep purple at the edge. The species occurs in Brazil and has a variable flowering time. It is used somewhat in hybridization.

Group III. Pseudobulbs similar to those of Cattleya. Includes those species with the largest and most showy flowers

Laelia crispa. A popular, summer-flowering species, its blossoms are large, fragrant, and white, except for yellow and purple in the lip. The petals and lip are attractively ruffled. Five or six flowers are produced per stem. The species is native to Brazil, and is popular in collections. This species crossed with *C. mossiae* gave the first bigeneric hybrid, in 1863.

Laelia purpurata. The largest of the Laelias, it has flowers up to eight inches in diameter. The petals are white, suffused with light rose, and the handsome, bell-shaped lip is a rich velvety purple. The plant occurs in Brazil and flowers in the spring. It is used in hybridization more than any other Laelia because of its large size and beautiful lip.

Laelia sawyeri. This newly discovered species will soon be sought after for collections because of its deep red-violet color and its wealth of flowers. It was found by H. D. Sawyer in 1942 in the mountains of Acuitlapan, and named after him. While the sprays usually hold ten to twenty flowers, plants with eighty to a spray have been found.

Laelia superbiens. A large plant, it has pseudobulbs a foot long, from which arise flower scapes five to six feet long. Ten to twenty flowers are borne in a roundish cluster. The flowers are about six inches across and are

Fig. 41 Three species of Laelia. Upper left, *Laelia crispa,* which has plant characters very much like Cattleya. Upper right, *Laelia flava,* lower, *Laelia an-ceps,* both of which are small plants with very tall, jointed flower stems. (*L. crispa* and *L. flava* courtesy of Rod McLellan Co. *L. anceps* courtesy of H. D. Sawyer)

lilac-purple. The lip has yellow side lobes with margins and stripes of purple. The front lobe is ruffled, yellow, with deep crimson margins and several toothed crests. This handsome but not much grown species is a native of Guatemala and has a variable flowering season.

Laelia tenebrosa. Sometimes given as a variety of *Laelia grandis.* This species has flowers which are a little better shaped than those of many of the Laelias. They range from coppery-bronze to citron-yellow. The lip is trumpet-shaped, deep purple with a border of white, marked with darker veins. A very striking and unusual flower, it is the parent of many hybrids. The plant occurs in Brazil and flowers in the spring.

Laelia xanthina. Yellow flowers, somewhat variable in intensity, ranging from buff to yellow to yellow-green, three to five to a stem. The front lobe of the lip is white streaked with crimson. The flowers have a somewhat leathery texture. This species occurs in Brazil and flowers in winter or spring.

Species Moved from Brassavola

Two species formerly included in Brassavola have long been considered better suited to membership with the Laelias and are now generally included in this genus. These are *Brassavola digbyana* and *glauca.* These, as well as many other species of Brassavola, have been crossed with Cattleya to produce the bigeneric hybrids, Brassocattleyas. However, *digbyana,* with its huge fringed lip, has been used more often than all of the others put together and is responsible for a particular concept among the Brassocattleyas. The influence of its lip, with or without the fringe, is recognizable through long lines of hybrids (as is its peculiarly long ovary). Sander's List still includes hybrids formed with *digbyana* among the Brassocattleyas, as well as those formed with *glauca.* Although it is difficult to give up a term, or a name (as witness the difficulty of changing from Cypripedium to Paphiopedilum), or an association of long standing, we should probably now call the hybrids made with *digbyana* and *glauca* Laeliocattleyas in-

stead of Brassocattleyas. It may be impossible in practice, especially where it concerns hybrids already named and registered, because it would involve looking up the ancestry to see whether indeed such and such a hybrid was made with *digbyana* or *glauca* or whether it included one or more of the species still correctly included in Brassavola.

Laelia digbyana. Slender pseudobulbs, bear a single leaf, rather slow growing and not too floriferous. The huge lip, often four inches across, is white or cream colored, its edges marvelously fringed. The lip remains wide where it folds up over the column, carrying the fringe around to meet at the top of the tube. The sepals and petals are slender and plain, pale green tinted with pinkish lavender. The flowers have a strong scent of citrus fruits. The species has eight pollinia, occurs in Honduras, and flowers in July and August.

Laelia glauca. Rather short slender pseudobulbs, somewhat compressed, bear a single leaf. The usually single flowers are fragrant, yellowish-green with a large spreading lip that is streaked with red in the throat. The plant occurs in Mexico and Guatemala and has eight pollinia.

Group IV. Pseudobulbs slender, reed-like, sheathed with scales and swollen at the base

Laelia cinnabarina. This attractive, reddish-orange flower is about three inches across, borne four to five on a stem which is fifteen to twenty inches high. Sepals and petals are slender. The lip has short, pointed side lobes, and a rather large, oval, ruffled middle lobe. This Brazilian species is valuable in hybridization and flowers in the summer.

Laelia harpophylla. A delightful species, which has five to ten brilliant scarlet-orange flowers on a short stem. It is quite similar to *L. cinnabarina.* The tubular lip has a ruffled front edge. The plant, which occurs in Brazil and flowers in February and March, is valuable in hybridization.

Laelia monophylla. Although it is interesting because of its unique habit, this species

Fig. 42 Left, *Laelia digbyana*. Right, the primary hybrid between this species and *Cattleya dowiana* (Laelio-cattleya Mrs. J. Leeman), showing how *Laelia digbyana* transmits its huge, fringed lip. (*L. digbyana* courtesy of H. D. Sawyer)

is not much grown. The rhizome is a matted mass, from which arise tufts of stems each bearing a short thick leaf. The single flowers are one to two inches across, vivid orange-scarlet, with a tiny, three-lobed lip. It occurs in the mountains of Jamaica, the only species of Laelia that grows outside of the Mexico-Guatemala and Brazil regions.

Brassavola

Of the twenty or so species in this genus, some are little known; but many are grown widely for their individual charms and are crossed with other members of this tribe. The plants have terete leaves, or leaves that are slender and so thick as to be almost terete, topping slender stem-like pseudobulbs. The flowers are basically similar, having very slender sepals and petals and a lip whose outer lobe spreads open from a slender tube. It occurs in Central and South America.

Brassavola cordata. This plant has pale green sepals and petals, with a pointed heart-shaped lip that is white. The flowers occur three to six on a stem shorter than the leaves.

Brassavola fragrans. As many as twelve of these fragrant flowers can occur to the stem. The sepals are yellowish-white, faintly spotted with purple; the petals are yellowish-white, and the white lip has a green spot at the base.

Brassavola nodosa. These flowers are delightfully fragrant from evening to the middle of the night, earning the nickname of "Lady of the Night." The sepals and petals are white or faintly greenish white. The front lobe of the lip is white, shaped like a long pointed spade. Several flowers are borne on long graceful stems.

Sophronitis

This is a genus (of about six species) of which one, *Sophronitis grandiflora*, is frequently used in hybridization for the sake of

Fig. 43 *Brassavola nodosa* 'Orchidglade'. Nicknamed "the lady of the night." (Courtesy of Jones and Scully, Inc.)

its red color. All are dwarf plants, with brilliantly colored flowers that bear eight pollinia.

Sophronitis cernua. These are very small plants. The flowers are colored like those of *Sophronitis grandiflora,* but are smaller and borne in clusters of four to eight. The species occurs near Rio de Janeiro and flowers in the winter.

Sophronitis grandiflora. This is a beautiful little plant, compact, with short, egg-shaped pseudobulbs and oval leaves, of a total height of three to four inches. The single flowers are bright scarlet, sometimes red-orange, one-and-a-half to two inches across, very plain and neat. The sepals are spatula-shaped, the petals more rounded, and the narrow, orange lip folds over the column. It occurs in the Organ Mountains of Brazil and flowers through the winter.

Sophronitis violacea. One of the smallest of cultivated orchids, this species has pseudo-

bulbs one inch long and leaves of two to three inches. The tiny flowers are only an inch across and are bright rose in color. The species occurs in the Organ Mountains of Brazil and flowers in the winter.

■ INHERITANCE IN ORCHIDS

The foundation of the individual in all species of living things, both plant and animal, lies in its genetic make-up. Every cell in a plant, whether of roots, leaves, or flowers, contains in its nucleus a set of microscopic structures called chromosomes. On each chromosome there are still smaller structures called genes, so tiny that they cannot be seen with the ordinary microscope. The genes (derived from genetics, which in turn comes from genesis, the beginning) control every single characteristic of the individual. Try to list all the observable traits of an orchid plant, from the most obvious to the most minute, including

Fig. 44 *Sophronitis grandiflora,* a delightful miniature. The plant is scarcely four inches tall, often two inches. (Courtesy of Rod McLellan Co.)

such things as: pseudobulbs, tall or short, thick or thin; leaves, long or short, wide or narrow; sheath, single or double; lip, bordered or plain, "eyes" present or absent, throat, open or tubular; texture of flower; substance, whether waxy or thin, and so on. You would soon have quite a list. The internal structure of the plant, if you could discern it, should be added to your list, as should its growth and flowering habits and the keeping quality of the flowers. Every one of these items is controlled by genes, and it probably takes several thousand, working together in a most complicated way, to produce the plant under scrutiny.

Environment cannot be overlooked in the making of a plant. Without the necessary growing conditions, a plant cannot develop properly. But proper growing conditions only give the genes a chance to express themselves. A plant that gives poor flowers under the best of care will never give good ones. It does not have the genetic make-up for good flowers. Such characteristics as petals that fold back too far, or misshapen flower parts, are genetic faults. (However, if a plant that has consistently produced good flowers suddenly gives

defective ones, you might look for insect injury, disease, or some environmental cause. Freak flowers appear occasionally but seldom repeat themselves.)

Every species has its own standard number of chromosomes. In man there are forty-six. In the fruit fly there are eight. The garden pea, used by Mendel in the experiments which gave the world the fundamentals of genetics, has fourteen.

Chromosomes exist in pairs, but the members of each pair actually stand side by side only during reduction division (see below). The two members of each pair of chromosomes are identical in shape and size, but not necessarily in gene content. Genes also occur in pairs, one member of a pair on each of the matched chromosomes. Each pair of chromosomes is different from every other pair in the cell. Fig. 45 shows a cell that has two pairs of chromosomes, which have been made black and white to distinguish the individual members of each pair. The shape and size of the chromosomes, as well as the total number, are standard for the species. Of the forty chromosomes in *C. trianaei*, there are twenty distinct kinds, two of each, and every cell in the plant, except the reproductive cells, contains the full complement.

Certain tissues of a plant are set aside for the formation of reproductive cells. In these tissues the cells divide in a special way, called reduction division. The chromosomes come together in pairs. Then the members of each pair of chromosomes separate, and travel to opposite ends of the cell, which then divides in half to form two new cells. Fig. 46 shows this proc-

Fig. 45 A cell with two pair of chromosomes.

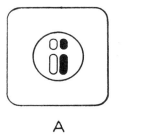
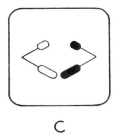
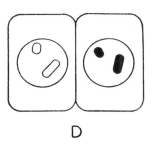

A   B   C   D

Fig. 46 Reduction division. A, the chromosomes pair. B and C, they separate. D, new cells are formed with half the original number.

ess. Each of the new cells now contains one member of each pair of chromosomes, or half of the original number. This is called the "haploid" number. The haploid cells later develop into sperm and egg cells, which in genetic terminology are called gametes. When fertilization takes place, see Fig. 47, and a sperm and egg come together, the full number of chromosomes, the "diploid" number, is again present. The new individual that develops from the fertilized egg thus receives half of its chromosomes from one parent, half from the other. The chromosomes never fuse, but remain separate and distinct from each other. Each chromosome carries with it its own gene content, and when it goes into the making of a new individual it takes its genes along with it to that new individual. It makes no difference genetically which of two plants is the male (pollen) parent and which is the female (pod) parent.

The haploid number is referred to as "n" for brevity and convenience. The diploid number then becomes "2n." We shall later talk about triploids, "3n," and tetraploids, "4n," plants that have three and four times the haploid number of chromosomes, and even pentaploids, "5n." Plants with more than the 2n number of chromosomes are called "polyploids."

During the development of reproductive cells, it is pure chance which member of a pair of chromosomes will go into a resulting sperm or egg cell. We can think of the chromosomes as pairing with one to the right of the other, but just as often, the position is reversed. If the members of each pair are identical in gene content, it does not matter how they separate, for

the resulting reproductive cells will be identical. But where the members of a pair differ from each other, if by only one gene, it makes a great deal of difference. Fig. 48 shows the possible combinations of genes in the reproductive cells arising from one that has two pair of unlike chromosomes. Where only one pair of unlike chromosomes is involved, there are two types of reproductive cells, or 2 to the first power, 2^1. Where two pair are concerned, there are four types, or 2^2, and where there are three pair of unlike chromosomes, there will be eight different types of reproductive cells, or 2^3. The figures become almost astronomical for cells that contain a large number of chromosomes. For instance, where there are 20 pair, if each member of every pair is unlike the other, the possible types of reproductive cells is 2^{20}, or 1,048,576 different kinds.

Such a figure gives some idea of the problems confronting geneticists who try to make a complete analysis of a plant or an animal. The genetic make-up of an individual cannot be known from its appearance. The only way to

Fig. 47 Fertilization brings together a set of chromosomes from each parent.

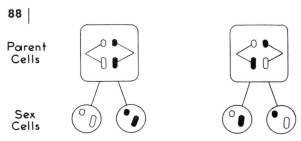

Parent
Cells

Sex
Cells

Fig. 48 Four types of sex cells arise from a cell having two pair of unlike chromosomes.

find out what genes it contains is to breed it and see what comes out in the offspring. This reveals why geneticists usually choose subjects that have a short life cycle. In contrast to orchids, the fruit fly produces a new generation every few days, and wheat and corn in a matter of months. A planned study of orchid genetics started now would take several lifetimes to complete. We do have quite a body of facts, however, collected by careful observers, that show how certain factors in orchids behave, and their pattern follows the same general behavior seen in plants that have been studied in more detail.

Genes are of two general types, "dominant" and "recessive." Dominant genes have the power to induce the appearance of the characteristic they govern whenever they are present. Recessive genes can manifest themselves only in the absence of the dominant. For instance, in Cattleyas purple is dominant over yellow. A cross between *Cattleya gigas* (purple) and *Cattleya dowiana* (yellow) gives all purple offspring. In Fig. 49, the dominant gene for purple is indicated by P, and the recessive

gene for yellow by y.° *Cattleya gigas*, the parent plant, has the pair of genes PP, and gives one to each reproductive cell. *Cattleya dowiana*, similarly, has the pair yy, so that each reproductive cell contains one y. Each individual among the offspring inherits a gene for purple, P and a gene for yellow, y, and, since purple is dominant over yellow, the offspring have purple flowers. On the other hand, the yellow of Laelia is dominant over the purple of Cattleya,† so that a mating between *Laelia flava* and *Cattleya gigas* would give all yellow flowers. This is shown in Fig. 50, where Y now stands for dominant yellow and p for recessive purple.

There are cases where the dominant gene can manifest itself fully only when present in a double dose, that is, when two dominants are present for the same characteristic, instead of one dominant and one recessive. This seems to be true of flower size; see Fig. 51, where L stands for large size and s for small size. If a large Cattleya, LL, is crossed with a small one, ss, each of the offspring will inherit one gene for large size and one for small, Ls. The size of the resulting flowers will be intermediate between the two parents. The gene for large size, when present in a single dose, is dominant to the extent that it can make the flowers of the

° The system of symbols used here has been devised for the sake of simplicity. It may well be that our single symbols may represent groups of genes.

† Species of Laelia that have been used to produce hybrids of various shades of yellow, orange, red-orange, and bronze, are *cinnabarina, flava, harpophylla, tenebrosa,* and *xanthina.*

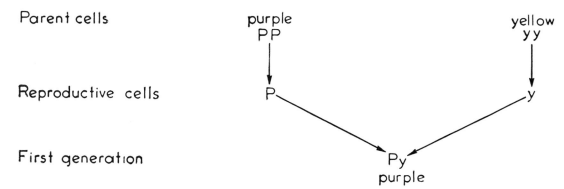

Parent cells   purple   yellow
                PP   yy

Reproductive cells   P   y

First generation   Py
                           purple

Fig. 49 A cross between C. *gigas*, in which purple is dominant, and C. *dowiana*, in which yellow is recessive, produces all purple flowers in the offspring.

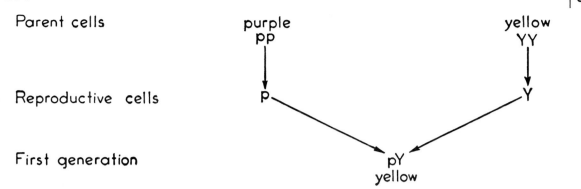

Parent cells purple yellow
              pp   YY

Reproductive cells p Y

First generation pY
                  yellow

Fig. 50 A cross in which the purple of C. *gigas* is recessive to the yellow of *L. flava* will produce all yellow flowers in the offspring.

Fig. 50 A cross in which the purple of C. *gigas* is recessive to the yellow of *L. flava* will produce all yellow flowers in the offspring.

new generation larger than the smaller parent, but it is not able to bring them up to the size of the larger parent. This is called "incomplete dominance."

Plants that have identical genes for any one character are said to be homozygous (pure) for that character. For instance, a plant that contains two genes for large size, LL, will give every one of its sperm and egg cells one of those genes, and when used as a parent, will transmit this gene to every individual among the offspring. The same is true of a plant that has identical recessive genes, such as one with two genes for small size, ss, which is said to be homozygous for this character.

A plant that contains unlike genes for any character is called heterozygous (impure, or mixed). If it is heterozygous for size, it means that it contains one dominant gene for large, and one recessive gene for small, Ls. The offspring of the two yellow-purple crosses described above are heterozygous for color, those of the Cattleya cross being Py, and those of the

Laelia × Cattleya, pY. When used as parents, heterozygous plants give half of their offspring the dominant gene and half the recessive.

The species tend to be homozygous. However, there are various types within a species, and these types pass their characteristics on to their progeny. There are, for example, good *Cattleya trianaei*, and poor ones. If the types are well separated geographically, the chances are that the good and the poor are respectively homozygous. But if there has been interbreeding among them, they may be heterozygous. The only way to tell whether a flower is homozygous is to pollinate it with its own pollen (self-pollinate it). If all the offspring are identical to the parent, you may know that the parent is homozygous. But if the progeny differ markedly from each other in any way, you will know that the parent is a mixture. A plant that is homozygous for all of its good qualities can be used as a "stud" plant. One that proves to be heterozygous is not a "stud" plant. Self pollination is not only valuable in "proving" an in-

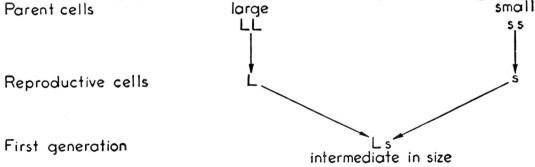

Parent cells large small
              LL   ss

Reproductive cells L s

First generation L s
                  intermediate in size

Fig. 51 Incomplete dominance. The incompletely dominant gene, L, for large size, when coupled with the recessive gene, s, for small size, gives offspring intermediate in size.

dividual, but is a means of obtaining pure strains, strains that are homozygous and which will all breed "true."

There are many dominant characters among Cattleya and its relatives which can be detected in their hybrids. The bi-foliate type of growth, with its slender, jointed stems and two or three leaves is dominant over the thick pseudobulbs and single leaf of the labiata group. So, also, is the spade lip dominant over the labiate lip, and although through successive generations it may be broadened, it can often be identified by the notches that separate the middle lobe from the side lobes. The characteristic veins in the lip of *C. dowiana* and the mottling in the lip of *C. mossiae* both persist in their hybrids. *C. labiata* contributes its day-length sensitivity to its hybrids. The reed-stem Epidendrums are dominant both for their growth habit and the size and character of their flowers. Of course, segregation of these dominant characters through successive generations will cause them eventually to appear only in a percentage of the hybrids.

Whether you intend to enter into a serious breeding program or just cross two orchids for the fun of it, it makes the work more interesting and insures a greater measure of success if you follow some plan based on genetic principles. If what you want is merely a large number of good flowers, perhaps to make your hobby profitable, you will be saved from making crosses that would produce a large number of poor flowers. Or if you want to obtain a unique combination of characteristics from two individuals, you will be spared much pain in knowing ahead of time that the type you want may be only one out of a wide assortment of types in the offspring.

It is interesting to go a little further into the inheritance of yellow in Cattleyas. The purple *Cattleya gigas* crossed with the yellow *Cattleya dowiana, aurea* gives a first generation (F_1 to geneticists) that is all purple, Cattleya Hardyana. Suppose Cattleya Hardyana is self-pollinated, and a second generation (F_2) of seedlings is raised. A person who did not know the inheritance of Cattleya Hardyana would be astonished to get some yellow flowers in this second generation. But those who knew its genetic make-up would have expected just that. Fig. 52 shows how this happens. Cattleya Hardyana is heterozygous. Its color genes are Py. In the formation of reproductive cells these genes segregate so that half of them contain P and half of them y. The second generation will recombine these genes in three ways, PP, Py, and yy. One-fourth of the plants will be homozygous purple, one-half of them will be heterozygous purple, and the remaining one-fourth will be homozygous yellow.

Again, someone who did not know genetics might think he could increase the "potency" of that homozygous yellow by crossing it back to the yellow *Cattleya dowiana, aurea*. It is true that he would get all yellow flowers, but the yellow always remains a recessive gene. If he is looking for a plant to use for breeding yellows when crossed with purple, he will not get it this way. Fig. 53 shows why. The only way to

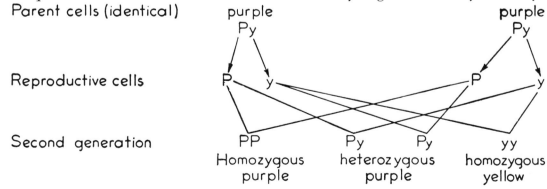

Fig. 52 The F_2 generation obtained by crossing members of the F_1 will be three-fourths purple and one-fourth yellow.

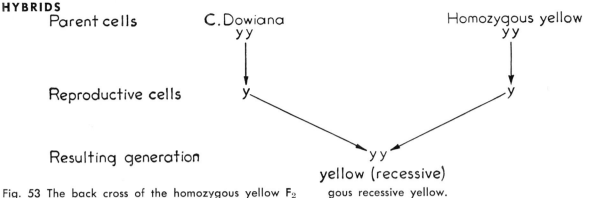

Fig. 53 The back cross of the homozygous yellow F₂ hybrid to *C. dowiana* simply produces another homozygous recessive yellow.

get a yellow that will always be dominant over purple is to use a yellow Laelia as a parent, as described below under Laeliocattleyas.

Laeliocattleyas

Laelias are used in crosses with Cattleyas to lend their bright coloring to the hybrids. *L. harpophylla,* a bright orange, can produce Laeliocattleyas of the same color. *Laelia tenebrosa,* which is reddish brown with coppery suffusion and a darker lip, when crossed with Cattleyas produces bronze flowers with deep purple lip, in which the bronze ranges from yellow-bronze to purple-bronze. *L. purpurata* has perhaps been used more than any other in hybrids with Cattleyas, partly because of the deep velvety purple of its lip, and partly because it is itself a large flower and the resulting hybrids are of good size from the beginning. Hybrids that have small Laelias for parents have to be crossed again with Cattleyas to bring the size up to the desired dimensions.

In the discussion of yellow-purple crosses above you will remember that the yellow of Laelias is dominant over the purple of Cattleyas. The great value of this type of cross is that it is possible to breed a stud plant that is homozygous for yellow (that carries the double dose) and in which the yellow is dominant. Such a stud plant should also be homozygous for large size, in other words, it should be a yellow Laeliocattleya that has the desirable Cattleya shape. Two steps are necessary to achieve this.

Suppose we choose the all-yellow *Laelia flava* and cross it with any Cattleya. Here we will be dealing with two characters, size and color. Fig. 54 shows the primary cross between these two, giving the first (F₁) generation. The Cattleya is LLpp, where L represents the gene for large size, and p the gene for purple, which in this cross is recessive. *Laelia flava* is ssYY, where s stands for the gene for small size, and Y for yellow, which is dominant. The reproduc-

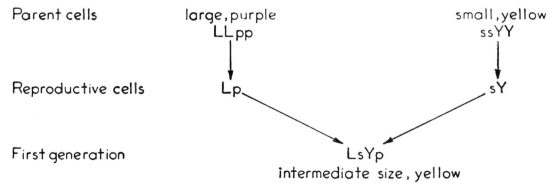

Fig. 54 The F₁ generation obtained by crossing a purple Cattleya with yellow *L. flava* gives all yellow flowers, which are heterozygous for both size and color.

tive cells from the Cattleya are all the same, Lp, and from the Laelia similarly are sY. The offspring combining these genes are therefore identical, LsYp. They are of a size intermediate between the two parents, and all yellow, though the yellow is not quite as clear and pure as where the double dose of Y is present.

The plant we want to make in the next step is one that will be homozygous for both large size and yellow color, LLYY. Off hand, you might think that the way to get it would be to cross a member of the F₁ generation back to the Laelia parent. The Laelia parent gives only one type of reproductive cell, sY. The plant

from the F₁ generation gives four types, LY, Lp, sY, and sp. Combine sY with each of these and you get LsYY, LsYp, ssYY, and ssYp. These come out in equal proportions as to the numbers of plants of each type. There are two types that are homozygous for yellow, LsYY and ssYY, but of these one is intermediate in size and the other is small. Nowhere can you find the plant you want, the LLYY type. The back cross to the Cattleya would not give it either, for here you would get Lp combined with the four types of germ cells from the F₁, and the results would be LLYp, LLpp, LsYp, and Lspp. Two would be homozygous for large size, but

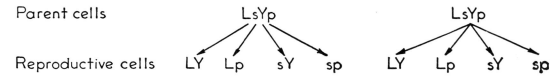

checkerboard to show all possible combinations in F₂

	LY	Lp	sY	sp
LY	LLYY homozygous large yellow	LLYp	LsYY	LsYp
Lp	LLYp	LLpp	LsYp	Lspp
sY	LsYY	LsYp	ssYY	ssYp
sp	LsYp	Lspp	ssYp	sspp

Fig. 55 Inheritance in the F₂ generation when members of the F₁ generation from Fig. 54 are crossed.

none for yellow. So we have to go at it another way.

Look at the four types of reproductive cells that arise from a member of the F₁ generation, LY, Lp, sY, and sp. The homozygous large yellow plant we want would have to come from the fertilization of an LY egg cell by an LY sperm cell, and we can get this by self-pollinating a member of the F₁, or by mating one F₁ plant with another. Fig. 55 shows all of the possible combinations, in checkerboard style. The four types of reproductive cells are written horizontally and vertically, and each line contains the combination of the genes at the left with each group on the top. The proportions of types in the second generation, F₂, are given in sixteenths. In the checkerboard the type LLYY occurs only once, so that this type will be one-sixteenth of the total number of offspring. (The large yellow plants in the offspring would have to be self-pollinated in order to discover which ones are the LLYY type.) Perhaps you will think it is hardly worth the trouble of making the cross to get only one out of sixteen. A plant breeder would consider it very worthwhile, for this LLYY plant when self-pollinated will give a whole generation of large yellow flowers, and when bred to any large Cattleya will carry its dominant yellow to every member of the offspring. Among the other types on the checkerboard, some will give good flowers of large and intermediate size, both yellow and purple, plants that will be an addition to your collection, though not useful in breeding.

Digbyana Hybrids

Laelia (*Brassavola*) *digbyana* has been combined with Cattleyas for the sake of its broad, marvelously fringed lip. In a primary cross with a Cattleya the offspring are intermediate between the two parents. The sepals and petals are reduced toward the size of the *digbyana* parts, but the lip is broadened and shaped more like that of *digbyana*, with the fringe present though not quite as long. (See Fig. 42 for pictures showing *L. digbyana* and a primary hybrid between this and *Cattleya dowiana*, Lc. Mrs. J. Leeman.) The colors of the primary cross are diluted with green, which makes them very delicate and beautiful. Subtle coloring is also obtained when *digbyana* is crossed with a lavender Cattleya, lovely tones of pink suffused with green for example. The colors become stronger when first generation hybrids are crossed with species or hybrids of darker tones, and some of the brilliant hybrids with large, full lip are among the handsomest of orchids. In a secondary cross, segregation of the genes causes both lip types to show up, so that there are some with the Cattleya lip as well as some with the digbyana lip, some with fringe and some without it, or with the barest denticulation of the edge of the lip. The fragrance of the *digbyana* hybrids, reminiscent of citrus fruits, is another characteristic that frequently follows through a line of breeding.

Laelia species, and hybrids containing them, are often crossed with *digbyana* hybrids giving what we know familiarly as "Brassolaeliocattleyas." It is interesting to note that a successful method for breeding yellows has been achieved through the use of Lc. Luminosa, *L. tenebrosa* × *C. dowiana*, a hybrid made in 1901, crossed with various hybrids containing yellow Laelia species and with some containing *digbyana*, such as Lc. Mrs. J. Leeman. Also, many rich vibrant tones of purple, violet, and rose are found among the "Brassolaeliocattleyas."

Sophronitis Hybrids

Sophronitis grandiflora, a gem of a flower in itself, has been made to contribute its redness to the large Cattleya and Laeliocattleya hybrids. The primary cross of *Sophronitis grandiflora* with a Cattleya necessarily gives quite small flowers, and even smaller and less well shaped with a Laelia. But when either of these is recombined with a Cattleya or Laeliocattleya, larger flowers of various deep rosy or red-violet tones appear. It has been hoped that the clear red tones would, through self-pollination or further breeding, be combined with the desirable size, but this happens rather infrequently. It may be that the chromosomes from Sophronitis are so unlike those of Cattleya and

Laelia that they fail to pair at reduction division and that many reproductive cells are therefore non-functional. This may account for the fact that the types for desired color and size are frequently lost from seedling progeny.

Potinara is the name given to the quadrigeneric cross, Brassosophrolaeliocattleya. It can easily be imagined that a combination of all the desirable qualities of the four genera would be an outstandingly handsome thing. However, plants in which all the desired qualities show up occur in only a small proportion of the offspring, and the percentage of plants homozygous for all qualities even less often. A rather extensive breeding program would be necessary to achieve the ideal results. Many lovely combinations do occur in Potinara crosses, although relatively few have been made.

White Cattleyas

Breeding white orchids has its own special problems genetically, as well as its own special appeal esthetically. The genetic problem has been pretty well worked out for Cattleyas, so that you will not have the troubles experienced by some of the early growers. You will not have the sorrow of crossing two pure white flowers only to raise from them a batch of all purple offspring.

Before we discuss their genetics, we must first define what is a pure white orchid, odd though it may seem to have to define "white." From the point of view of its appearance, a pure white orchid is one in which there is not the slightest trace of purple pigment, either in the plant or in the flower. Plants that give purple flowers show purple pigmentation in the plant, in the new growths, sheaths, or leaves, even though their flowers may be extremely pale. Plants that give pure white flowers are all pure, bright green. Nor is there any trace of purple in the flowers. Green and yellow plastids are present, and the white flower may have yellow markings in the throat, but the rest of the flower must be a chaste paper-white, not tinged with color in any way.

The necessity for this definition arises from the carelessness of people who call any very pale flower white, even one that has the veins or the tips of the petals and sepals obviously tinged with color. These tinged whites are nothing but dilute color forms. It is not so significant when the tinged whites are sold by the florist for pure white, because the recipient of the corsage probably does not mind the slight tinting of the flower, may even prefer it that way. But a tinged white cannot be crossed with a pure white without giving colored offspring, at best a mixture of colored and white. Pure whites must be used if you want all pure white progeny. Or, if you are buying seedlings with the intention of having all pure white flowers, be sure that the parents are pure, and not "almost white" or "nearly white."

As if purposely to confuse the matter and make the breeding of whites more difficult than colored orchids, white Cattleyas (and other genera, too) divide themselves into two groups genetically. It is simple when understood, but it puzzled early growers to find that combinations of the albino forms of some species gave all purple flowers, while different combinations of the same parents would give all white.

The mystery was solved by Charles C. Hurst, an English geneticist, who published his interpretation in *Experiments in Genetics* in 1925. He figured out the probable genetic make-up of white orchids from the way they behave in breeding. His deduction is briefly this. Manifestation of color in orchids depends on at least two types of genes working together. In order that a specific color may appear, there must be a gene, which Hurst calls R, to govern what color it is to be. And in order for that color to manifest itself, there must be another gene that allows color as such to be formed, which he calls C. In a colored orchid these two types are both present in their dominant form. However, if only the recessive form of the first type is present, no color may be made in the flower, even though the gene for color as such, C, is present. Or, if the situation is reversed and the plant contains only the recessive form of the second type, c, no color will show, even though the gene for specific color, R, is present. The two types of albinos are therefore, according to Hurst, ccRR and CCrr.

Any pure white when self-pollinated will give all white offspring, and any two of the same type when crossed will produce all white. You can see at a glance, however, that if ccRR and CCrr are crossed, the offspring will inherit c and R from its ccRR parent, and C and r from the CCrr parent, so that both types of genes will be present in the dominant form. The offspring will have the genetic make-up CcRr, and the resulting flowers will all be colored.

Hurst figured out to which of the groups, ccRR or CCrr, the various albino forms of the species belonged, according to the way they behaved when intercrossed. The Cattleya species from his list are given below, with the addition of other species that have shown their make-up by their behavior.

Group I, ccRR	Group II, CCrr
C. mossiae, Wageneri°	C. harrisoniana, alba°
C. gaskelliana, alba°	C. mendelii, alba°
C. intermedia, alba°	C. schroederae, alba°
C. labiata, alba°	C. gigas, var. Firmin
C. speciosissima, alba	Lambeau°°
C. trianaei, alba°°°	C. trianaei, alba°°°
C. skinneri, alba	
C. loddigesii, alba	

° Hurst's original list. All others have been added.
°° Pure white C. gigas are very rare. The var. Firmin Lambeau by its behavior seems to fit in this group, but there is no data on other white C. gigas.
°°° C. trianaei, alba seems to include both genetic types. Only breeding with other whites can prove to which group a particular plant belongs.

Any of the members of Group I when intercrossed will give all white offspring, and any of the hybrids made from these species may be crossed to produce all white. For example, C. mossiae, Wageneri × C. labiata, alba = pure white; C. trianaei, alba × C. gaskelliana, alba = pure white, and the offspring of each when crossed will also give pure white. Similarly, any members of Group II and the hybrids derived from them will give all white offspring.

Semi-Alba

Cattleyas and their hybrids which have pure white sepals and petals and a purple lip are called semi-albas or are designated W-C-L, white-colored-lip. We prefer the term semi-alba. Here we must emphasize that by pure white we mean the absolute absence of any color in the sepals and petals. Flowers that have a tinge of color in the sepals and petals, no matter how slight, would not come in the category of semi-alba, but instead would be considered colored flowers. There was for a while a tendency to call white with purple lip "alba," which was very confusing. Since the term alba means white, it should be used only for flowers that are all white. Semi-alba indicates half white, in other words, white sepals and petals and a colored lip.

The fact that a flower with pure white sepals and petals could have purple pigment in the lip indicated long ago that inheritance of lip color was separate from inheritance of color in the rest of the flower, and was therefore governed by an independent set of genes. We saw, above, that a flower will be white if it has a double recessive in either the C or R category, that is, if its makeup is ccRR or CCrr no color at all will be formed. It would follow that for color to appear in the lip, there must be at least one dominant C and one dominant R present. How, then, would another set of genes operate to prevent this color from showing in the sepals and petals, but allow it to be expressed in the lip? G. A. L. Mehlquist proposed a solution, upheld by W. B. Storey and H. Kamemoto, based on studies of various crosses.

They postulate (and this is a clever piece of deduction and seems very logical) that a pair of genes, **PP**, or **Pp**, or **pp**,° are present in all flowers, which control the distribution of coloring, whether the sepals and petals and lip shall all be colored, or only the lip. (These genes have nothing to do with the yellow coloring in the lip of a flower.) When the genes C and R are both present in a flower, the gene **P** (whether present along with **p** or as **PP**) causes

° By coincidence these workers chose the symbols **P** and **p** to represent color distribution, while I have used them to represent simply purple in the flower. In order to distinguish the two different sets they are given here in boldface type.

the color to appear in both sepals and petals and in the lip; but where the genes for color distribution are recessive, **pp**, color shows up only in the lip. White flowers, in which no color at all can be manufactured, due to the genetic constitution cc or rr, are obviously not influenced by the color distribution genes. White flowers can have **PP, Pp,** or **pp.**

Great confusion as to how to breed semi-albas has arisen from the fact that sometimes a cross between two semi-albas gives all semi-alba, sometimes both semi-alba and white, in the offspring. In crosses between two colored flowers, semi-alba and white sometimes occur among the colored flowers in the offspring. Two white flowers can give all colored progeny or a mixture of white and semi-alba, or even all semi-alba. The great difficulty in predicting what a cross will yield stems from the fact that you cannot know the exact genetic makeup of a flower by looking at it. Recessive genes are hidden when the plant is heterozygous, that is, when dominant genes are present to counteract their influence. Fortunately, hybridizers have been using for breeding only whites that have been proven to give all white progeny, and their descendants when crossed in the proper cc or rr group will give only whites. The danger of getting mixed progeny in a white cross would come from using whites of unknown heredity, such as whites that crop up in crosses between semi-albas or from colored parents. Let's look at the possible theoretical makeup of white, colored and semi-alba flowers, and then see how these could react with each other.

White flowers can have the following genetic makeup: ccRRPP, ccRRPp, ccRRpp, CCrrPP, CCrrPp, CCrrpp, and to these we would have to add Ccrr and ccrR, each combined with **PP, Pp,** and **pp.** In other words, white flowers are always homozygous for either the cc or rr genes, and may have any combination of the color-distribution genes.

Possible colored types are CCRRPP, CCRRPp, CcRrPP, CcRrPp, CCRrPP, CCRrPp, CcRRPP, and CcRRPp. They must have at least one C, one R, and one **P,** but the other member of each pair may be dominant or recessive.

Possible semi-alba types are: CCRRpp, CcRrpp, CCRrpp, and CcRRpp. They must have at least one C and one R, and are always homozygous for the **pp** genes.

As you glance through the lineup of types, you can see that whenever you mate two flowers that could bring together a combination of C, R, and **P** in the offspring, you will get some colored flowers. Whenever you mate flowers that offer the possible combination of C, R, and **pp,** you will get some semi-albas. And when two flowers offer the combinations of cc or rr, regardless of the **P** or **p** genes, you will get some white.

Let's work out a few semi-alba crosses. These must be considered hypothetical crosses, because not all of them have actually been performed, or if performed have not been studied. First we will self-pollinate a homozygous semi-alba, or cross it with another homozygous semi-alba. This would have the genetic make-up CCRRpp. Only one type of sex cell could be produced, CRp, and the recombination of these would re-create the CCRRpp make-up. In other words, a homozygous semi-alba crossed with a homozygous semi-alba always gives semi-alba. Incidentally, if you wish to find out what a semi-alba contains in the way of genes, the best thing to do is self-pollinate it.

Next let's take a heterozygous semi-alba, CcRrpp, and self-pollinate it or cross it with one exactly like it. This is more complicated because four types of sex cells are produced. CRp, Crp, cRp, and crp. The following checkerboard shows this cross and the resulting types of offspring.

	CRp	Crp	cRp	crp
CRp	CCRRpp semi-alba	CCRrpp semi-alba	CcRRpp semi-alba	CcRrpp semi-alba
Crp	CCRrpp semi-alba	CCrrpp white	CcRrpp semi-alba	Ccrrpp white
cRp	CcRRpp semi-alba	CcRrpp semi-alba	ccRRpp white	ccRrpp white
crp	CcRrpp semi-alba	Ccrrpp white	ccRrpp white	ccrrpp white

Self-pollination of a semi-alba having genetic makeup CcRrpp. Ratio of offspring = 9 semi-alba to 7 white.

(Upper) Laeliocattleya Bonanza 'Cornucopia'. (Lower) Laeliocattleya Bonanza 'Giant' AM/AOS. (Courtesy of B. O. Bracey and Company)

Cattleya Lorna 'Corona'. (Courtesy of Kieswetter's Orchid Gardens)

A third possible cross would be between the CCRRpp and the CcRrpp semi-albas. Here the single type of sex cell from the first plant, CRp would combine with the four types from the second, CRp, Crp, cRp and crp, to give offspring CCRRpp, CCRrpp, CcRRpp, and CcRrpp, all semi-albas.

The possible combinations among white types are almost too numerous to give, but let's try a few. As we said before, crosses between any of the ccRR types will give all white, regardless of the P or p content, as will crosses between any of the CCrr ones. But when we mate plants from opposite sides of the table (see page 95) many combinations might result. The color distribution genes now become significant because we are crossing plants that contain the dominant C with those that contain the dominant R. A ccRRpp white crossed with a CCrrpp white gives sex cells cRp from the first and Crp from the second, which combine to give CcRrpp offspring, all semi-albas. A ccRRPP white mated to a CCrrPP white would give sex cells cRP from one and CrP from the other, which would combine to form CcRrPP all colored flowers in the offspring. A third cross might be between a ccRRPp white and a CCrrPp white, both heterozygous for Pp. The first would give sex cells cRP and cRp, and the second, sex cells CrP and Crp. Combined in the offspring these would give CcRrPP, CcRrPp, CcRrPp, and CcRrpp, a ratio of three colored flowers to one semi-alba.

It is not so easy for plant breeders to attain the desired results as for us to set up crosses on paper. They must come at it the other way, by making the crosses, raising large numbers of progeny and then, by studying the types and the ratios among them, figure out what the various contributions of the parent plants may have been. Geneticists who study these problems are often foiled by not having access to large enough populations of the progeny from certain crosses, or by not having complete records of crosses to study. They can be greatly assisted by growers, and will therefore be of greatest help to them in return, (1) if growers would call them in when a large population of seedlings from one cross is in flower; (2) if growers would note the characteristics of the offspring as to size, color, whether the color is dilute or strong, pattern of color, blooming period, and other characteristics of each plant, and the numbers of plants among the various types; and (3) if growers would be willing to make certain critical crosses that would give the geneticists needed information. The ratio of one type to another in a generation of seedlings gives the geneticist a great deal of information, because it shows what the parents contain in the way of dominant and recessive genes.

■ POLYPLOIDS

A polyploid is a plant that has one or more extra sets of chromosomes. In a normal Cattleya, the basic number of chromosomes is forty, and the reproductive cells (gametes) contain the haploid number, or twenty. We refer to this haploid number as "n," and to a plant that has two sets as a 2n, or diploid plant. Each haploid set represents the set of chromosomes inherited from one parent. A plant with three sets of chromosomes is a 3n, or triploid plant. One with four sets is a 4n, or tetraploid. Five sets makes a 5n, or pentaploid, and six sets a 6n, or hexaploid.

Polyploids occur occasionally in nature, usually arising from an abnormal genetic event. The first polyploids among orchids occurred in some such way, either in their native habitats or in the greenhouses of orchid growers. Only when the science of cyto-genetics was developed, however, did growers know about polyploids as such.

If the chromosomes of a plant give it a happy combination of good qualities, the plant may be superior to other members of its group. If a plant has an extra set of the chromosomes that bear genes for the good qualities, it is likely to be quite superior. This is the case with the polyploids. Tetraploids, with four sets of chromosomes, are likely to be very large, heavy plants, with large flowers of heavy substance, broad parts, and wonderful keeping qualities. Triploids are also large and heavy, somewhat faster growing than tetraploids, and they often give more flowers. We must not give the impression that all polyploids are superior to all diploids. A diploid with all dominant genes for its good qualities may compare very favorably with the polyploids. The triploids have the disadvantage of being partially or completely sterile. This means that they may fail to make functional reproductive cells, or they may make but few, and are seldom successful as parents. If the triploid is exceptionally fine, or embodies qualities that are most unusual, the grower may be happy to have the few offspring he can obtain from it. Whereas diploids may produce eighty to ninety per cent viable seed, triploids may give as little as five per cent, and sometimes five-tenths per cent viable seed. Pentaploids have been rare, and have not always been of as good quality as triploids and tetraploids although some are very fine. With the help of the geneticists we are learning much more about them and they may soon be more abundant.

Through the years, growers have selected the best individuals for hybridization, and the best often included some that were polyploid. Thus polyploids began to play their role in hybridization without anyone's having knowledge of their genetic make-up. Some of them became famous as extraordinary parents, such as the tetraploid Cymbidium Alexanderi 'Westonbirt' and Cymbidium Pauwelsii 'Compte d'Hemptinne,' the triploid *Paphiopedilum insigne* 'Harefield Hall,' and the hexaploid (6n) *Phalaenopsis amabilis* 'Elizabethae.' It is almost impossible to tell just when, and through what plants, polyploidy entered many of the lines of Cattleya hybrids. Chromosome counts made upon named varieties of a number of species have turned up the fact that some are polyploid, for example a tetraploid *Cattleya labiata* 'alba,' the tetraploid *Cattleya trianaei* 'Llewellyn,' and the triploid *Cattleya mossiae* 'Mrs. Butterworth.' Undoubtedly other polyploid Cattleyas have existed and been used as parents, both species and hybrids, but in the ensuing years their identity has been lost and they are not now available for study. Even now, crosses are being shown to be largely polyploid which had not been created with that intent, and often it is not known through what ancestors the polyploidy entered the line.

What brought about the occasional polyploid in nature and the first ones to occur in cultivation? The spontaneous appearance of triploids and tetraploids in an otherwise diploid population is felt to be caused largely by nonreduction in a few reproductive cells. It occasionally happens that in the formation of reproductive cells, one or more may fail to go through reduction division, and these thus become functional gametes with the full or 2n complement of chromosomes. Fertilization of a 2n gamete by one that has the normal haploid number creates a 3n individual, a triploid plant. Fertilization of a 2n gamete by another 2n gamete creates a tetraploid or 4n individual. There are other possible ways in which polyploidy can be caused. One is the chance fertilization of one egg by two sperms. Another is that in the interval between pollination and the arrival of the pollen tubes in the ovary, a few egg cells may undergo division of the nuclear material without dividing into two separate cells, thus doubling their number of chromosomes. As soon as man got hold of polyploids he, of course, began creating more and more of them by breeding them.

It should be emphasized that only an actual count of the chromosomes, in material especially prepared for microscopic study, can show the chromosome number of a plant. The large size of a plant or its flowers cannot be taken as an indication of its ploidy. Although a cross can be almost entirely polyploid, the discovery of a number of polyploids in a certain cross does not mean that all of the other members of the cross are also polyploids. In fact, it is often the case that 2n, 3n, 4n, and even occasionally 5n plants occur among the plants from the same seed pod. Individuals whose chromosome number is ascertained should have this information recorded both in the grower's file and on the label that stays with the plant. If the plant turns out to be diploid when it was hoped that it might be a polyploid, the information is no less valuable, for fine diploids are very important in hybridization. Counting chromosomes is a time-consuming process, and can be done only by people who either are trained or who have the background to train themselves to do it. Therefore it is not practical for a grower to have chromosome counts made on any and all plants. Plants which have proved valuable in breeding, or which have qualities that lead the grower to think they should be useful as parents, or plants which win awards or are interesting for some particular characteristic or behavior pattern, are worth having counts made upon. Geneticists make numerous counts in species and in hybrid progeny in order to

now, they have not been available in large numbers. A rare tetraploid can show up in a 2n × 2n cross, but they occur more often in crosses involving one or more polyploid parent, in 3n × 2n or 3n × 4n crosses. A cross between two tetraploids regularly produces a tetraploid progeny, so that, now that growers have increasing numbers of tetraploids to work with, they can create more by mating them with each other. The chief lack of tetraploids is in certain color ranges, or in certain lines. Cymbidium growers, for example, are hopefully waiting for tetraploid greens to show up. Since tetraploids have a double dose of genetic material, their influence is quite strong in

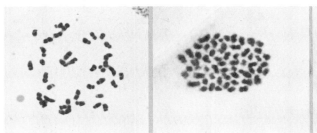 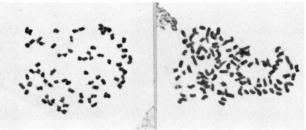

Fig. 56 Chromosomes in root tip cells of Vanda. From left to right: a diploid, with 38 chromosomes; a triploid, with 57 chromosomes; a tetraploid, with 76 chromosomes; and a pentaploid, with 95 chromosomes. (Courtesy of H. Kamemoto)

obtain information on how polyploidy occurs and is transmitted.

Much breeding at present is aimed toward the production of triploids, which, because they flower so profusely are often preferred by amateurs and by the commercial cut-flower grower. Triploids are made by crossing a diploid by a tetraploid. Both diploids and tetraploids, having even sets of chromosomes, form abundant numbers of reproductive cells, and the combination of the haploid gametes from the diploid and the 2n gametes from the tetraploid give the 3n number that creates the triploids. Given an abundance of tetraploids, tremendous numbers of triploids of a wide variety of colors and types can be bred.

While the tetraploids themselves are very handsome plants, their value lies especially in the field of hybridization, for, at least up to

crosses where they are mated with diploids. Hence, once a tetraploid of a certain type or color occurs it can be used in crosses with diploids to produce triploids that come close to having the desired characteristics.

The more equally balanced in number and character are the chromosomes in a plant, the more regular is the formation of reproductive cells. Each chromosome must have a like chromosome to pair with at reduction division in order for the process to proceed in a regular fashion. The members of each pair are called homologous chromosomes, and are inherited, as you will remember, one from the male and one from the female parent. Pairing is less efficient when chromosomes are unlike, as is often the case when they are derived from species that are quite widely separated, and when odd numbers are present. Lack of pairing of the chromosomes gives rise to reproductive cells with odd numbers, and these cause the formation of aneuploid plants.

The term "aneuploid" is used to describe the condition of having a chromosome number over or under an exact multiple of the basic haploid or "n" number for the species. It is derived from the term "euploid" which means "true ploid." Euploid forms have exactly twice, or three times, or four or five times the n number. If Cattleya is used as an example, the euploid forms have exactly 40, 60, 80, or 100 chromosomes. Aneuploid means "not true ploid," and refers to plants that have something over or under 40, 60, 80, or 100 chromosomes. In plants that have two sets of unlike chromosomes, inherited from widely separated parent species, these chromosomes may not be able to pair at reduction division. Instead, they become assorted in odd ways, and, if functional sex cells are formed at all, they will probably contain odd numbers of chromosomes, such as 17 and 23, or 15 and 25, instead of the even 20 chromosomes each. Such sex cells will, when fertilized, give rise to aneuploid individuals, plants with chromosome numbers such as 37, 43, etc. The many failures to form functional sex cells accounts for the relative sterility of hybrids from quite unlike parents, as for example, Cattleya and Schomburgkia. (See Hybridization in Vanda, Chapter 12, for other examples.)

Aneuploids can also result from polyploid crosses. For example, in a triploid plant, which has three sets of chromosomes (60 in Cattleya) you might think that 30 of these would pair with the other 30. This is not what happens. A chromosome can pair only with its homologue. In a triploid there are three of each homologous type, instead of the usual two. Some chromosomes may form pairs, leaving the third homologue standing alone. Sometimes three will come together. As reduction division takes place, some of the pairs will separate normally. The unpaired chromosomes may drift to one pole or the other, but some may get stranded and, not arriving at either pole, fail to be included in the newly forming

nuclei. The chromosomes that have come together by threes may separate so that two of them go to one pole and one to the other, or they may travel together so that one newly forming nucleus will receive all three while the other is left entirely without the genetic material they took with them. Some cells may be formed with only a few pairs and a few stragglers and thus have a very incomplete gene content. Most of such erratically formed cells cannot develop into functional sex cells, which accounts for the high degree of sterility in triploids. The same thing takes place in pentaploids.

A higher percentage of aneuploids occurs in some crosses than in others, showing that some plants are less regular in the formation of reproductive cells than others. Studies upon aneuploids show that those that have just one or two more or less than the euploid number can be quite normal. But plants whose chromosome numbers range far to one side or the other of a euploid number may suffer lack of vigor or be quite abnormal in some way. For instance, aneuploids with chromosome numbers of 58, 59, 61, 62, or 78, 79, 81, 82, etc. may be normal plants, while those with something like 50 or 70 may be abnormal.

We mentioned earlier that occasionally gametes are formed without having their chromosome number reduced. The cells which are destined to form the sex cells go through the process retaining their full complement of chromosomes. It appears that some of the functional sex cells of triploids are of this nature. Crosses between triploids and diploids, and triploids and tetraploids seem to be more fruitful if the triploid is used as the female, or pod, parent. Diploids and tetraploids, having even sets of chromosomes, produce large numbers of functional reproductive cells, and when these types are used as the male, or pollen, parent, there is greater likelihood of obtaining some viable seed than if the triploid were used as the male parent. Although the fertility of triploids is notoriously low, Cattleya Bow Bells seems to be an exception. A number of triploid Bow Bells have been the parents of a long line of successful hybrids. We do not have all the data we could wish on these crosses, but it appears that successful matings have been made between triploid Bow Bells and diploid plants, as well as with triploid Bow Bells and tetraploids. Both tetraploids and pentaploids are among the progeny. The unusual fertility of these Bow Bells individuals seems to indicate that they are better able to form non-reduced gametes than many other triploids, and form them more freely. Since these Bow Bells crosses have appeared, some other crosses between triploids and tetraploids have been unexpectedly successful. It may well be that success depends on finding the more fertile of the triploids in any one group and then finding plants that will be compatible with them.

Pentaploids have been far fewer in number than tetraploids and triploids. Individual pentaploid plants have sprung from various polyploid crosses. In some cases these have not been as handsome or as vigorous as triploids and tetraploids, but this is not continuing to be true. Pentaploids can be formed by 3n × 4n matings, where the 3n parent contributes a non-reduced gamete and the 4n contributes a 2n gamete. A fairly high percentage of pentaploids occurs in crosses where Cattleya Bow Bells has been mated with a tetraploid.

Attempts to create pentaploids and to use them as parents have been frustrating. However, work that is being done now may point the way. Theodore Zuck reports that efforts to cross the pentaploid Lc. Rosa Kirsch with 2n and 3n plants failed, but that a fairly good number of seedlings was obtained when it was crossed with a tetraploid C. Titrianae. From among the seedlings ten plants, counted at random, were all pentaploid. This would seem to have been brought about by fusion of 3n gametes from Lc. Rosa Kirsch with 2n gametes from C. Titrianae. Whether the 5n Lc. Rosa Kirsch also produce 2n gametes is not known, but if such were produced and functioned, it would be expected that this cross would also produce tetraploids. It is possible that no 2n gametes were functional. Another case of the

successful use of a pentaploid as a parent is reported by D. H. Niimoto and L. F. Randolph, who are doing other valuable work in orchid genetics. This case involves the mating of a pentaploid with a diploid, a type of cross that has failed heretofore. The pentaploid parent is C. North Star 'Niimoto,' one of several pentaploids from a cross between a 3n C. Bow Bells and a 4n C. Helen P. Dane. Large numbers of vigorous seedlings are now being raised, but their ploidy has not yet been reported. Much information should result from their study. It should be added that the pentaploids Lc. Rosa Kirsch and C. North Star are very lovely, vigorous plants, which gives hope that a new horizon in Cattleya breeding is in view.

■ COLCHICINE

The chemical, colchicine, has been used by horticulturalists for a good many years to create giant sized plants and flowers (tetraploids) and to make otherwise sterile hybrids capable of producing seed. Both results come from the same function of the chemical, which is to double the number of chromosomes. We often see tetraploids advertised in garden catalogues, for instance tetraploid snapdragons. The progenitors of most of these have been man-made tetraploids, formed by the use of colchicine. Success with colchicine on orchids has been slow to appear, for there are many problems to be solved along the way, but as more is learned it may become a useful tool.

In some orchid genera there is a lack of tetraploids in certain colors, for instance in green Cymbidiums. It would be a great boon if diploid greens could have their chromosomes doubled so that the resulting tetraploids could be used in breeding. Where hybrids are sterile, because they are triploids, or because they contain chromosomes from unlike parents (See Chapter 12 for examples in Vanda), or because of an aneuploid condition, they would become fertile if their chromosomes could be doubled. Whether we will ever be able to achieve this on a practical basis remains to be seen. At present there is little work reported. Gavino

Rotor reported preliminary work that showed promise in 1957. His paper may be found in the Proceedings of the Second World Orchid Conference.

Colchicine upsets the normal process of cell division. Vegetative cells divide by a process different from that of reduction division. The process through which vegetative cells divide (as in the growing parts of plants) is called mitosis. In this process each chromosome duplicates itself so that each resulting cell receives the full complement of chromosomes. As a cell with forty chromosomes divides, each newly forming cell receives a complete set of forty chromosomes.

The steps in mitosis are diagrammed briefly

would momentarily contain 80. The peculiar action of colchicine is to interfere with the division process just at the point when the chromosomes have become duplicated. The cell is made to cease its activities and return to a resting condition, carrying the double number of chromosomes. When the effects of colchicine wear off, the cell begins the division process all over again. This time, the 80 chromosomes duplicate themselves so that there are 160. Half of these are drawn to each pole, so that the two new cells each receive 80 instead of the original 40. Thus the cells become tetraploid cells. Typical action of colchicine is shown in Figure 58.

The action of colchicine is not always per-

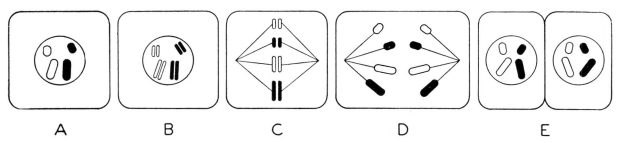

A   B   C   D   E

Fig. 57 Mitosis, the division of vegetative cells. A, the resting cell. B, each chromosome duplicates itself. C, the chromosomes gather in a plane through the center of the cell. D, opposite duplicates of each chromosome are drawn to opposite poles. E, the new cell wall comes between the newly separated sets of chromosomes, and two cells, each with a full complement of chromosomes, are formed.

in Figure 57, using a cell with 4 chromosomes for the sake of simplicity. In this diagram, A shows a resting cell. In B, the chromosomes are shown after each one has duplicated itself. In C, the chromosomes are lined up in the center of the cell, with a protoplasmic strand attached to each. This arrangement of protoplasmic strands or fibers is called the "spindle." In D, the strands appear to pull the attached chromosomes to the poles of the cell, half of them to one pole, the other half to the other pole. In E, the chromosomes are reconstituted into two nuclei, and a cell wall grows between them, forming two separate cells.

In Figure 57, the cell with 4 chromosomes has, for a brief interval, 8 chromosomes. In a cell with 40 chromosomes, at the time when these have duplicated themselves the cell

fectly regular. Sometimes an odd number of extra chromosomes is produced. Occasionally the doubling action is repeated, giving rise to cells that have four or eight times the normal chromosome number. Often not all cells are affected, so that the resulting plant may have some tetraploid parts mixed with normal parts. The ultimate aim is to produce plants that have tetraploid flowers, which will give reproductive cells bearing double the number of chromosomes. Plants that are entirely tetraploid might be created by treating very young seedlings. Tetraploid flowers might be achieved by treating a developing lead on a mature plant, the aim being to affect the cells that go into the formation of flowers at the tip of the pseudobulb. In either type of treatment, many failures may accompany an occasional success, so that the worker must have a great deal of patience and be willing to perform a great many treatments.

Treatment of seedlings is probably best administered when they are just large enough to be removed from the flask, about six months of age. Two methods are suggested. One is to wrap the roots in wet cotton (colchicine is injurious to roots so they must be handled with great care) and immerse the leaves and stem in colchicine solution. Concentrations must be

is more difficult, for the colchicine must be made to penetrate the tough outer coverings of the stem in order to reach the dividing cells at the stem tip. Treatment is suggested at the time the growth has reached a length of an inch or so. A small tube containing an agar gel to which the colchicine has been added may be inverted over the lead. Perhaps these inner cells may be reached by injecting the colchicine solution into the very base of the new lead (so as not to injure the stem tip), or by

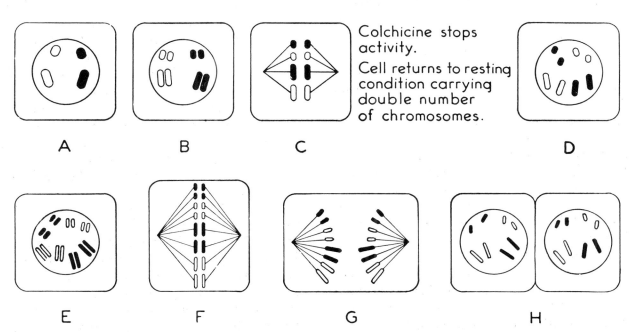

Colchicine stops activity.
Cell returns to resting condition carrying double number of chromosomes.

A   B   C   D

E   F   G   H

Fig. 58 Action of colchicine. Mitosis proceeds normally, A, B, and C, until colchicine is applied. Colchicine prevents the migration of the chromosomes to the poles, C, and returns the cell to resting condition, D. When mitosis resumes, after the influence of colchicine has worn off, the chromosomes duplicate themselves again, E. The process goes to completion F, G, and H, producing new cells with double the original number of chromosomes.

very weak (see below), and the exposure to the solution should be varied with different groups of seedlings in an attempt to find a period of time that is effective. Another method is to lay a little wad of cotton wet with colchicine solution in the axil of a leaf. A drop or two of solution would be added from time to time to keep the cotton wet for the desired period. In this case, the colchicine would penetrate the stem and affect cells from which future growths are to come.

Treatment of new growths on older plants

drawing a fine string through the base of the lead and keeping the outer end immersed in a container of solution, the string acting as a wick.

Colchicine is poisonous to plants and to human beings. It must be used on plants in very weak dilutions, measured very carefully. Too strong a concentration may kill the plants, yet the dose, to be effective, must be very near the lethal strength. Workers are cautioned not to let colchicine remain in contact with the skin, and particularly not to get it in the eyes.

It should be kept out of the reach of children.

Suggested concentrations to start with are between 0.05% and 0.20%. Not all plants respond to the same concentration or duration of exposure. Since there is little data on its use with orchids, your trials will be purely experimental, and should in fact be set up as an experiment.

You might make up (or have your druggist do this for you) three concentrations, 0.05%, 0.10%, and 0.20% colchicine in tap water. Each concentration would be applied to separate plants for three different intervals of time, four, six, and twenty-four hours. For your experiment, you would pick out nine groups of plants. To the first group you would apply 0.05% solution for four hours, to the second 0.05% solution for six hours, and to the third 0.05% solution for twenty-four hours. To the next group of three plants you would apply 0.10% solution in the same manner, and to the third group the 0.20% solution. Somewhere out of the nine groups there might be one for which the treatment proved just right. A record of the treatment given each plant would be kept, so that conditions that prove favorable can be repeated. If none of the treatments is effective, the concentration might be increased, but probably should not be made stronger than 0.30%. Perhaps it would be better to use the weaker dilutions for longer periods.

The first reaction to colchicine among seedlings is a slowing of growth rate. The effect may be so pronounced for some that they may not recover. Some may resume normal growth, but in others the growth of the main stem tip may cease, to be replaced by growth from an axillary bud. As growth is resumed it may proceed more slowly than in untreated seedlings. Tetraploid growth is often slower than diploid growth, and tetraploids may be slower in reaching maturity. Growth of a treated lead on an older plant may proceed quite normally, or it, too, may be slowed down. Also, if not all cells were equally affected, growth may be heavier on one side than the other.

Chromosome counts are usually made on root tip cells because these tissues are easy to obtain and, being constantly growing, show all stages of mitosis. Counts made on root tips from the second growth of a treated seedling may show whether tetraploidy has occurred. In order for the seedling to become a tetraploid plant, the colchicine must have penetrated and acted upon the stem and the bud from which the new growth is to arise. Roots formed from this new growth should be tetraploid if the colchicine was effective. Determining whether a flower has been made tetraploid is another matter. Chromosome counts can be made upon the cells that are to become reproductive cells. But this event takes place in the very early stages of flower bud formation, and dissecting out these tissues would, of course, spoil the developing flowers. Therefore, in order to determine whether tetraploid flowers have resulted from treating a developing lead, one must use the pollen from the flower on another of known ploidy and then study the resulting seedlings.

Gavino Rotor reports a case in which fertile flowers were produced on a plant that had previously always been sterile. Pollen from a flower on a plant of Cattleya Mary Schroeder, treated with colchicine, used on another plant of the same cross, produced a good quantity of viable seed. The production of functional reproductive cells by a plant that had previously been sterile is good evidence for the induction of chromosome doubling. By doubling the chromosome number, odd chromosomes that could not pair for lack of homologues are given duplicates of themselves with which to pair. Thus a plant that could not form functional sex cells has been enabled to do so. Study of the resulting seedlings would be decisive proof.

Plants which form flowers differently from Cattleya, that is, on an axillary stem that differentiates the flower buds as it develops, can be approached in a different manner. In such plants the developing flower spike itself may be treated, while it is still small and before the buds become apparent. Colchicine may have a number of effects. It may cause the spike to fail completely, or it may cause dropping of the buds. But if it is successful at all, some or all of the flowers may become tetraploid. When just the flower spike is treated, the plant itself will be unaffected; future spikes from the same plant will have the same ploidy as the plant.

You cannot expect simply to apply colchicine to a plant and come out with a tetraploid. However, we need only a few tetraploids in certain types to add greatly to the possibilities in hybridization, and only a few to break the sterility barrier in some breeding lines. Obtaining them may be well worth the effort involved.

9 | *Growing and Sowing Your Own Seed*

ONE of the main cares of nature, after assuring the nourishment and growth of a plant, is to insure its reproduction and the continuation of the species. Various ways have been devised for scattering the seed, for moving it away from the parent plant to more open ground.

The diversity of such mechanisms is a fascinating study in itself. There are plants that have ways of forcibly ejecting the seed from the pod or capsule, such as the Siberian pea and Oxalis. Others offer fruits tender and tasty, brightly colored, which attract birds and animals that carry away their seed. The cockleburs make a nuisance of themselves by their method of forcing their seed upon whatever agent happens their way. The exquisite forms of wind-borne seed are well known for their delicate umbrellas and parachutes.

But not every seed that is produced finds conditions suited to its germination. Only those fortunate enough to land in just the right spot can grow to maturity. Hence plants in even the best of circumstances must produce more seed than will ever grow.

Epiphytic orchids face a special problem in seed dispersal. The chances are slim that a seed will find some obscure crevice in the bark of a tree where it can germinate, or that it will have there the necessary conditions of air and light, moisture, and mineral nutrients. If only one seed from each plant should germinate and survive to maturity the continuation of the species would be well assured. In order to guarantee this against such odds, each plant produces hundreds of thousands of seeds every year.

The formation of so many seeds by rather small plants means that the seeds must be very tiny, which is true of all epiphytic orchid seeds. The seed of Cattleyas is as fine as powder, and close to a million are formed in one capsule. Its small size allows it to be carried by the gentle air currents in the jungle which are not strong enough to lift heavy particles to great heights. As the seed capsule ripens and splits open, the drift of pale yellow powder is picked up by the moving air and dusted from branch to branch. Some of the seed is blown away by stronger winds that meet the upward air currents above the jungle. Much of the seed, of course, drifts down to the ground where it has no chance to grow.

Because of its small size, the seed contains

little, if any, food to nourish the embryo during germination. It must find a ready supply where it falls. In a pocket of decaying vegetable matter, there will be available minerals and sugars released by the decomposing action of fungi and bacteria. And as will be seen in a moment, the presence of sugars is all-important to bring about the germination of the seed.

Even after successful germination, the seedling still faces hazards of destruction, overgrowth of fungi, burning by the sun if it has not enough shade, or even desiccation if it does not receive frequent enough rain.

The first growers who tried to germinate orchid seed ran into problems that plagued them and their followers for three-quarters of a century. Various methods were tried to induce germination. The seed was sown on leaf mold, decaying bark, sphagnum moss, etc. More often than not, if the recalcitrant seed did germinate, much of it was killed by invading bacteria and fungi. When these attempts failed, growers set to work on the theory that germination might be induced by contact of the seed with some fungus found in association with parent orchid plants. The experiments that followed were intricate, and consisted of infecting the seed with isolated strains of fungi, called the symbiotic method. Enough success came from this work to carry the fungus method on for many years. But it was a technique that could be used only by experts, and even in their hands there followed frequent destruction of the seed by the fungi.

It remained for Dr. Lewis Knudson of Cornell University, in 1922, to find a completely controlled, standardized, simple method for germinating orchid seed. He had done previous work which showed that sugars had a favorable influence on plant growth, which suggested to him that orchid seed might require the presence of sugar in order to germinate. He interpreted the success with fungi, not to its effect on the seed itself, but to digestion by the fungi of some of the carbohydrates and nitrogenous substances present in the growing medium. Sugars would be among the materials released in this process.

This proved to be true. Dr. Knudson found that the seed germinated readily without the presence of fungi when sown on an agar jelly to which had been added the necessary mineral nutrients plus sugar. Patiently he worked to find out what was the best sugar to use, and in what concentration. He also had to adjust the proportions of the mineral nutrients. The flasks containing the agar-nutrient mixture were sterilized, and the seed was disinfected to kill foreign organisms that might enter the flasks with it. The flasks were stoppered after being sown, and left untouched until the seedlings were well developed, some eight months to a year later. The flasks were perfect little glass houses, protecting the tiny plants from insects and contamination, and providing them with a constantly moist atmosphere until they were well developed. This is called the asymbiotic method.

Dr. Knudson's method revolutionized orchid growing. He removed the guesswork, the confusion and the hazards, and gave growers a technique that was easy to use and certain of success. It is simple enough to measure out the ingredients for making the agar-nutrient jelly, and now it is even possible to buy the mixture all prepared except for the addition of water.

In the jungle, only an occasional seed of the tremendous numbers produced has a chance to germinate. Now, in the hands of man, nearly every seed may become a plant. Growers who once zealously guarded every hybrid seedling, now hardly know what to do with the countless thousands they produce. One grower estimates that he has 80,000 seedlings in flasks at present. This has put orchids on a par with other greenhouse crops, and made orchid plants available to all who would buy.

Needless to say, Dr. Knudson's flask method has given a tremendous impetus to orchid growing, not only by increasing the numbers of plants grown commercially, but by making it possible for amateurs to grow their own.

■ POLLINATION

A simple maneuver with the forceps starts a seed pod on its way in your greenhouse. The human hand can perform in an instant the function of pollination, which in nature requires the most elaborate preparation and clever groundwork. Few orchids are capable of self-pollination. In fact, most orchids are constructed so that self-pollination in nature is impossible. It almost looks as if, in the long struggle for survival, those orchids which were perpetuated by cross-fertilization were the more vigorous, and lived to maintain their kind.

Orchids are equipped with fascinatingly ingenious mechanisms by means of which insects are practically forced to carry the pollen from one flower to another. Each mechanism is so well designed as to be almost foolproof, but an individual orchid lives under a perpetual handicap. Its mechanism will work only if an insect of just the right size and shape enters the portals so attractively spread for its reception. A tiny orchid, just one-quarter inch in diameter, requires a very small insect, while another, whose nectar tube is in the form of a spur ten-inches long, needs the services of a species of moth with a ten-inch proboscis. A flower may be visited by scores of insects, yet may wither and die before the kind comes along that can serve as bearer of its pollen. However, when the right one does visit the flower, the insect is not allowed to leave without carrying with it a parcel of pollen glued to its anatomy.

The pollen grains are fastened together in rather large waxy masses called pollinia, each of which contains enough pollen to fertilize another flower satisfactorily. Cleverly enough, in order to insure cross-pollination, orchids fasten the pollen masses to the insect as it leaves the flower.

Fig. 59, A and B show in detail the reproductive parts of the Cattleya. The column is shown from its under side in A, and cut in half lengthwise in B. The anther (*a*), the cap that covers the pollinia, is fastened by a tiny hinge (*h*) to the end of the column. Protruding slightly from under the anther are the tips of the four caudicles (*c*) attached to the pollinia (*p*). The rostellum (*r*), the partition between the anther chambers and the stigma, has on its under side a gland that secretes a sticky fluid. The stigma, which is really two stigmas grown together through the processes of evolution, is indicated by (*s*). The lip (*l*) presses up close under the column, forming a narrow passageway down which an insect must travel to reach the nectary (*n*) at its base. Fig. 59C shows the pollinia as they are situated in the anther chambers, after the anther has been raised, and Fig. 59D shows a single pollinium with attached caudicle.

The flower is pollinated by any rather large bee. When the bee lights on the lip its weight depresses the lip somewhat, and it then passes down the tube to get nectar. As it backs out of the tube, it pushes against the rostellum (*r*), ruptures the gland and becomes smeared with its sticky secretion. The force of the bee against the rostellum tips up the anther cap, touching off the spring. The anther flies back, rotating the pollinia so that the caudicles are exposed. As the bee backs farther out, the caudicles are caught in the sticky fluid on its back, and the pollinia are pulled out.

When the bee visits the next Cattleya, the pollinia on its back are forced into the stigmatic cavity. The stigmatic fluid is so sticky that it grips the pollen masses and tears them from the caudicles. After its feast of nectar, the bee leaves the flower with only the stumps of the caudicles attached, but in the process it will take with it the pollinia from this flower (if they have not already been removed) and bestow them on the next one it visits. You can imitate this by using a cotton swab for a bee. Push it down between the column and the lip, and as you pull it out watch the pollinia come with it. Then push it back into the flower and watch the pollinia stick to the stigma.

The simple sleight of hand that human beings can substitute for the natural process is to remove the pollinia from one orchid and place them directly on the stigma of another. But there is a difference between your respon-

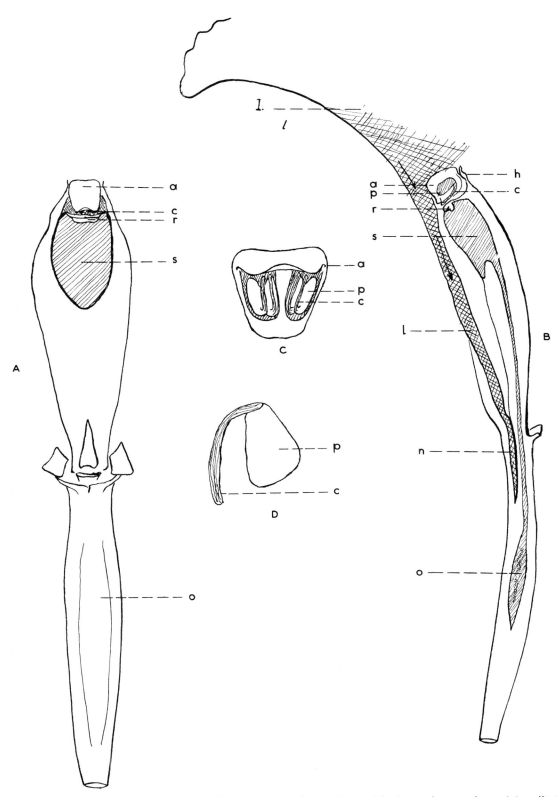

Fig. 59 Reproductive parts of a Cattleya. A shows the column from its under side, with the flower parts removed. B is a view of the column cut in half. It is seen from these drawings that what appears to be the stem of the flower is actually the ovary. (a) anther, (h) hinge that holds the anther in place. (p) pollinium, (c) caudicle, tail of the pollinium, (r) rostellum, (s) stigma, (l) lip, (n) nectary, (o) ovary. C is a view of the anther from its under side, showing the pollinia. D is a single pollinium with its caudicle.

sibility and that of the flower where pollination is concerned. The flower makes elaborate preparations to insure pollination and the production of a huge number of seeds, from which possibly only one or two seedlings will grow. Your preparation consists of giving great care to the choice of parent plants so that the innumerable seeds you germinate will be worth your energy to raise.

If the flowers you wish to cross are of about the same size, and the plants are equally strong, it does not matter which one bears the pod. However, if one flower is much smaller than the other, it is better to put the pollen from the larger one on the stigma of the smaller. The reason is of a purely mechanical nature. The pollen from the small flower may give rise to pollen tubes too short to reach into the ovary of the larger flower, or at best they may reach only as far as the apex of the ovary. The cross might then produce little or no viable seed (seed containing an embryo).

A seedling blooming for the first time, or a propagation having only two or three bulbs, should not be allowed to bear a seed pod. The production of seed would take more food than it can afford and still be able to make good growth. Such a plant should donate the pollen and the larger, stronger plant should grow the seed. A very large, heavy plant may carry two or three pods at the same time or may bear pods in successive years. If you wish to cross the same plant with two or three different others, use a separate flower for each kind of pollen. Never put two kinds of pollen on one flower.

A flower must be allowed to reach its prime before it is pollinated, that is, it must have been open for several days. Remove its own pollinia before placing on its stigma the pollen with which you desire to cross it. If you have a particularly handsome flower with nothing else at the moment to match it in quality, it is possible to keep its pollen for use in the future (see below under storing seed and pollen).

It is not necessary to use all four pollinia in the pollination of one flower. Actually, nature has provided enough pollen in one pollen mass to produce a pod full of seed. The other three might be called a safety factor. However, it is customary to use two pollinia, one on the left lobe and one on the right lobe of the stigma.

To obtain the pollinia, hold a clean piece of paper under the tip of the column and gently tip up the anther cap with a clean toothpick or other pointed instrument. The anther chambers (actually the whole tip of the column) will come loose and fall onto the paper. Push the pollinia out of their chambers with the same instrument, being careful not to touch them with your fingers. An easy way to transfer a pollinium to the other flower is to touch the stigma with your instrument and then touch the pollen mass. The pollinium will stick to the viscid drop on the instrument. Pollination is performed simply by pressing the pollinia well into the stigmatic fluid, one on each side. Once covered by the sticky substance, they will not fall off.

The first reaction of the flower after pollination is to wilt, sometimes within a few hours, certainly after two days. After the flower parts have wilted they should be cut off at their base to prevent decay and possible infection of the column. The column is, of course, left intact during formation of the seed pod.

■ DEVELOPMENT OF THE SEED POD

Within a week after pollination, the tip of the column becomes swollen and the pollinia seem to have been drawn deeply into the cavity. At about the same time, the ovary begins to enlarge. These reactions are merely the first responses to the presence of the pollen in the stigma. They are not a sign that fertilization of the eggs has taken place.

Each pollen grain, stimulated by the action of the stigmatic fluid, sends out a long slender tube. The pollen tubes grow down through the channel of the column, along the walls of the ovary, and eventually each tube penetrates an ovule. Fig. 61A shows this process, and Fig. 61B pictures sprouted pollen grains. During the growth of the pollen tube, two sperm cells are formed within it, one of which unites with the egg nucleus in the ovule. (The other sperm cell unites with other nuclei in the ovule to form the endosperm, tissue used as food by the developing embryo.) It takes sixty

pollen tubes were able to find their mark. How the 500,000th tube manages to find a still unfertilized ovule is something to puzzle over. That many pollen tubes are not successful is

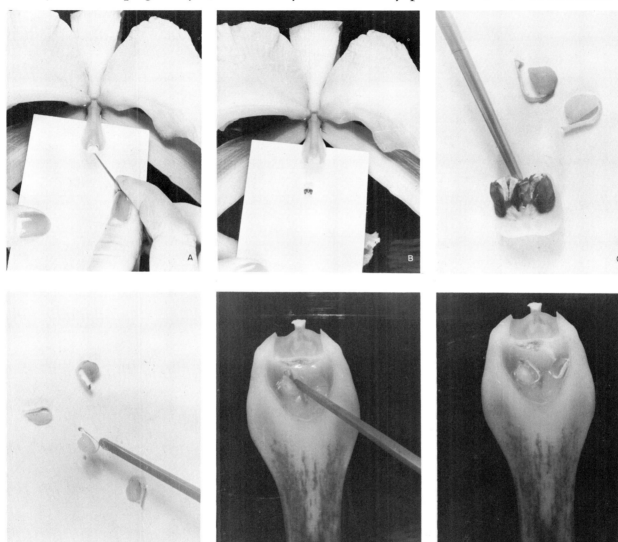

Fig. 60 Steps in pollination. A, remove the anther from the flower selected as the pollen parent. Hold a clean piece of paper under the column and tip off the anther onto it. B, the anther separated from the column. C, nudge the pollinia out of the anther. D, in order to pick up a pollinium, use a clean toothpick. Touch its tip first to the sticky fluid of the stigma and then touch the caudicle of a pollinium. The pollinium will adhere to the drop of fluid. E, place the pollinium on the stigma. F, pollination completed, two pollinia on the stigma.

to ninety days for the pollen tubes to complete their growth and penetrate the ovules.

Every viable seed formed is the result of the penetration of an ovule by a pollen tube. Production of 500,000 seeds means that 500,000

attested by the fact that often the greatest concentration of viable seed is found near the top of the ovary.

Incompatibility between the pollen and the flower on which it is placed often occurs. Some-

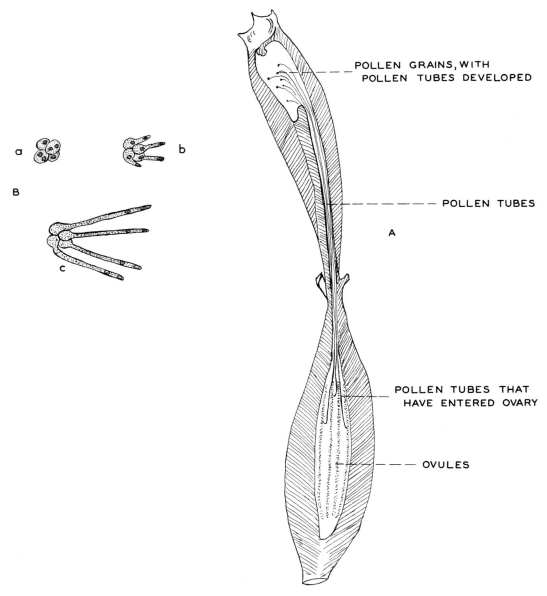

Fig. 61 Process of fertilization. A is the column and ovary sixty days after pollination. The pollen tubes have grown from the pollen grains in the stigma down into the ovary, which by this time is definitely enlarged. During this sixty days the ovules have been maturing so that they are now ready to receive the sperm cells brought to them by the pollen tubes. B shows pollen grains at various stages: a, as they originate, usually in groups of four; b, with tubes just starting; c, tubes elongating, and the nuclei carried along near the tips.

times it shows up within a few days by the shriveling of the column. The same pollen used on another flower might, however, have effected a successful mating. Sometimes a seed pod that seems to be progressing will turn yellow and drop off after two or three months. The ovules are immature at the time of pollination. Their maturation proceeds and the ovary enlarges while the pollen tubes are growing the necessary length. If for some reason the pollen tubes finally fail to effect fertilization, growth of the seed pod ceases.

If the cross is compatible, the ovary enlarges steadily. During its development it becomes marked with three deep flutings, corresponding to the three faint linear depressions visible on the ovary before pollination. The seed pod is completely hollow, containing three broad bands (placentae) to which the ovules are attached.

At six months the seed pod is about the size of a lemon and it does not enlarge much after this time. It ripens at about nine to ten months, occasionally later, and cracks open down the center of the flutings. The time to remove the pod is just when the cracks begin to show, before they have opened wide enough to allow the seed to spill out. To prevent losing any seed, it is a good idea to tie tissue paper over the seed pod a few weeks beforehand, and examine it from day to day. When the time comes for its removal, cut the stem that holds it to the pseudobulb, and place the pod in a clean glass jar to dry. Set the jar in a dry place, leaving it uncovered. Do not leave it in the greenhouse. If your climate is damp, the seed pod should be wrapped lightly in tissue paper and dried in a desiccator containing calcium chloride. When the pod is dried and split completely open, the seed can be shaken out into a clean container. It is ready to be sowed at this time, if you desire, but excess seed should be properly stored.

■ STORING SEED AND POLLEN

A desiccator is a glass container having two chambers, one holding calcium chloride which absorbs water vapor and the other containing the stored material. They can be purchased, but are rather expensive. A makeshift one will do as well. Use a wide-mouthed jar, and put two tablespoons of calcium chloride in the bottom. Make a shelf, out of hardware cloth or screen, that will rest in the center and divide the jar into two compartments, separating the calcium chloride from the upper part. A layer of paper over the screen will afford additional protection, yet still allow free circulation of air. Put the material to be stored in the top section, and screw on tightly a vacuum sealing lid. While drying the seed pod in the desiccator, let it remain at room temperature, as it will dry more rapidly this way than under refrigeration.

After the seed is removed from the pod, it should be kept under refrigeration. Cut pieces of writing paper (not wax paper) about four inches square, and in the center of each write the names of the parent plants so that the label will be visible after the seed is wrapped. Then put a small amount of seed in each paper, and fold carefully, fastening the ends with a paper clip. Place the packages in the desiccator, screw on the lid, and put in the refrigerator.

Seed retains its viability for a long time when stored in this manner, sometimes as long as six years. The percentage of germination decreases gradually, however, so that it may give only twenty to forty per cent after a long period.

Pollen does not remain viable for as long as seed, but may be kept for at least six months. Its viability is highest during the first few weeks. To store pollen, place the pollinia in a tiny glass tube, cork it tightly, and dip the corked end in paraffin to seal it. Then keep the tube in a refrigerator. Some advise the addition of a few granules of calcium chloride to the tube (in which case the pollinia must be wrapped in tissue paper to prevent contact with the calcium chloride), or else that the pollinia be dried in a desiccator for two days before placing in the glass tube.

■ CHECKING VIABILITY OF SEED AND POLLEN

Crosses between closely related species usually produce viable seed and pollen. Sterility is more likely to occur in complicated hybrids, particularly those derived from extremely dissimilar flowers. Testing the viability of seed and pollen is a simple matter, though in nine cases out of ten it is not necessary for amateurs to bother with it. Commercial growers and those who are carrying on serious breeding programs find it a necessary procedure. Discovery ahead of time that a certain pollen is not viable enables the grower to choose some other pollen for use on a choice flower. Otherwise he may have to wait another year to mate that particular plant. The benefit of checking the viability of the seed before sowing a hundred or more flasks is obvious.

To test the pollen, place a little of it on a flower that you do not wish to save, a "cull." Pollen tubes commence to grow within forty-eight hours and can be seen under a microscope. Remove some of the stigmatic fluid on a pin point, mix it with a drop of water on a microscope slide, and cover with a cover glass. The sprouted pollen can be seen unstained, but if you wish to stain them add a drop of crystal violet solution to the water. Fig. 61B, mentioned above, shows the pollen grains with tubes in various stages of growth. If you do not have a spare flower for this process, the pollen may be tested in a 0.2-molar sucrose solution (about one teaspoon of sugar in thirteen teaspoons of water) with agar added, kept at seventy-two degrees.

In any batch of seed there are some that do not contain embryos. Figs. 63A and 63B show a sample of Cattleya seed, with and without embryos, as seen under a microscope. To observe your own seed, mix a small amount with water, and place on a slide under a cover glass. Count the seed with and without embryos and estimate the relative percentage of good seed; eighty to ninety per cent is good. If no seeds have embryos, the lot must be discarded. You will have to use your own judgment as to whether to use seed that shows only a low percentage with embryos. Perhaps it will pay to try it for the sake of obtaining a few seedlings from a most unusual cross, or from one that rarely gives seed.

A further check of seed viability, and the one of real significance, is to sow a flask or two and see how well it germinates. This necessitates waiting three or four weeks, or until the seed swells and turns green. It sometimes happens (though rarely) that seed that appears under the microscope to be good is actually not living. This check would be well worth your while for seed that has been stored an excessively long time or has not been kept under good conditions.

■ **PREPARATION OF THE FLASKS**

The agar-nutrient medium for growing flask seedlings can be bought ready-mixed, so that beginners need not be awed by the list of chemicals involved. It can be obtained either from the Difco Company, Detroit 1, Michigan under the name of "Bacto Orchid Agar," or from Daniel M. Hill, Chemist, 605 East Granada Court, Ontario, California. Daniel M. Hill has two preparations, one for Cattleya, Vanda, and most other kinds, and one for Cymbidium and Cypripedium. Complete directions are given (requiring only the addition of distilled water and warming), and if followed carefully, results should be perfect. The mixtures are adjusted to the correct acidity, so that the beginner does not even have this to worry him.

Usually, 500 cc. Ehrlenmeyer flasks are used, but wide-mouthed clear glass bottles are frequently preferred. The latter may have bakelite screw caps or be fitted with rubber stoppers. They must be capable of sterilization, and be large enough to give several square inches of surface of agar. Large test tubes may also be used, although these will hold fewer seedlings. Everything should be washed thoroughly and be rinsed several times.

Rubber stoppers are much easier to handle than the conventional cotton plug. They should be boiled for fifteen minutes before being used. The stopper should have a hole in the center, through which is put a piece of glass tubing bent over at the top, for ventilation of the bottle or flask. The bent-down end of the glass tubing is closed with cotton. This arrangement helps prevent the latent contamination of the flask, which is a nuisance with the cotton stoppers. Also, it is easier to sterilize the rubber stopper and neck of the flask at the time of seed sowing or transplanting.

When the agar-nutrient mixture has been prepared, it is ready to be poured into the flasks or bottles. These may be slanted, if you wish, or kept in an upright position. If you prefer them slanted, build a rack beforehand to hold them in the desired position. Many prefer the "slants" as they afford a somewhat larger surface area. Use a long-stemmed funnel for pouring the agar, so that it will reach

Fig. 62 Preparing flasks and sowing seed. Upper left, add measured amount of prepared agar-nutrient mixture to one liter of distilled water in double boiler. Heat until thoroughly dissolved. Lower left, pour the melted agar-nutrient mixture into flasks, using a long-stemmed funnel. The flasks are then stoppered and sterilized in a pressure cooker. Upper right, disinfecting the seed. Calcium hypochlorite solution from the flask at the left is put in a small vial, to which is added a bit of seed on the tip of a knife. The dropper to be used in the sowing process is put to soak at the same time in a cup containing calcium hypochlorite solution. Lower right, flasks are taken one at a time from the pressure cooker, in which they were sterilized and allowed to cool. Here we have used cotton stoppers, but it is recommended that rubber stoppers be used instead (screw caps for bottles). These last should be put in a dish of sterilizing solution while the seed is being sown. Place a few drops of the suspended seed in the flask and replace the stopper. Cover the stopper and neck of the flask with foil or film.

down into the flask and obviate splashing agar on the sides or, most important, on the neck. This is essential to prevent the sticking of the stopper and to avoid giving molds a place to grow. The agar should be about an inch and one-half deep.

The flasks or bottles should be stoppered before sterilization. Screw caps should be tightened firmly and then released one-quarter turn.

Laboratory workers will be able to sterilize the flasks in an autoclave, but home canning equipment does just as well, either a pressure cooker or a hot-water-bath kettle, preferably the former. In either case, you must be sure that no water enters the flasks. In a pressure cooker, twenty minutes at fifteen pounds pressure is sufficient. If a canning kettle is used, adjust the water level to the level of the agar in the flasks to prevent their tipping while boiling. Cover the kettle and boil for one hour. After sterilization, remove the flasks while still hot, pour out the water from the kettle or cooker, and quickly put the flasks back in and cover with a clean cloth. This will allow them to cool without becoming contaminated. If possible, keep them thus protected until you are ready to use them. They are ready as soon as they are cool and the agar is jelled.

■ SOWING THE SEED

This process is so simple that the doing of it takes no longer than the telling. In fact, none of the procedures is difficult, and if the detailed descriptions make any part of them seem so, you have only to try it all, step by step, to realize that each is essentially easy. The second time you go through the process, you will wonder that you could ever have thought it complicated.

Sowing the seed consists of two main steps: (1) disinfecting the seed by soaking it in an antiseptic solution, and (2) putting a little of the suspended seed in each flask. We shall give you several methods—take your choice. In each method cleanliness is an important factor. The air is filled with mold spores. You are going to have to open the sterile flasks briefly to insert the seed, and you must take every precaution against contamination of the flasks during this time. Wait until the day's activities are over in the kitchen and the air has had time to settle before you begin your work. I like to spread damp dish towels on the work surface as a protection against dust, and the effect is better if they are wrung out of a 10% Clorox solution (one part Clorox to nine of water).

Method # 1. Equipment you will need includes a one-quarter-ounce vial with a cork, a new medicine dropper, a glass or china cup, a graduated cylinder that holds 100 cc., two empty bottles, filter paper, glass funnel, an open flame (gas burner or alcohol lamp), and a paring knife.

The seed may harbor mold spores acquired during handling and must therefore be disinfected. A solution of calcium hypochlorite* is standard for this purpose. Buy a bottle of it at the drugstore and keep it tightly stoppered in the refrigerator. To make up the solution put ten grams of the solid calcium hypochlorite in one bottle and add 140 cc. of distilled water. Shake thoroughly, let stand for one hour, shaking it at intervals. Then filter off the clear solution into the other bottle. This must be used at once. (Any amount left over must be thrown away, and fresh solution made up each time you prepare to sow flasks.)

Fill the little vial two-thirds with the calcium hypochlorite solution, and add a tiny bit of seed. The amount you can pick up on the tip of a paring knife will sow ten or a dozen flasks. (The knife, incidentally, should be sterilized by flaming and completely cooled before touching the seed.) Cork the vial tightly. The seed must be thoroughly wetted with the calcium hypochlorite solution, which requires that it be shaken vigorously and continuously for at least twenty minutes to break up the minute air bubbles that surround each seed.

* Note that calcium hypochlorite is an entirely different chemical from the calcium chloride used in the desiccator. Calcium hypochlorite may be purchased as chlorinated lime.

While you are shaking the seed, put some of the remaining calcium hypochlorite solution in the cup and place the dropper in it to soak, being sure to fill the bulb as well as the glass part. You might also check on the arrangement of your equipment. Everything should be close together, the flasks, still in their covered container, and the cup with the dropper. In the cereal bowl put a solution of 10% Clorox, for disinfecting the stopper while it is removed during sowing.

When the seed has been disinfected, you are ready to sow the flasks. The work will move more smoothly if you can have a helper at your first session, either to attend to the flasks or to drop the seed into them, but you can manage alone if you must. The following operations must be performed quickly so that the flask will be open to the air for as short a time as possible.

Take one flask at a time from the covered container and remove the stopper or screw cap. Place this in the bowl of Clorox.

The seed will by now either have risen to the surface of the solution in the vial or sunk to the bottom, and you do not want to remove all of it in one dropper full. It should be quickly stirred up by putting the end of the dropper down in the bottom of the vial and forcing the air out of it. The bubbles will swirl the fluid and the seed, and you can then take up a few drops to be transferred to the flask. Hold the dropper in the neck of the flask so that the drops will not run down the sides. Four drops is a good amount to put in each one, and if you move the dropper slightly in a circle you can put each drop in a different place on the agar. As soon as the seed is dropped in, take the stopper from the bowl, drain off any excess Clorox so that none will enter the flask, and replace it on the flask.

When all of the flasks are sown, pick up each one and gently tilt it back and forth to spread the seed over the surface of the agar. The screw cap or stopper must be covered, preferably with foil fastened with tape. Be sure that all flasks are labeled and dated.

One or two of the flasks may have become contaminated at the time of sowing and they will show growth of molds on the agar within a few days. It is to be hoped that not all of them will be so affected. If you work very carefully you may be able to get rid of a single spot of mold, provided you find it while it is still small. Swab the neck, rim and stopper with 10% Clorox. Sterilize a long handled instrument. Working in an area prepared as for flask sowing, open the flask, reach in and cut out the spot with the surrounding agar, and gently lift it out. Be sure that you do not touch the sides of the flask in the operation, else the mold may thus be spread. Drop a few drops of Wilson's Anti-Damp on the area and re-stopper the flask. The more quickly this procedure is done, the less chance for further contamination. As your speed and dexterity increase with experience you will be less likely to have contamination in the flasks.

Method #2. This method employs a hypodermic syringe to inject the seed into the flask. Instead of a bent glass tube in the rubber stopper, a short straight tube is used, with cotton placed in it as before. Put a few drops of 10% Clorox on the cotton. The seed in suspension is picked up with a sterile hypodermic (a large bore needle is necessary). The needle is then dipped in 10% Clorox, forced between the cotton and the glass of the tube, and the seed squirted into the flask. R. H. Higgins suggests that if the seed tends to stick to the needle, this can be alleviated by adding a bit of 10% warm agar solution to the vial containing the seed and disinfectant. The stopper should be covered with foil after the flasks are sowed.

Method #3. The McEwan Flask Method. This method is detailed farther on, under transplanting flasks. It is an entirely new method, the equipment and procedure designed by Wm. S. McEwan, and if you plan to sow many flasks over a period of time, it would be well worth your consideration.

Method #4. The actual process of sowing the flasks is the same as described in Method

#1, but the danger of contamination is reduced by the use of a "sleeve box." This is a box constructed with a slanting hinged glass lid and holes in the front or ends through which you can put your hands. Some growers like to add sleeves made of cloth and fastened on the outside to the holes. These have elastic in the ends so that they fit well up over the forearm. The inside of the box should be sprayed with 10% Clorox before each use, and a cloth wrung out of the Clorox solution should be laid on the floor.

Have everything you need in place in the box before inserting your hands: sterilized flasks, sterilized dropper in cup of calcium hypochlorite solution, vial of disinfected seed, saucer of 10% Clorox for holding stoppers or lids, and squares of foil or polyethylene film for covering the flasks. You may wish to wear rubber gloves while working. It is not recommended that these be fastened to the ends of the sleeves, as the struggle to put them on often causes air to be sucked into the case with some force. After you have everything in readiness, put on the gloves, wash them in Clorox solution, insert your hands through the sleeves, and then wipe off the gloves with a cloth wrung out of Clorox solution placed in the box for this purpose.

■ CARE OF FLASKS

Cattleya seed germinates and grows best at temperatures between 70° and 75°. The temperature may rise a little in warm weather. Ideally the temperature should be 70° to 75° at night also, but if you cannot maintain this, let the night temperature drop to 65°. A fluctuation of more than 10 degrees either way is not good for the developing seedlings and will retard their growth. Flasks may be kept on a shaded shelf in the greenhouse, or in a glass case with added humidity in the house. The latter is necessary to keep the flasks from drying in the drier atmosphere of the house. They need only 200 foot-candles of light.

In extreme cases of drying, it is necessary to add a little sterile distilled water to the flask.

This is a risky procedure, however, and unless done expertly may result in contamination. The screw cap or stopper and the rim and neck of the flask must be thoroughly swabbed before opening with 10% Clorox. Then lift the lid only high enough to admit the dropper (previously sterilized) and replace it quickly after the water is added. If you have used a stopper with a short straight tube, as in method #2, put a few drops of 10% Clorox on the cotton and inject the sterile distilled water by means of a hypodermic syringe, inserting the needle between the glass and the cotton. Cover the stopper with fresh foil afterward.

During the development of the seedlings, disturb the flasks as little as possible. Jostling the flasks sometimes allows mold spores that have settled on the neck or the stopper to drop into the agar and cause contamination.

■ DEVELOPMENT OF THE SEEDLINGS

About ten days or two weeks after the seed is sown it begins to swell. Within six weeks the seed turns green, showing the development of chlorophyll. Fig. 63 shows the stages of development of the seedling. The embryo continues to increase in size until it is a little green spherule, about $\frac{1}{16}$ inch in diameter, shaped like a top, with a depression in its upper surface. Absorbing hairs soon cover the surface. Between two and three months after the seed was sown, the first leaf point makes its appearance in the middle of the depression, and the spherule becomes larger and somewhat flattened. This disc-like structure is called the protocorm. Soon a second and third leaf appear, the stem elongates, and the first root grows down. By the sixth month the seedling is well developed. During the following months the leaves grow larger, and additional roots may form. Nine to twelve months after sowing, the seedlings are ready to transplant to community pots.

When the flasks are first sown, it is not possible to control the number of seeds per flask. Some will be very crowded, others not so heavily populated. There is always some difference in the growth rate among individual

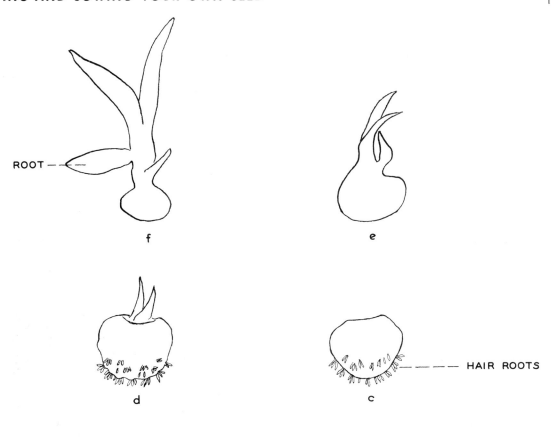

ROOT

HAIR ROOTS

f

e

d

c

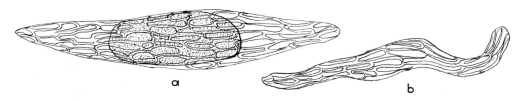

a

b

Fig. 63 Development of Cattleya seedlings. A, a seed with an embryo. B, a seed without an embryo. C, spherule developed; the embryo increases in size until it bursts the seed coat, and then enlarges. Absorbing roots (small hair roots) develop on its surface. D, proto-corm, the first leaves developing (two to three months after sowing). E, elongation of the stem, with more leaves appearing. F, seedling at about six months, showing first root growing from the stem, below the second leaf.

seedlings; some take hold and grow rapidly while others develop more slowly. Some never go past the protocorm stage. The differences are more marked in crowded flasks where competition for the nutrients allows the faster growing ones to gain an advantage over the slower ones. After about six months, the growth rate in general slows down a little, due possibly to the accumulation of metabolic products in the agar as well as to depletion of the nutrients.

At the six-month stage, or even a little earlier, most commercial growers and many ambitious amateurs like to transplant the seedlings to fresh flasks. The seedlings receive quite a boost by being put into fresh medium. The commercial grower has a dual purpose, first to produce flasks with a uniform number of plants so that one customer will not receive 500 plants and the next only 50, and also to have flasks of transplantable size ready for the market in a shorter time. Amateurs are motivated by the desire to have their seedlings come along as fast as possible, and also to have them as large as possible when the time comes to put them into community pots. Transplanting flasks is, however, a ticklish business, and the average grower need not feel at all compelled to undertake it. The process is described later on in this chapter.

■ KNUDSON'S FORMULA "C"

After you have grown seedlings with the prepared products, you may want to mix your own medium. You should start with a standard formula, and later, if you want to join the ranks of experimenters, you may want to try the addition of vitamins or other growth promoting substances to the media. It should be said here that, up to now, research has produced no better formulas than those of Dr. Knudson. Therefore, Knudson's "C," is given as the standard.

the ingredients, or will sell them to you himself.)

Add the ingredients, one at a time, to one liter (1000 cc.) of distilled water, and dissolve completely. Then add fifteen grams of plain agar, and warm in a double boiler until all of the agar is dissolved.

After the medium is thus prepared, and before sterilization, it is necessary to check the pH (which means hydrogen ion concentration). The pH scale is based on units from zero to fourteen, which indicate the degree of acidity or akalinity of a solution; seven is neutral. Below seven the solution is acid, and the lower the number the more acid it is. Above seven it is alkaline. Cattleya seed (and that of most orchids) grows best in a solution that has a pH of 5.0-5.2. This degree of acidity is necessary to make the minerals available for the use of the seedlings. Too great an acidity often kills the seed, and a too alkaline condition impoverishes the seedlings by preventing the plants from obtaining the necessary minerals. Equipment to test pH can be bought from most supply houses, and ranges from the expensive electrode type to the cheaper color indicator kind. Full directions come with the equipment.

Checking the pH consists of removing a small amount of the agar-nutrient medium as

KNUDSON'S FORMULA "C"

Chemical	Symbol	Amount
Calcium Nitrate	$Ca(NO_3)_2 \cdot 4H_2O$	1.00 gram
Monobasic Potassium Phosphate	KH_2PO_4	0.25 gram
Magnesium Sulfate	$MgSO_4 \cdot 7H_2O$	0.25 gram
Ammonium Sulfate	$(NH_4)_2SO_4$	0.50 gram
Sucrose	$C_{12}H_{22}O_{11}$	20.00 grams
Ferrous Sulfate	$FeSO_4 \cdot 7H_2O$	0.025 gram
Manganese Sulfate	$MnSO_4 \cdot 4H_2O$	0.0075 gram

These chemicals must be weighed with extreme care, using a fine balance. Any discrepancy in the proportions of the chemicals, even of the sugar, may be disastrous to the seedlings. If you do not have access to a fine balance, or are unaccustomed to its use, you had better ask your druggist to do the weighing for you. (Incidentally, he will also assist you with the name of a chemical supply house where you can buy

soon as it is prepared (before sterilization), and testing it with whatever type of equipment you have. If it is found to be too alkaline, add a drop or two of 0.1 normal hydrochloric acid to the whole amount of medium, mix thoroughly, and then remove a small quantity again for checking. Continue until the pH reads between 5.0 and 5.2. If the medium as first mixed turns out to be too acid, add 0.1 normal potassium hydroxide solution, and proceed in the same manner.

■ USE OF WIRE LOOP FOR SOWING SEED

Experts prefer a fine wire loop instead of a dropper for sowing seed. The loop is a bit difficult for beginners to use, so the dropper has been suggested to simplify things at first. The loop has the advantage of picking up the seed with very little of the sterilizing solution clinging to it, and in an expert hand the seed may be spread evenly on the agar. It is particularly useful in handling seed that sticks to the sides of the vial—Cymbidium seed, for instance.

The end of a fine platinum wire is made into a loop about $\frac{3}{16}$ inch in diameter, and attached by the other end to a long slender handle. When the loop is dipped into a suspension of orchid seed, it comes out with a thin film of fluid spread within the loop, holding a good number of seeds. For seed that floats, the loop is dipped only into the upper surface. Where the seed sinks, the sterilizing solution can be poured off first, leaving the collection of seed in the bottom of the vial.

The loop is sterilized by flaming, and completely cooled before touching the seed. To be sure that it is cool, you might dip it into another vial of the disinfecting solution you are using. To sow the seed, the loop is drawn lightly across the agar, not really touching the agar but merely the moisture that has exuded on its surface.

■ SLANTING FLASKS OR BOTTLES

Many growers prefer to have the agar on a slant in flask or bottle. This gives a little wider growing area, and with the flask held on a slant during the sowing process mold spores are less likely to enter the mouth. A simple rack can be built to keep the flasks tipped at the desired angle. The sterilized flasks are placed in the rack before the agar jells and covered to prevent contamination. After the flasks are sown they are kept in the rack.

■ OTHER METHODS FOR DISINFECTING SEED

Calcium hypochlorite solution has long been the standard means of disinfecting seed. It is gentle yet efficient, and it does not harm sensitive seed such as Vanda, Phalaenopsis and Cymbidium. Cattleya seed can remain in it for several hours without harm, giving the beginner the advantage of extra time and allowing the seed to be kept over in case of an interruption during the seed sowing process. Some growers like a three per cent hydrogen peroxide solution as a disinfecting agent, and some prefer a solution made by adding one Clorazene tablet to two ounces of distilled water. With these last two time is saved by not having to make up the calcium hypochlorite solution, but the seed should be sown immediately.

For seed that is not sensitive to a disinfecting agent, Clorox may be used, but always with extreme caution. The solution must be quite weak and the seed should not stand in it for very long. We recommend one part of Clorox to ninety-nine parts of water, although one of Clorox to fifty-four of water has been used. Shake the seed in the solution for exactly ten minutes, no longer, as after this length of time the percentage of germination may be reduced. As much as possible of the Clorox solution must then be removed and be replaced with sterile (boiled and cooled) distilled water. If the seed has sunk to the bottom of the vial, gently draw the Clorox solution off from above it with a sterilized dropper. If the seed is floating, insert the dropper below it and draw the solution into it. Replace with sterile distilled water and shake thoroughly. This may be enough rinsing for most seed, but the process can be repeated. Then sow the seed at once.

Another method for rinsing the seed is to filter off the Clorox solution. Fit filter paper into a small glass funnel and pour the contents of the vial into it. Then pour sterile distilled water through and let it drain. The seed must now be re-suspended. Hold the end of the funnel into a sterile vial, add enough distilled water to well up in the filter paper, and then with a sterile instrument quickly poke a hole in the bottom of the filter paper so that water and seed will run through into the vial.

■ OTHER MEDIA FOR GERMINATING SEED

Research goes on to find new media for germination—media that will speed up the growth of seedlings and shorten the time they must be in flasks. So many things enter into such research that obtaining results that can be generally useful is a long, slow process. A substance that may stimulate the growth of one species may inhibit, or at least not benefit, the growth of another. A substance may be beneficial to some kinds in one concentration and to others in a different concentration. Thus it sometimes occurs that a report by one group of workers may seem to be in conflict with that of another, simply because seed from different individuals was used, or because of other differences in the work. It would take a tremendous amount of space to summarize what work has been done on various modifications of formulas and on the additives and substitutes that have been tried, for instance, additions of substances from various plants, different sugars, numerous vitamins, growth promoting chemicals, and so on. Such work is discussed by Carl Withner in his chapter on "Orchid Physiology" in *The Orchids,* edited by him and published by Ronald Press in 1959. Anyone interested in doing studies along these lines will find his bibliography most helpful.

However, from among the various plant substances tried in media, two have been found useful in germinating seed. These are coconut milk and tomato juice, which can be substituted for some of the chemical salts ordinarily combined with the agar. Not all genera respond when tomato juice is used alone, but a mixture of coconut milk and tomato juice seems to be quite satisfactory for most genera. Coconut milk has been used in a great deal of work with seed germination. It contains some substance that stimulates growth, but the exact nature of the substance has not yet been found.

Rev. Masao Yamada of Hawaii, who has in the past published formulas using coconut milk and tomato juice, has kindly given me by letter a revised formula. He emphasizes that best results are obtained with milk from green coconuts, in which the meat has just begun to harden. The milk at this stage is at its sweetest and is also in greatest quantity. Obviously, his formula will be most useful in areas where coconuts can be obtained at just the right stage of development.

YAMADA'S FORMULA

For one liter of medium:
250 cc. of coconut milk
750 cc. distilled water
5 teaspoons granulated table sugar
1 teaspoon Peptone (powder, Difco Co.)
¼ teaspoon Gaviota Organic Orchid Fertilizer
3 tablespoons canned unsalted tomato puree (any standard brand)
15 to 20 grams of agar (Difco Co. plain agar)

A tomato juice formula as reported by J. Meyer is very simple and may be useful for some things.

TOMATO JUICE FORMULA—J. Meyer
250 cc. fresh strained tomato juice
250 cc. distilled water
7.5 grams stick agar

If you wish to try a new medium, or to experiment on your own, it is advisable to have on hand a large quantity of seed from one seed pod. You can then germinate some on a standard medium such as Knudson's "C," or the Difco or Hill prepared media, for comparison, as well as for safety. Don't risk a small amount of precious seed on a medium with which you are not familiar.

■ GERMINATING GREEN SEED

Cattleya seed is easy to disinfect and germinates readily. Some kinds, however, are sensitive to disinfecting solutions and others are reluctant to germinate. Research has been carried on with a view to finding some stage in the development of the seed when it may be removed from an unripe pod and will germinate when thus planted green. Seed from most genera will germinate when removed a month before the pod would normally ripen. Cattleya seed will germinate as early as six months after pollination.

Sowing seed from the green pod can be helpful in many ways. The seed within the unopened pod is absolutely clean and sterile, free from any contaminating organisms. If the pod is harvested before it begins to split and is thoroughly washed with a disinfecting agent, the seed can be removed under sterile conditions and be sown without having to be treated itself with a disinfectant. This eliminates the danger of harming sensitive seed, and also does away with one step in the usual procedure. Some kinds that are slow to germinate may do so more rapidly if sown before the seed coat is fully hardened. Although not all growers have difficulty with Vanda, Phalaenopsis, and Cymbidium, some definitely do, and these find that sowing the seed green gives them a better percentage of germination in these genera. Paphiopedilum is a problem unto itself. Poor germination is caused largely by the genetic makeup of the plants, but often apparently viable seed fails to germinate. It is thought that in Paphiopedilum, as in many other kinds of plants, the seed coat contains an agent that inhibits germination. Sowing the seed before the seed coat is fully developed has given better germination in some instances.

The flasks are prepared in the usual way and are kept covered until time to use them. In a pressure cooker or an autoclave sterilize the following equipment, wrapped in a towel: a small glass vial with a stopper for the seed, an eye dropper, a sharp stainless steel knife, and a shallow bowl. Also, sterilize at the same time a flask of distilled water. Prepare a sleeve box by spraying the inside with 10% Clorox solution and lay on its floor a towel wrung out of 10% Clorox. Place the prepared flasks in it, along with the sterilized package of equipment and the flask of sterile distilled water. Also place in the box a small towel wrung out of the Clorox solution, for wiping your hands.

Wash the seed pod thoroughly with 10% Clorox, scrubbing it gently all over including the seams with a soft brush, and then wrap it in a piece of toweling also wrung out of the Clorox. Some growers like to peel the outside layer off the pod at this point, and re-dip the peeled pod in Clorox. There is danger in doing this, for you may cut too deeply into the pod and expose the seed, so be careful. Exposure to the air will contaminate the seed, and contact with the Clorox will injure it. Place the wrapped pod in the sowing box.

If you have many flasks to sow, or if you are sensitive to Clorox, you should wear rubber gloves. Rinse the gloves in 10% Clorox after you have put them on, and then wipe them with the Cloroxed towel after inserting them through the sleeves. No Clorox must touch the seed. Open the sterile package. Pour some of the sterile distilled water into the bowl, and rinse your gloves in it. Then pour a little distilled water from the flask into the seed vial. Now rinse the seed pod in the bowl, and cut it open with the sterile knife. Scoop out some of the seed with the knife and put it in the vial. Stopper the vial and shake it to suspend the seed. Sow the seed with the dropper, stoppering each flask as you do so.

■ TRANSPLANTING FLASKS

The greatest hazard in transplanting flasks is the danger of contamination. The flasks must be open for quite a while, and you must move an instrument in and out of them as you transfer groups of seedlings, thus multiplying the chances for mold spores to enter the flasks. The professional grower, whose first failures are but a dim memory, can turn out clean flasks day after day, but the amateur is lucky if he doesn't have some troubles. Amateurs, being what they are, however, usually persist until they are successful!

Flasks for transplanting are prepared in the same way, and with the same medium, as the original ones. The work of transplanting must be done under cover, and the usual equipment is the sleeve box described above. The fresh flasks are placed in the prepared box (sprayed with 10% Clorox, etc.). The flasks from which the seedlings are to be taken are thoroughly washed off on the outside with 50% Clorox, including caps or stoppers and the area between rim and stopper. The instrument for moving the seedlings may be a wire loop on the end of a handle, or a long-handled spoon with a small bowl. It should be sterilized with 10% Clorox after it is placed in the case and must then be rinsed in sterile distilled water just before use.

It would be well to have a shallow dish of a fungicide solution, such as Wilson's Anti-Damp, in the box, because as you work from flask to flask you may find some seedlings large enough to go into community pots. These can be set aside in the bowl for later attention.

Open the flask from which seedlings are to be removed, and a flask into which they will go,

placing the stopper of the latter in the dish of 10% Clorox. Gently dip out a group of seedlings, skimming them off the old agar, and place them in the new flask. Repeat until you have enough, perhaps about fifty, and then with the same instrument nudge them apart so as to space them more or less evenly. They will regain an upright position as their roots go into the new agar.

If the seedlings are definitely different in size, it might pay to put the larger ones in a flask together and the medium and small ones in other flasks, saving the occasional huge ones

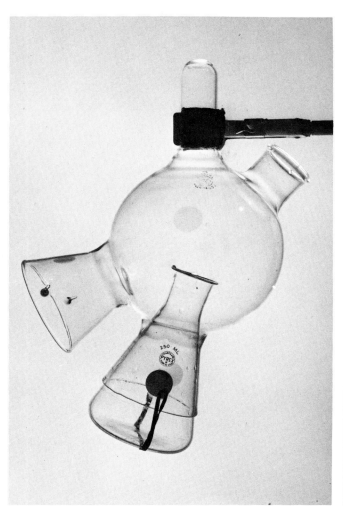

Fig. 64 The McEwan flask for sowing seed or transplanting flasks. Left, the McEwan flask, with two projecting bells into which the flasks are inserted for working, each attached by rubber bands to hooks on the sides of the bells. At the upper side is an open neck through which sowing or transplanting tools are inserted, and a handle by which the flask is held in a clamp. Upper right, transplanting seedlings from one flask to another. Lower right, stoppering the finished flask. (Courtesy of W. S. McEwan)

for community pots. If you have a large number of seedlings from one cross, you may not care to save the ones that are still in protocorm stages. Some of these will never go beyond it. But surprisingly enough, many will perk up and grow nicely when transplanted. As we shall see in the next chapter, it is even possible to transplant very small seedlings, including protocorm stages, into media other than agar, although they will make faster growth in agar in flasks.

A new apparatus for transplanting seedlings was devised by Wm. S. McEwan,[*] and is pictured herewith. The advantage of this device is that it has a small volume of air and, being glass, can be sterilized more efficiently than the sleeve box. It is a custom made glass sphere to which have been fused two bell shaped glass collars on the lower side and a single collar on the upper side. The sphere has a handle on top by which it is held in place by a clamp on a ring stand. The flasks to be sown, or the flasks to be transplanted, are held in the lower collars by rubber bands hooked over horns fused to the sides of the collars. You reach in through the upper opening with long handled instruments to sow the seed or transplant the seedlings.

The general method for transplanting seedlings is as follows. The inside of the sphere and

[*] Wm. S. McEwan has made arrangements to have these flasks made for any who care to buy them. The cost at present is twenty-five to thirty dollars. Interested persons may write to him at 513 A Lexington Ave., China Lake, Calif.

the collars are swabbed with 50% Clorox, by means of a piece of toweling wrapped around the end of a stick. The stopper and the neck of the fresh flask is thoroughly washed with 10% Clorox, and then, under cover of an inverted cereal bowl, the stopper is removed to a saucer of 10% Clorox where it remains until it is reinserted in the flask. Keeping the open flask in a horizontal position so as to prevent spores from entering, move it into one of the collars and hook it into position. The flask from which seedlings are to be taken is then washed off with 50% Clorox, opened and inserted into the other collar. The seedlings are moved from one flask to the other by means of a long handled spatula, or handle with a wire loop, which has been sterilized before use. When the new flask is ready, the stopper is removed from the dish of Clorox; and the flask is edged out from under the collar just far enough to allow the stopper to be inserted while still under the protection of the collar.

Seed sowing is accomplished in much the same way. The sphere is swabbed with the Clorox solution, the flask is swabbed before opening and the stopper placed in a dish of Clorox. The flask is hooked into one of the collars. The sterilized seed is transferred from the vial to the flask either by means of a long pipette or, as McEwan prefers, by means of a little beaker holding 1 cc. and held by a ring on the end of a rod.

10 | *Seedlings from Flask to Bloom*

Even if you do not indulge in growing your own seed and sowing flasks, you will at some time or other want to obtain some flask seedlings, certainly some community pot seedlings. Flasks can be bought for between twenty-five and thirty dollars, and are usually transplanted flasks. That is, the seedlings have been moved from the flasks in which they were germinated into fresh flasks, and are of fairly uniform size and close to an estimated number. The price is low per plant, something like twenty-five cents each. The seedlings will be ready to go into communities as soon as you receive them.

Community pots may be bought, either freshly established from the flasks or with the seedlings ready to be moved on. Prices vary according to the number of plants per pot and their size. However, seedlings of community pot size are often sold individually, ranging from seventy-five cents to a dollar and one-half each. They are ready for individual pots. They are removed from the community pots or flats in which they are grown, and are shipped in little polyethylene bags. The grower with limited space or a desire for greater variety can thus obtain a few each of many different crosses.

Seedlings of larger sizes are also obtainable, on up to flowering age. We suggest that you buy them not larger than two and one-half inch pot size, however, as their price is still very reasonable at this age and you can have several for the price you would pay for one nearly mature plant.

When you buy seedlings, you make your choice from a list that gives the names of the parents, and usually a description of their size, coloring, and flowering season. The grower often adds helpful information as to what he expects from the cross, based on how the parents have behaved in previous crosses. Occasionally, crosses are offered that are repetitions of previous crosses, which have proved successful and for which there is still demand. If you know the history of the cross, and if the re-make is done with the original parents, it will undoubtedly be a good value. However, when re-makes are not done with the original parents you have to be wary. Such a cross is bound to be different from the original—it may be better or it may be worse. If you know the hybridist, and his work, and if he has selected parents superior to the original ones for a definite purpose, you might like to try some of the seedlings on an experimental basis.

■ FLASK TO COMMUNITY POT

The flasks are packed in boxes and sent by railway or air express. Sometimes they arrive in perfectly undisturbed condition, depending on the care with which they are handled and the distance they travel. Occasionally the soft jelly is jumbled and the little plants are clustered in tangled masses, which does not seem to harm them. If the flasks arrive in the latter condition, it is necessary to transplant them at once, but undisturbed flasks may be kept for a time.

If you have not seen flask seedlings before, nothing I can say will prepare you for their sheer beauty, the delicacy of their little shiny green leaves, and their tiny translucent roots. The plants are so small and fragile that you will handle them with tender awe, wondering that it has taken a year for them to grow to this size. There will be a few larger seedlings, perhaps an inch and a quarter from tip to tip, with several leaves and three or four roots. Most of them will have leaves and roots a quarter of an inch long, and in some the leaves and roots will be mere pin points just starting to form. Also, in non-transplanted flasks, you will see some that are no farther than the spherule stage (see drawing, p. 119), the little round green ball stage that precedes leaf formation.

These little seedlings, when removed from the flasks, will be put into "communities," either pots holding about fifty or flats holding around a hundred plants. The communities not only save space and facilitate handling a large number of seedlings, but they can be kept more uniformly moist, thus providing better growing conditions than small individual pots afford. They will remain in communities about a year.

Before removing the seedlings from the flask, prepare the pots or flats, whichever you decide to use. The former should be of clay, the shallow type called bulb pans, three inches

Fig. 65 A flask of seedlings ready for community pots.

or, preferably, five inches in diameter. Flats may be made at home using strips of wood two inches wide for the sides and window screen for the bottom, making them about six by eight inches large.

Of course, osmunda may be used for communities, and it is good in many ways. As the roots grow into it there is little danger of washing the plants out of the pots, and they need not be watered very frequently. However, removing the seedlings from the fiber after their roots have become intermingled causes many roots to be broken. We are going to suggest that you use bark instead, and for small seedlings I believe fir bark is best, or one of the mixtures given below.

For plants just out of the flasks the bark should be very fine and should contain some of the "screenings," the material screened out of the coarser grades. A seedling grade of bark is available in which the size is given as zero to one-quarter inch, undoubtedly containing much fine material. If you have a bag of any grade of bark, you may be able to obtain enough material for a few community pots by screening it through a one-quarter inch mesh screen. Although the coarser grades are pretty clean as they come from the producer, there is still some fine material in them.

Some growers like a mixture of three parts bark screenings, mixed with one part sand. Another mix is one part one-quarter inch bark, one part finely screened peat moss, and one part sand. Still another is eight parts screened peat moss, two parts sand, and one part granulated charcoal. Growers in areas where fresh sphagnum moss is obtainable, as in the Pacific Northwest, can use it to advantage in the seedling mix. A fine grade of chopped tree fern is good, either plain or mixed with seedling grade bark. Whatever the composition of the mixture, it should be fluffy or open, and should not pack hard in the pots. It should be easy to keep damp.

Flask seedlings are subject to "damp-off," an infection by a soil fungus that rots the stem at ground level and can destroy seedlings overnight. Although bark is less likely to carry infection than osmunda or soil, it is wise to sterilize it, or any of the mixtures, before put-

Fig. 66 Transplanting flask seedlings into a flat. Make a little hole in the medium, set a seedling in place, and press the material around its roots.

ting seedlings in it. Put the potting material in a large pan, dampen it, and bake it for an hour at 250° in the oven. After it has cooled you may need to dampen it again before using it.

Pots should have one-third of their depth filled with broken crock topped by a layer of one-quarter inch size bark. Flats should have a layer of fine gravel laid over the screen. They are then filled with potting medium to within one-half inch of their rim.

Now remove the seedlings from the flask. Open the flask and pour into it one-half cup of water that is about room temperature. Swirl the flask, and pour out the water and the seedlings that have come loose from the agar into a shallow bowl. Repeat a time or two. If some of the seedlings are deeply embedded in the agar, reach into the flask with a dinner knife and cut out the section of agar containing them. Let them remain in the water until all of the agar is dissolved from their roots. You can tease away stubborn bits if necessary.

The seedlings are then put in a fungicide solution, such as Wilson's Anti-Damp, made up by adding two teaspoonfuls to a quart of water, or Natriphene made up according to the directions on the label. They will remain in this until you pot them. Set out three shallow bowls and put some of the fungicide solution into each. Then sort the seedlings as to size, putting the largest into one bowl, the average size into the next, and the smallest ones and those that have not gone beyond the spherule stage in the last. Sorting them at this time will facilitate potting, because it is wise to put plants of about equal size together. Also, it saves the eye strain that results from looking through the whole batch each time for another seedling of the size you want at the moment.

I like to use small forceps to pick up the seedlings and put them in the pot. An old pair from someone's high school biology dissecting kit is good. Bend the tips a little so that they come together with just enough space between them to lift a seedling but not to pinch it. A pointed stick or a pencil will do for a tool to make the hole into which the seedling will go.

Beginning at one side of the pot or flat,

make a little hole in the potting material, set a seedling in it, and gently push the material together around its roots. The seedlings should be set so that the level of the potting material comes just at the juncture of roots and stem. Some little plants will have nice straight short roots that are easily put in the hole. Others may have long curled roots that defy being set in place. Don't worry if the tips of the roots protrude above the surface. They will continue growth, and the plant will make new ones that will go into the medium. Just be sure that the plant itself is firmly in place. Place the seedlings about a half inch apart, allowing perhaps a little more space between very large ones. Fill a pot by putting the plants in concentric circles, and a flat by putting them in rows.

Prepare a dilute fertilizer solution, one-quarter teaspoon of any complete orchid fertilizer to a gallon, and give each pot or flat a mist spray with this as soon as you finish potting it. Label each community with the name of the cross and the date.

After you have potted all of the large and average size seedlings, you are faced with the problem of what to do with the smallest ones and those that are still spherules (protocorms). If the flask yielded a generous number of seedlings, you may by now have all that you can take care of, and you may not wish to keep the less well developed ones. But if the flask was sparsely populated, or if the cross is a particularly valuable or intriguing one, you should save every plant. The left-overs may take longer to reach flowering size, but on the other hand, if their small size was the result of crowding in the flask, they will make a spurt of growth when they are transplanted. Early in my growing experience, after potting a tremendous number of seedlings, I ran out of pots. Yet I didn't want to discard the least seedlings. So I put clean sand in a glass pie plate, wet it with nutrient solution comparable to "Ohio W.P." and set the little plants in it, even the protocorms. I covered it with a pane of glass and set it on the living room table. As the months went by I sprayed the plants with nutrient solution whenever the sand appeared to

Fig. 67 Community pots and flats need a damp atmosphere. A wooden box with a hinged glass lid makes a good growing case for them.

be drying. Each day I propped open the glass lid for a little while for ventilation. A large percentage of the seedlings grew very nicely. About half of the protocorms died, but to my surprise the rest developed good little leaves and roots. Although these were way behind their sisters out of the flask, they eventually matured into flowering plants.

A better method for handling these smallest seedlings is to put them in a community pot in bark screenings dampened with fertilizer solution, and then put the whole pot in a polyethylene bag and close the top with a rubber band. In place of the pot a glass jar can be used, filled two-thirds of its depth with bark screenings dampened with fertilizer solution, and then covered with polyethylene film fastened by a rubber band. Such pots or jars may be kept along with regular communities in a seedling box.

Community seedlings need a constantly damp environment, which is most easily furnished by a box or case such as shown in Fig. 67. One can be made from a fruit lug, or any wooden box about eight inches deep. The lid can be covered with polyethylene film or be made of glass, and should be hinged to the box. If you have a great many community pots you can keep them on a bench with board sides and covered by a hinged sash.

A night temperature of 60° is neces-

Fig. 68 Glass jars containing fir bark screenings (with sand added if desired) make good growing cases for seedlings just out of the flask. The jar at the right has newly transplanted seedlings, the one on the left older ones. This method is especially useful for the smallest, least well developed seedlings from a flask. (Courtesy of A. J. Pillichody)

sary to keep the seedlings growing well, and they can be grown at this night temperature until maturity. They will grow a little faster if you can give them a night temperature of 65°. Perhaps a heating cable in an enclosure will do the job.

Community seedlings should be started with about the same amount of light they had in the flasks, about 200 foot-candles. Strong light will bleach the leaves and stunt their growth. Shade can be furnished by laying two thicknesses of cheesecloth over the lid of the box, or the boxes can be kept in an area curtained by cheesecloth. After about two months, gradually increase the light so that by the latter part of the year they are receiving 500 foot-candles.

It is important to keep the seedlings growing vigorously, and for this reason they should not be allowed to dry out. Spraying with a fine mist once a day may be all the watering necessary. The spray will wet the box and the pots, and so help maintain a humid atmosphere. But

watch the potting material closely, checking down into the pots from time to time. It must be kept soft and moist, and water should be given in the pots when needed. Young seedlings require more water than mature plants, yet they must not be allowed to remain sopping wet. It doesn't take a very strong stream of water to wash the little plants out of the pots. For watering, either let the mist sprayer run long enough to wet the medium thoroughly, or use a very gentle water breaker. Once a week add fertilizer to the water, one-quarter teaspoon to the gallon at first, and then increase the strength to one-half teaspoon per gallon.

Although the seedlings require a humid atmosphere, they will benefit from some ventilation. Moisture will condense in drops on the lid during the night. During the warm part of the day, prop the lid open a few inches to let this excess moisture dry off. Then close the lid. Ventilation will discourage the development of fungus infections. If the box stays too wet even with ventilation, drill a few holes in opposite sides to allow a little air movement, or leave the lid open for longer periods. Pots enclosed by film do not have to be opened in this way, for the film excludes fungus spores. However, spores that were present when the film cover was put on can germinate, so watch them carefully.

Damping-off can occur even though the potting medium and seedlings were disinfected originally. An occasional preventive spray with Wilson's Anti-Damp, Natriphene, or a fungicide containing captan is wise. If you notice any seedlings turning brown and watery, remove the whole container from the box and drench it thoroughly with the fungicide.

Slugs and snails are vicious enemies. One slug can mow down a pot full of seedlings in short order. Slugs are easier to control than snails, however, and they are easier to see. Poisons containing metaldehyde are used to control both, but you should not wait until you see them. Dust the communities with a powder form, or spray them with a liquid containing metaldehyde every month or six weeks.

Some seedlings may make exceptional growth during the first six months of their stay in communities. Even though you may be tempted to put them in individual pots at this time, it would be best to separate them and replant them in communities, with more space per plant, continuing their care as before.

■ INDIVIDUAL POTS

After a year in communities, most of the seedlings should be ready for individual pots. They will now be fat little plants, with thick waxy leaves. Some will have outstripped the rest, so that while the average plant may be an inch and one-half tall, with leaves one-half inch wide, others may be taller or broader. As always, a few will lag behind

Fig. 69 A flat of husky seedlings ready to be moved into individual pots. (Courtesy of Rod McLellan Co.)

the rest, and these slower ones can well go back into communities for another few months.

You may now switch to osmunda fiber if you prefer it for your plants in general. However, if you are going to use bark for most plants, you may as well continue the seedlings in it. There are advantages to each. Little seedlings are not difficult to pot in osmunda, as are larger plants, and the fiber holds them firmly in the pot. Osmunda requires less frequent watering than bark. However, after this stage bark is easier to use than osmunda. Plants can be shifted from pot to pot with great speed. Bark requires more frequent watering, and greater care must be taken not to tip the plants out of the pots. Many growers, incidentally, are now using plastic pots for bark because they hold moisture a little better. Do not use plastic pots for osmunda fiber.

For osmunda we generally choose two sizes of pots, one-and-three-quarter-inch for the average plants, two-inch for the largest ones. For bark we put the average plants in two-inch pots and the largest ones in two and one-half inch ones. Bark should be a seedlings grade of perhaps one-eighth to one-quarter inch size, not the very fine material used for communities. A mixture of bark and tree fern may also be used. Osmunda fiber should be the soft brown kind, sometimes called "golden." Pots should have two or three pieces of crock in the bottom.

Chunks of osmunda fiber should be thoroughly wetted and allowed to drain, and then be cut into various size pieces. Take a seedling in your hand and lay a small chunk of fiber on each side of the roots, forming a cube-shaped sandwich. The circumference of the cube should be about twice that of the pot. Then, squeezing the sandwich together firmly, push it into the pot. If the amount of fiber was correctly estimated, it should completely fill the pot and be quite firm in consistency, not as hard as for adult plants, but not open or loose either. If you underestimated the amount of fiber to give the desired result, work in a little more, pressing it between the sides of the pot and the fiber already in place. The plant should be situated with the level of the fiber just above the juncture of roots and stem, and the fiber should be a little below the rim of the pot.

Prepare the bark by soaking it long enough to wet it thoroughly. Then drain off the water. Hold a seedling in the pot so that its root crown comes just below the level of the pot rim, and pour the bark in around it, wiggling it in among the roots with your fingers. When the pot is full, thump the pot firmly on the bench a few times to settle the bark, and add more if needed. Then gently press the bark down all around the inside edges of the pot with your fingers. Do not force it in too roughly, else you may break the roots between the pieces. A piece of stiff wire, cut just longer than the diameter of the pot, can be used to hold the plant in place. Press it across the rhizome, wedging it into the pot.

Put a label in each pot. This should be a routine part of the potting process, not only because it is more interesting to know what each plant is, but because a plant without a label is technically an "unknown" for the rest of its life. You may think you can remember that this group is cross such-and-such, and that that group is cross so-and-so. But pretty soon the plants will all look alike to you. Groups may be shoved together to make room for additional plants, and soon their identity is lost.

The newly potted seedlings should be shaded for the first few weeks to receive about 500 foot-candles of light. During this time, which is a recovery period, they should be syringed lightly several times a day in bright weather to reduce loss of water until their roots are again active. Night temperature can be 60°, but as with communities, they will grow a little faster with nights of 65°. They benefit from somewhat higher humidity than needed by adult plants, and although they should not be kept in as close an atmosphere as the communities, some means of giving them a humid atmosphere should be devised. A covered bench, suggested above for accommodating a large number of community pots, can be used for seedlings newly put in individual pots. The cover of the bench should be propped open for a fair part of each day.

Fig. 70 Transplanting from community pot to individual pot in osmunda fiber. Upper left, a community pot of seedlings removed from the pot. Upper right, seedlings separated from the fiber. Note difference in rate of development. Lower left, place a chunk of fiber on each side of the roots. Judge amount necessary to fill tightly the pot into which the seedling is going. Lower right, the potted seedling. If fiber is not firm, press the ball toward the center and add a few more pieces of fiber.

Another method is to fasten polyethylene film to a frame built around the seedlings. After the recovery period, the light should be gradually increased until they are receiving 1000 foot-candles.

As with younger seedlings, plants of this age should not be allowed to become dry. Whether they are in bark or osmunda fiber, water them often enough to keep the medium damp. For bark, this will mean a daily watering until the bark begins to hold water efficiently, then perhaps they will need watering only every other day, or in cool weather every third day. Osmunda fiber will not need to be watered as frequently. Use a water breaker for either medium, as the full force of the hose can not only wash the bark out of the pots, but can tip over the pots themselves.

Plants in bark should be given fertilizer once a week for a while, and then every other watering as they resume vigorous growth. One-half teaspoon of fertilizer to a gallon of water is a good concentration. Plants in osmunda fiber should not be fertilized until they are making active new roots, and then they may be fed every other week with the same strength used for plants in bark. For osmunda fiber use a 10-10-10 fertilizer, and for bark a 30-10-10.

■ TO THREE- AND FOUR-INCH POTS

After the first eight months in individual pots, the plants will show quite a striking difference in size. They are then between two and a half and three years old. A few will be large enough to go into four-inch pots, while most will require only three-inch pots. Seedlings appreciate being shifted to fresh medium, so that even those that have not made much progress should be repotted at this time.

It is a simple matter to remove a seedling from a pot of bark. Tap it out, give it a few gentle shakes and separate the roots a bit to loosen the bark and allow most of it to fall away. It is not necessary to remove pieces that cling tightly to the roots. This is a good time to check for evidence of snails. If any are found, or if the roots look as if they have had bites taken out of them, dust the roots with a metaldehyde powder or dip them in a metaldehyde solution. Examine the roots and trim away any that are rotted. Roots that have grown over the side of the pot may be put inside of the new one if they will conform to the space. Otherwise trim them back to a two-inch stub. All of the roots, including the cut stubs, will send out branch roots in a short time.

Place the plant in its new pot, prepared with a few pieces of broken crock in the bottom, and fill in with fresh, dampened bark. This time the grade may be a little coarser, perhaps the one-quarter to one-half-inch size. But in a dry climate it may be well to continue with the seedling grade for another year, or to use some tree fern mixed with the bark. To hold the rhizome down in the pot at the proper level, use a piece of wire described above.

If osmunda fiber is to be used, prepare the fiber and the pots as before. It is not necessary to remove the fiber from around the plant; many growers just transfer it intact. We like to loosen the ball a little by pulling away some sections of fiber that do not have roots in them. We then fit a few pieces around the old ball, set it in the new pot, and fill in with chunks of fiber that can be worked in with a potting stick. The fiber should be quite firm, but not hard.

Plants of this age should be staked as the next growth will double the present height of the plant. Stakes especially made for use with bark can be obtained from orchid supply companies, and these are a great help. They come in a number of designs, but all hold firmly to the rim of the pot, giving a rigid support for the plant. A straight steel stake can be used for osmunda, driven into the center of the pot beside the plant. Gently tie the tallest growth to the stake.

Seedlings in three- and four-inch pots can be placed on the open bench. Starting with 1000 foot-candles of light, gradually increase the light so that by the end of the year they are receiving 2000 foot-candles. Since they now occupy a larger area it may be difficult to continue the 65° night temperature for them. They will do very nicely with the 55° to 60° nights usually maintained in the Cattleya house. If you have a way of maintaining a 60° to 65° night temperature, they will grow a little faster, however. After this, their fourth year, the vigorous ones are going to be treated in the same way as adult plants, and should be gradually worked up to adult conditions. Keep them growing steadily. Do not let them dry out, and give them a mist spray on bright days. Continue the same vigil against slugs, snails and insects, and include the seedlings in the general treatment of the greenhouse for these pests. As before, give fertilizer to the plants in bark at every other watering, and to those in osmunda every other week.

■ FOUR- AND FIVE-INCH POTS

Plants that have outgrown the three- and four-inch pots are shifted on to the next size, the threes into fours, and the fours into fives. Some will have developed two or three leads, an indication of vigor that is most welcome. Do not divide them. These are the specimen plants of the future. If they are large enough to justify it, move them into six-inch pots. If one of these plants with many leads turns out to be of fine quality, and if it carries on its eagerness to multiply its leads, some day you will have many wonderful plants from this one seedling.

Heretofore we have not had to consider any particular growth phase in repotting seedlings. But from now on it is best to pot them just as a new set of roots begins to form. Those in osmunda should be potted hard, as for adult plants. When they have resumed active growth, put them alongside the mature plants in your greenhouse and care for them in every way as you do the older plants.

■ FIRST FLOWERING

It would be difficult to choose any one stage in the life of a seedling as the most exciting. Their development in the flask is beautiful to watch. Their year in communities, which sees them transformed from fragile little things into husky youngsters, is a joy. Their further development in individual pots is most rewarding, for you can see that they are beginning to grow up. An array of healthy, perky, bright green seedlings is a sight almost as lovely as an array of flowers, and an achievement to be proud of. But it is really thrilling as they approach maturity and you know that flowering is not far off. A few may flower at the age of four years, many at the age of five years, while some will take longer. The average age of flowering used to be seven years, but better cultural methods have shortened the time and we do not have to wait so long nowadays for their first blooms.

There are always some laggards in any group of seedlings. Some may still be only large enough for three-inch pots when the rest have moved on to fours and fives. The rate of development is not necessarily related to the quality of the flowers they will eventually produce. Some of the slow ones may give just as good flowers as the faster growing ones, a few even better.

The most vigorous of the plants are usually the first to flower. Others may produce sheaths but no flowers, showing at least that they are nearly ready to bloom. The first flowers may or may not show what a plant is capable of doing. A big stocky plant should give good flowers its first time, with more than one to the stem. But many give only one flower, and often the first effort is smaller and not so well colored or of as heavy substance as subsequent flowers will be. The second flowering is a better test of the capabilities of a plant. Don't write off a plant that performs poorly the first time. We can't say that it will necessarily do better the next time, but at least give it a chance to do so. Sometimes the second flowering is an incredible improvement.

You can get some idea of the value of the cross from the flowering of the first group of seedlings. If it is uniformly good, it indicates that the rest will also be good. If only one or two of a fair number have good flowers, you may have a cross in which the percentage of good plants will be low, but perhaps the good ones will by themselves make up for the trouble of raising the cross.

■ ACCELERATING THE GROWTH OF SEEDLINGS

Seedlings make their best growth during the long days and warmer nights of summer. Their growth is speeded up somewhat during the winter by giving them a night temperature of 65°, as suggested earlier in this chapter. Growth can be speeded up even more by giving them a 16 hour day by means of artificial lighting. It is not too difficult a matter to give additional light to a few community pots. A single incandescent light, 100 watt size, placed in a reflector two feet above the plants will cover a radius of about three feet. Additional lights should be used for a larger bench area. The light is turned on at sundown and turned off when it has brought the total daylength to sixteen hours. Care must be taken not to let the light reach other plants in the greenhouse whose flowering schedule might be altered by it (see Chapter 7). Long days may be started while the seedlings are in the flask, and continued until the plants approach flowering size. Each phase of their growth should be shortened by a few months, bringing them into flower perhaps a year or a year and a half earlier than normal. Perhaps, however, you can manage lights only while the plants are in flasks and communities, finding it difficult to light the greater area they will occupy when they go into individual pots. Giving them long days for just their first year or two will give you an advantage in the ultimate time it takes them to reach flowering size.

Herbert Hager has worked out a schedule by which he is able to bring ten per cent of a batch of Cattleya seedlings into flower in two and a half years from seed. About eighty per cent of the batch will flower at three years, and the remaining few will flower a year or so later. His program involves stepping up the night temperature, increasing the daylight intensity by faster jumps and giving them a 16 hour day all year round. It is truly a forcing program, but its advantage is that you can very soon learn whether a cross is a valuable one or whether it should be culled. Mr. Hager warns that in order to make use of the higher night temperature along with the 16 hour days, the plants must have a great deal of natural sunshine, and that it is therefore wise to try his program only in areas where this is possible. At the time of his published report he was growing his plants for the most part in osmunda fiber. He does not specify the concentration of fertilizer to use, or the frequency of applying it, but indicates that the plants should be fertilized heavily. We would venture a guess that in a bark medium this would mean fertilizing at every watering, either with the one-half teaspoon per gallon concentration we have recommended elsewhere, or possibly even up to one teaspoon per gallon. In order to carry out Mr. Hager's program, an amateur should have a place where the high night temperatures will not affect other plants, where he can maintain a high humidity, and where the continuous long days will not affect the flowering of other things.

Here is his schedule. The night tempera-

ture maintained through all stages of growth is 68° to 70°. Daylength of 16 hours is produced in winter and summer by the use of 100-watt incandescent bulbs in reflectors placed two feet above the plants and five to six feet apart. The day temperature for plants in flasks should be between 80° and 85°, and the relative humidity should be between 50 and 70%. Natural light intensity is started at 200 foot-candles and is gradually increased to 400 foot-candles after germination. Plants are left in flasks from four to six months.

For plants in flats, the day temperature should be between 80° and 90° and the relative humidity is from 50 to 70%. The natural light intensity is started at 400 foot-candles and is increased to a maximum of 600 foot-candles. Plants are left in the flats for about six months.

The young plants are kept in one- and one-half inch pots for a year. During this time the temperature and relative humidity are the same as they are for the flats, but the light intensity is increased up to 1500 foot-candles. The orchids are then moved into three-inch pots. The day temperature is then between 80° and 90°, and the relative humidity is usually between 50 and 70% although it may sometimes reach 80%. The intensity of natural light is gradually increased from 1500 to 4000 foot-candles. The first ten per cent will flower at two and one-half years; about eighty per cent will flower when they are three years old.

■ OTHER KINDS OF ORCHIDS

The techniques described in this chapter may be used for any kind of orchid. In some kinds the seed pod takes a longer or shorter time to mature than in Cattleya, and the length of time for the various stages—flask, community pot etc.—may be different. Some kinds reach flowering size earlier. But essentially the same methods are used for handling the seed, sowing the flasks, transplanting to community pots, and carrying the plants on to flowering size.

11 | *The Orchid Tribes*

Wᴴᴇɴ Nature drew the designs for the orchid family, she combined and recombined the basic flower pattern in every conceivable way and decorated her handiwork with all of the colors at her command. She created forms of beauty so serene, so pure, as to be almost sublime. She created other forms rich and showy, almost sensual. And then she turned or twisted, reduced or enlarged, shortened or lengthened each floral part to make thousands of new forms, lurid or beautiful, giant or pigmy, satanic or humorous. If a mathematician or a statistician were to try to compete with her, he would find that he could put together no new combinations that did not already have a counterpart in her work.

Man has been at work for more than a hundred years, naming and classifying the myriad orchids that have so far been discovered. Yet many are still hidden in jungle wilds or remote places, and each passing year brings to light some form new to his knowledge. It is characteristic of human beings that they must put a name to everything. And it is characteristic of scientists that the name must be so definite, so specific, that there can be no possible confusion of one object with another.

When a new orchid is found, even after it has bloomed and its major characteristics have been observed, it takes patient hours of dissection and study to determine with what group of orchids it belongs. Perhaps it does not fit with any established genus or tribe, and a new category must be made for it. Often the experts do not agree. One may feel that some slight difference is significant enough to warrant the creation of a new genus. Others may insist that it is only a variation of a kind already classified. When you look up almost any orchid in Bailey's "Standard Cyclopedia of Horticulture," or any comparable work, you see evidence of past confusion in the chronology of names that have been given to a single species.

The major sorting process, which gives a starting point in the classification of the 20,000 species, is the division into tribes. Each tribe of orchids might be compared to a deck of cards, which you sort into a pack because of the distinctive design on the back of each one. As the deck is divided into suits, each with its outstanding mark, so the tribe is divided into

137

genera, each with its own characteristic features. Every card in a suit differs from every other by the picture on it, or the number. Which brings us to the final division of the genus, the species. The species belonging to any one genus bear the hallmark of the genus, but each is different from the rest by some individual feature.

When you see the six of hearts, you have no doubt in what suit it belongs, or which card in the suit it is. But you cannot say just "six" or just "hearts." Similarly you cannot specify what member of the genus you mean by saying just "Cattleya," for there are many members of the genus Cattleya. Nor can you say just "labiata," for that name may refer to a member of another genus. As soon as you say *Cattleya labiata* you erase all confusion, for there is no other kind of orchid that goes by those two names together. For clarity and convenience, it is an established rule to give the name of the genus first, as *Cattleya,* and then the specific name, as *labiata.*

Through the years past it has been more or less customary to capitalize those species names which have been created from proper nouns and to use lower case for all other species names. It is now becoming a general practice to use lower case uniformly for all species names, whether purely descriptive or made from proper nouns. Therefore, in this book (and in most current literature) you will find that species names are not capitalized. *Cattleya Mossiae* becomes *Cattleya mossiae; Cattleya Trianaei, Cattleya trianaei,* and so on. The species name is often followed by the name of the person who first described it, as *Cattleya labiata* Lindley (or Ldl., an abbreviation of Lindley). Hybrid names have always been capitalized and still are, and are not italicized in this book so that they can easily be distinguished from species names.

A species often has a number of botanical variations distinct enough to merit an additional descriptive or varietal name. For instance, *Cattleya dowiana* has a yellow form designated *Cattleya dowiana,* variety *aurea, Dendrobium fimbriatum* has a form with a spot of deep purple on the lip called *Dendrobium fimbriatum,* variety *oculatum.* These botanical varieties (which might also be considered subspecies) occur in nature, usually in some numbers and often in a separate geographical location. The word variety may be abbreviated var., or v.

A grower who owns a particularly fine individual plant, whether species or hybrid, may designate it by a varietal name of its own. This name is added to the full name of the plant and is set off in single quotes. A famous example is Cymbidium Alexanderi 'Westonbirt,' a hybrid that has become the ancestor of many of the fine modern Cymbidiums. Suppose you own a particularly beautiful *Cattleya trianaei,* of richer color or heavier substance than other members of the species, and you wish to mark this plant to separate it from the others. You could call it *Cattleya trianaei* 'Supreme' or *Cattleya trianaei* 'Aristocrat,' or 'Jones,' or anything else you wished. When you divide this plant you would put this name on each division, and when you again divide the divisions the name would still follow, so that you would keep track of each and every division made from the original plant. The original plant and all of its divisions are called a "clone." The importance of identifying with certainty the divisions of a valuable plant is obvious. The members of a clone have an additional value in experimental work, because results are more decisive when the plants used are identical in every way. An individual plant designated by its own varietal name is considered a horticultural variety, as opposed to a botanical variety.

Most orchid tribes are so prolific that it would take a lifetime to collect a single specimen of all of the species included in just one tribe, to say nothing of the varieties of each species. Should you start on such a project, you might run into difficulties. Some tribes spread over a geographical area that includes all sorts of climatic conditions, so that its members may not be suited to the conditions of a single greenhouse. In any tribe, of course, there are some members more desirable for cultivation than others. Unless you have the urge to own every species in a tribe, you will select from many tribes those that have a special appeal for you. You may choose a plant for its graceful habit, its showy flowers, its intriguing shape, unusual coloring, delightful fragrance, or even for its size, for instance, a dwarf plant whose minuteness is a charm in itself.

Botanists are interested in all kinds of plants, however insignificant they may seem to most people. Because of this, orchids that are of no commercial value, or that are not widely known, are often called "botanicals." Many of the botanicals are every bit as lovely as those with which we have better acquaintance, and these are now finding a place alongside their more popular relatives. Many amateurs find their chief interest in orchids not usually seen in the florist shop or in general collections.

Genera are known which have as many as 1000 species. For others only two or three species are known, and the rest run somewhere between these extremes. Obviously nothing less than an encyclopedia could describe all of the species.

Certain genera have been acclaimed by the public as the most beautiful and the most useful. Others, not as valuable commercially, are loved by collectors. Instead of presenting them to you as disconnected genera, each will be introduced along with the other members of its tribe. Many lovely orchids exist in the less well-known genera. To learn to know them in their relation to the more famous ones is to acquire a better understanding of them.

The presentation of the orchids in this book follows the system given in Bailey's "Standard Cyclopedia of Horticulture." Another system of classification, held in high esteem by botanists, is that of Rudolph Schlechter, a very comprehensive work organized somewhat differently from Bailey's. Schlechter divides the orchids into four large tribes, and groups the closely related genera within these tribes into sub-tribes. Bailey carries his division directly to the groups of related genera, which he calls tribes, and does not employ sub-tribes. Bailey's tribes include essentially the genera grouped by Schlechter into sub-tribes. Bailey's key carries the classification to genera and is therefore especially useful to amateurs, particularly beginners. Bailey's "Standard Cyclopedia of Horticulture" is available at most libraries, another point in its favor. By using Bailey's key, a person wishing to find out "what kind of orchid this is" can readily track it to its genus. Many kinds can then be identified as to species by the descriptions in Bailey's text. The text does not contain every species of every genus, nor does any other work. There are 1000 species of Dendrobiums alone, perhaps that many Oncidiums and Epidendrums, and hundreds in many others of the some 600 genera. Bailey gives many of those with which we are likely to come in contact, and books devoted to the orchids of specific regions are a great help.

The key to the tribes is given in the appendix and contains more kinds than can be included in this book, for example the terrestrial ones native to the temperate zones. The tribes we shall discuss are those that contain the kinds most popular with and interesting to amateurs, and their less well known relatives, some of which are becoming better known every day.

The genera included in any one tribe are closely related. Certain basic structural similarities bind them together in spite of such apparent gross differences as size of plants and flower parts. Also, they are closely related genetically, for most of the genera within a tribe will interbreed. Inter-generic crosses are more fruitful with some genera than others, however, and, of course, some are more desirable aesthetically.

12 | *The Aerides Tribe*

THE genera belonging to this tribe number about eighteen, and include some of the loveliest orchids known—Phalaenopsis and Vanda, whose sprays of subtly tinted, sweetly rounded flowers are sublime among flowers; Angraecum, one species of which was made famous by Darwin's speculation about its long spur; and Aerides, which has dense clusters of fragrant little flowers of crystalline or waxy texture. Many of the other genera are attractive and well worth growing.

The growth habit of the Aerides tribe is monopodial, illustrated by the drawing on page 12. They do not have a rhizome, but instead have a single upright stem and grow by adding new leaves to the top and new roots from between the leaves along the stem. Flower stems come from the axils of the leaves. They are epiphytic, but do not withstand drying as well as kinds equipped with pseudobulbs. Their fleshy leaves, heavy stems, and large roots do store some water, however.

The genera range natively from the Philippine Islands through the Asiatic tropics and into Australia and Africa, although each genus inhabits its own particular area in this vast range. For the most part, they live in climates that are warm and humid, some being subjected to heavy rains the year round, others to more moderate amounts of precipitation. They are found growing mostly on trees, occasionally on rocks.

PHALAENOPSIS

The "moth orchid" (Greek, *phaluna* meaning moth, *-opsis* meaning resembling) receives its name from its similarity to some tropical moths. There are about fifty species, not all of which are well known in cultivation. Some which are quite rare are now proving their worth in hybridization. The beautiful flowers would be worth growing even if they lasted only a few days, but the fact that many last for from two to five months and that bloom succession keeps them in flower for much longer makes them all the more desirable. They are not light-demanding, a fact which, together with their preference for sixty-five degree nights, makes them easy to grow in the house. (See *Orchids as House Plants,* Northen.)

The foliage is attractive. The long, broad curving leaves may be shiny or leathery, plain green or mottled with grayish green, often purple underneath. They are from eight to fifteen inches long, so that a mature plant covers a fairly broad area. The plants increase in height only slowly, and add but one or two new leaves a year. Mature plants retain an average of five or six leaves, although a few individuals may retain more. The robust, often flattened roots appear from the stem between mature leaves and grow down into the pot or outside of it to wander to some lengths. The flower spikes come from the axils of the lowermost leaves, often from the region where leaves have fallen, and therefore from the older portion of the plant.

The flowers divide themselves structurally into two groups. The first group, called Euphalaenopsis, is characterized by antennae-like appendages on the lip and by petals much broader than the sepals. The second group, Stauroglottis, has petals similar to the sepals, and a lip without appendages. In both groups the variously shaped lip is united with an extension of the basal part of the column, called the column "foot."

In general, the growing season, the period during which new leaves and roots are produced, is from spring through fall, with the flower spikes appearing from late summer into winter. Some individuals are quite orderly in this matter, but a large percentage vary, particularly among the hybrids, so that flower spikes may be started at almost any time of the year without regard to the state of growth of the plant.

The flower spike is tall and arching in most species, usually unbranched in the white species, branched in the colored ones. As it reaches maximum height, the end section elongates allowing the buds to become spaced apart. Some plants develop all of the buds on a spike at about the same time so that the whole spray is open at once. This habit is particularly true among the pink species. Others open the basal flowers first, while the tip of the spike continues to form more buds, a situation likely to be true of the white ones. Plants with the latter habit can remain in flower for the better part of a year, since individual flowers keep for several months and new ones

Fig. 71 A house of Phalaenopsis, where breath-taking beauty abounds for months on end. (Courtesy of Jones and Scully, Inc.)

open to replace those that fade. Do not cut off a spike until you are sure it has ceased to form new buds. There is sometimes an interval between fading of the first flowers and development of succeeding ones. In the white species and hybrids, if the flower stem is cut just below the node that produced the first flower, a branch stem may come from one of the lower nodes, giving a second spray of flowers. Such branch stems may not bear as many flowers as the original spike and sometimes the flowers are smaller. But this is not always true, for we have had excellent secondary spikes of twenty flowers. When a plant is grown under less than ideal conditions it may not form new flower spikes when an old one is making a branch, so the grower must decide from experience whether to remove a spike entirely or leave it to form a secondary one.

■ CULTURE

Potting. Phalaenopsis requires rather small containers in proportion to their size and need be repotted infrequently. A plant should never be allowed to become run-down, however. Osmunda fiber is still regarded by many experts as the best medium, but bark or chunks of charcoal are used by some growers. A plant should be repotted when the medium is no longer good, or when the plant has lost a good many lower leaves and roots, leaving the active part of the plant standing above the potting medium on a naked stem. Repotting should be done when new roots are developing.

To repot, remove the plant and clean off the old medium. With your fingers break off the old inactive stub of the stem below the ring of living roots. Cut back the lower roots to a length that will fit in the new pot. These stubs will branch, giving new roots that will go directly into the medium, providing a firm foothold for the plant. Allow the upper roots to maintain their natural position, whether in or out of the pot. Osmunda fiber need not be packed as hard as for Cattleyas, but it should be firm. Bark, or chunks of charcoal, should be of very coarse grade (large size pieces), and potting is done as directed for Cattleyas. The plant should be centered in the pot, and in any medium the basal part should be placed an inch or so down into the potting material.

After potting, water sparingly until new roots are well formed. Keep the atmosphere humid (fifty to sixty per cent relative humidity) and spray the plants with a fine mist once or twice a day. Since Phalaenopsis is not grown in strong light, additional shade after potting is not always necessary, but if the leaves become limp in spite of mistings the light should be reduced to about 500 foot-candles till the plants recover.

Temperature. These plants from the hot, humid tropics of Asia must be kept gently warm. The night temperature should not go below sixty degrees, as temperatures below this cause growth to be poor and flower buds to drop. Actually, the plants do better with temperatures somewhat above 60° at night, preferably closer to 65°. Day temperature should be ten degrees higher in the winter, but can go higher in the summer with the usual precautions about excessive heat.

Water. The plants should be watered frequently enough to prevent the medium from ever becoming bone dry, but they do not like to be kept sopping wet. Watering needs to be more frequent in dry climates than in damp ones, and of course, more frequent when plants are in bark than in osmunda fiber. The atmosphere should be kept humid, around fifty to sixty per cent relative humidity, which may be achieved by damping down and spraying the benches between the plants if humidity is not a great problem in your area, or by means of humidifying equipment in dry climates. The plants welcome light mist sprays on bright days, but they must dry off by night. The growth tends to be succulent and is particularly liable to damage if kept wet. During the winter, watch for drip from the roof and move any plants that might catch the water.

Feeding. Phalaenopsis benefits from applications of fertilizers. In osmunda a 10-10-10 formula given every two or three weeks at a concentration of one-half teaspoonful to a gallon of water is about right. More frequent applications are necessary with bark and a 30-10-10 formula should be used, unless some other means is devised for giving the higher nitrogen needed. As with other plants in bark, an exact system for fertilizing has yet to be worked out. Watch the plants carefully and adjust the frequency and concentration to their needs.

Light. Strong light makes small hard plants that do not do well. Phalaenopsis does best in less than half the light intensity allowed Cattleyas. During the summer they should be given between 500 and 1000 foot-candles. Toward fall increase the light gradually to encourage flowering and toughen the plants somewhat, and by winter let them have about 1500 to 2000 foot-candles.

Ventilation and air movement. In a greenhouse, air movement is absolutely necessary for Phalaenopsis. The moving air should be damp, and this means that unless the climate provides a high humidity some means of adding water to the moving air should be provided. Whenever possible open the ventilators, at least a crack, but do not let cold air blow on the plants. Ventilation and air movement help keep the plants healthy at all times but are particularly important to prevent spotting of flowers by the Botrytis fungus.

Propagation. Phalaenopsis do not lend themselves as well to vegetative propagation as some other kinds. When side shoots develop on the plants they can be removed after they have started their own roots. Sometimes young plantlets form from nodes on the flower spike. If a plant that you are repotting is fairly tall and has a good array of roots, you can divide it to leave a basal stump with a few living roots. Often a young plant will develop at the top of the old part. When growing rapidly it can be removed. Any young plantlets such as those described should be potted in sphagnum moss or soft osmunda fiber, and then pot and all should be enclosed in a polyethylene bag to give a damp atmosphere. When such plants are growing vigorously, they can be cared for like seedlings of a comparable size. Very rarely a plantlet is developed on a root.

Growing Phalaenopsis from seed. Pollination is carried out by hand as for other genera. The seed pods mature quickly, about five to six months after pollination. When the pod matures it dries and splits open quite suddenly, so that it should be covered in advance to prevent loss of seed. The seed loses its viability rather soon after it ripens, and while it may be stored in a refrigerator for a while, it should be used before very long. Also, it is more sensitive to disinfecting agents than other kinds. Calcium hypochlorite is the safest to use, and the seed should be sown rapidly so that it does not remain in the solution any longer than absolutely necessary. If you are very speedy, you can use a solution made by dissolving one clorazene tablet in two ounces of water.

The best method is to sow the seed from the green pod. Remove the pod at least a month before it would normally ripen; four to four-and-a-half months from pollination is generally accepted as the best time. Proceed according to the directions given in Chapter 9.

The seedlings grow rapidly and are ready to move out of the flask in six months or so. They may be transferred to flats or to five-inch community pots. They should be kept covered with glass to give them a warm, close atmosphere. When they are ready for individual pots, use the three-inch size. They reach flowering size in about three years, sometimes even less.

The Species; Group I, Euphalaenopsis

The lip in this group bears a pair of appendages, either antenna-like cirri, or slender horns. The petals are broader than the sepals and are contracted at their base into a slender "claw."

Phal. amabilis. This is one of the most popular of the genus, and, with *Phal. aphrodite*, is the basis for most of the modern white hybrids. The leaves are plain green, six to twelve inches long. The tall arching flower stems carry many flowers, each three to five inches in diameter. The pure white sepals and petals are set off by a lip which is tinted with yellow and spotted and streaked with red, and which bears two wavy cirri that fold back from the outer end. Secondary sprays will develop if the stem is cut just below the node that produced the first flower. The plant— which occurs in Java, Borneo, Amboina, and the Philippines—flowers in the fall and early winter. A form with large well shaped flowers is var. *rimestadiana*, and one that is pink or deep rose is var. *sanderiana*. Two famous plants which formed the background for the breeding line that led to our present day hybrids were the polyploid (6n) *Phal. amabilis* 'Elizabethae'. (*Phal. amabilis* × *Phal. amabilis* var. *rimestadiana*) and Phal. Gilles Gratiot (*Phal. amabilis* var. *rimestadiana* × *Phal. aphrodite*). From this line came Phal. Doris, Chieftain, and Winged Victory. With the advent of the tetraploid Phal. Doris new possibilities arose as this hybrid proved to have far better

Fig. 72. Phalaenopsis Grace Palm, one of the hybrids from the Phalaenopsis Doris line.

keeping quality than others. Phal. Doris has contributed this quality to subsequent hybrids such as Grace Palm, Juanita, Dos Pueblos, Vallemar, etc. Recrossing of selected individuals of these, plus back-crossing to plants used previously has led to a group of hybrids that are very much alike genetically and which exhibit near uniformity of perfection.

Phal. aphrodite. White flowers, sometimes flushed with pink, similar to *Phal. amabilis* but smaller, and borne in a drooping raceme. The lip is tinted pink and yellow and has two fine, twisted cirri. The leaves are browish green, ribbed down the center, and about a foot long. Occurs in Java and the Philippines. Flowers in the spring and summer.

Phal. lowii. The plants of this species are not so vigorous as some, and the flowers are small, one and a half to two inches in diameter. They make up for their size by their lovely coloring. The sepals and petals are white, flushed with amethyst toward the base. The middle lobe of the lip is deep violet-purple. The sprays may carry as many as twenty flowers. The species is deciduous in its native environment, Borneo and Burma. It flowers in the summer and requires a drier atmosphere than some.

Phal. pulcherrima. This species has some distinct differences from other members of the genus. It has a varied history, having long been

accepted in a separate genus as *Doritis pulcherrima* and having also been named *Phal. esmeralda.* It has pointed leaves, eight inches long. The tall slender stem bears many flowers, one inch in diameter. The sepals and petals vary from white to amethyst. The side lobes of the lip range in color from purple to orange to brownish red, while the middle lobe is purple and pointed in shape. Two cirri are situated behind a crest at the base of the middle lobe. This species occurs in Cochin China.

Phal. schilleriana. Marvelous drooping flower sprays, branched and carrying as many as a hundred flowers in tones of rosy-lilac, make this a favorite species. The plants have long leaves, mottled with grayish white, and purple underneath. The roots are flat and rough. The flowers are about three inches across. The rosy tone of the petals and sepals pales toward the edges. The lip is of the same color, dotted with red. Instead of cirri, it has a pair of divergent horns at its tip. It occurs in the Philippines and flowers in the spring. This species is much used in hybridization, for the purpose of combining its branched, heavily flowered inflorescence with the heavier substance and larger size of the white hybrids.

Phal. stuartiana. This charming species has small, oddly colored flowers. The leaves are mottled when young, grayish-green with purple undersides when mature. The sepals are white, the lateral ones pale yellow on the inner half and speckled with red at the base. The petals are white, lightly dotted with purple at the base. The golden-yellow lip is margined with white, spotted with purple, and has a pair of horns at its tip. The flowers have especially good keeping qualities and are borne on generously branching sprays. This species occurs in the Philippines and flowers in the winter. It is also used in hybridization.

Phal. intermedia. A natural hybrid between *Phal. aphrodite* and *Phal. equestris* (*Phal. rosea*), which has been repeated in cultivation. The leaves are generally green above, purple underneath. The flower stem is sometimes branched and bears flowers two inches in diameter. The sepals and petals are white, the petals speckled with rose at the base. The lip has violet side lobes dotted with crimson, and a deep crimson middle lobe bearing a pair of short horns at its apex. It occurs in the Philippines and flowers from March to October.

The Species; Group II, Stauroglottis

The lip of this group is without appendages, and the petals are more nearly the size of the sepals. The plants are smaller than those in Group I, and the flowers, though also smaller, are usually brightly colored, often strikingly barred or spotted. The species in this group have been less widely grown than those in Group I, but now that the ultimate in white hybrids has been reached, hybridists are turning to this group, and to the pink species in Group I, for the variety they offer in the creation of new things.

Phal. cornu-cervi. Yellow-green flowers barred with brown and having a white lip are produced freely on a stem whose shape resembles that of a stag horn. The species is deciduous natively, but apparently requires no rest period in a greenhouse. It occurs in Burma and Java and flowers throughout the year.

Phal. decumbens. For a long time called *Phal. amethystina*, this species is a small plant with leaves waved at the edges. The cream colored flowers have a lip of rich amethyst-purple, barred and margined with white. It occurs in Java and Sumatra and flowers in the fall.

Phal. equestris. This is the correct name for the species so familiarly known as *Phal. rosea*. The plant has small leaves, plain green with a pronounced notch at the tip. It produces several flower spikes a year and the flowers open over a period of months, keeping the plant in flower nearly all year long. The small flowers have white sepals and petals with a rose-purple stain in the middle. The side lobes of the lip are pink, while the mid-lobe is brown at the base and bright rose-purple at the end. It occurs in the Philippines and is now being used in hybridization.

Phal. lindenii. A free flowering species which has narrow mottled leaves, this species bears one and one-half inch flowers with pink petals and sepals. The side lobes of the lip are spotted with brown and the pink mid-lobe has purple streaks. The species occurs in the Philippines and flowers from March to August.

Phal. lueddemanniana. Another small species, this one has narrow shiny green leaves that are six to eight inches long. The flower spike is short and bears few blossoms, but they are most attractive. The sepals and petals are white, marked with bars that are purple toward the base and brown toward the tip. The lip is violet with yellow blotches, having a thickened ridge in the center covered with bristles. The flowers keep well. An odd characteristic is that the flowers turn green when pollinated. The plants are easily propagated by plantlets that form on the old flower spikes. It occurs in the Philippines and flowers throughout the year.

Phal. mannii. This species has small golden-yellow flowers blotched and barred with red-brown. The leaves are six to twelve inches long, green spotted with purple toward the base. The flower stem is branched and bears ten to fifteen flowers that measure from one and one-half to two inches across. The side lobes of the lip are white, streaked with purple, while the middle lobe is yellow, anchor shaped, with a fringed crest in its center. This species requires somewhat cooler temperatures than the others. Although not widely grown, it is being used in the formation of yellow hybrids, crossed with the large white hybrids. It occurs in Assam, India.

Phal. mariae. Resembling *Phal. lueddemanniana*, this species has yellow flowers that are marked with four transverse bars. The flowers are one and one-half inches across, and the lip is rose-purple with white margins, without bristles. It occurs in the Philippines.

Phal. micholitzii. Another species that resembles *Phal. lueddemanniana.* This one has yellow flowers that are not barred. It occurs in the Philippines.

VANDA

This genus of sun-loving, robust plants has won the hearts of orchid growers everywhere. Their flowers are beautifully shaped and exhibit a wondrous blending of colors. They are of excellent substance, keep well, and are adaptable to many uses. According to the habit of the species, from three to eighty blooms may occur on one stem. Their name is the Sanskrit word, Vanda, which was applied in ancient India to the Vanda of Bengal and related orchids.

The fifty or more species range natively through a variety of climates in tropical Asia. If the native habitat of each kind had to be reproduced in cultivation, it would make their

Fig. 73 Vanda Waipuna 'Hodama' A.M.—A.O.S., A.M.—H.O.S. (Vanda Ellen Noa × Vanda Rothschildiana). (Courtesy of Wm. Kirch)

culture quite difficult. Fortunately, Vandas are most adaptable. They can be grown in either an intermediate or a warm greenhouse, with the possible exception of *Vanda coerulea* which prefers cooler nights. Even this species can be grown in a cool spot in a Cattleya house.

The majority of the species have strap-shaped leaves, a few have cylindrical leaves, called the "terete" species, and a few come in between and are called "semi-terete." Each group breeds freely within itself. However, hybrids between leaf types can usually be carried no farther than the primary cross, for they are almost entirely sterile. The low degree of fertility in the inter-type groups and the few exceptions to this are discussed later.

Large, fleshy roots are produced from the stem between the leaves, which may grow into the pots, but which are likely to grow straight out into the air or into the pots of neighboring plants. The flower sprays arise from the axils of the leaves on the newly matured part of the plant. (See illustration, page 12.) The flower stems alternate from side to side of the plants, each one being produced from the axil of the next higher leaf. One, two, or sometimes three sprays appear at once, or they may come in succession through the year.

The sepals and petals are usually similar in size, though in some the lateral sepals are larger. They are narrowed toward the base, rounded toward the apex, and usually flat and spreading. The lip is attached to the short foot of the column and is spurred at its base, with the side lobes fleshy and erect, the middle lobe spreading. Colors include white, yellow, rose, purple, blue, and brown, often fantastically combined or fused in single flowers.

■ CULTURE

Potting. Vanda requires a large amount of growing medium and much nourishment. Osmunda fiber and tree fern have long been used, but bark is quite satisfactory for them. In fact, since bark allows the grower to keep up with the rapid growth of young plants, and since all ages do well in it, it is rapidly becoming the preferred medium in this country. The pots should have good drainage. Potting young seedlings simply requires that they be moved on into larger pots as they outgrow the smaller ones. After a plant has matured and flowered, it need be repotted only when the medium breaks down or the pot is no longer adequate. One could never use pots large enough to contain all the roots, so the aim is to furnish a size in proportion to the plant and its need for water and fertilizer.

Vandas increase rapidly in height. Some will grow to six or seven feet. This is not always an advantage. A large, heavy plant will produce more flowers for a while, but when it begins to lose the basal leaves and become straggly, flowering is sometimes reduced and the plant is no longer neat and handsome. Rather than allow them to become so tall it is better to cut off the top half and pot it in fresh material. New hybrids tend to be more compact and height is less of a problem with them.

To divide a plant, make a cut through the stem so as to leave a goodly number of roots on both halves, and a number of leaves on the older part. Choose a time when new roots are growing and old roots are branching. Wet the roots thoroughly to make them more flexible; it may then be possible to wind them around in the new pot without injury. If they break, cut them off at the break and put the stubs in the medium. Roots that grow too high upon the stem to go into the pot are left as they are. Center the plant so that the base of the stem is two inches or so in the medium. Fill in with bark (or osmunda or tree fern). Stake the plant so that it will not wobble. Repot the good section of the old part. Given a damp atmosphere, new growth may break from a dormant bud along the stem. If the roots of the old part remain good, the new growth can be allowed to continue to grow upon it. However, most growers prefer to remove the new plantlet when it has made roots of its own. It will take such a plantlet several years to reach flowering size. Incidentally, any plantlets that develop along the stem of a plant may be removed in like manner.

Water. Vandas require abundant water during their growing season, with somewhat less during the winter, though not to the point of dryness. They can withstand drying far better than Phalaenopsis, however. After potting, water sparingly until the roots take hold again. Roots that have been disturbed by potting will rot if they are kept wet, whereas they will start branch roots if they are kept on the dry side. Although Vandas can take a drier atmosphere than Phalaenopsis, they appreciate a humidity of forty to fifty per cent. In a very damp atmosphere, the plants will be larger and less tough than in a drier environment, although they will grow and flower well with a lower daytime humidity. A mist spray on bright days is beneficial, both to aid in furnishing humidity and in giving water to the aerial roots. Where an evaporative cooler or a humidifier is used, misting is not necessary.

Temperature. Vandas will do well with a night temperature of from 55° to 65°. This means they can be grown well either with Cattleyas or with warmer growing kinds. They can very well withstand an accidental cold spell, such as that produced when trouble arises with the heating system, although they should, of course, not be allowed freezing temperatures. While they are not as susceptible to burning as some, they should be protected from excessive daytime heat.

Light. The terete-leaved species require stronger light than the strap-leaved ones, and in warm areas are grown out-of-doors in full sun. The strap-leaved kinds and hybrids between these and the terete will adapt themselves to about the same amount of light as Cattleyas. Not all of them do well where winters are dull, however, but selected kinds, chosen for their adaptability, may. If you live where the sun shines all year round, you can grow almost any kind of Vanda. If you have long spells of dull weather, buy Vandas from growers who have chosen kinds for that type of climate. Give them the brightest spot in either the Cattleya house or the warm greenhouse.

Ventilation and air movement. Just as moving air and ventilation help to keep other orchids healthy, so do they benefit Vandas.

Feeding. Vandas are heavy feeders. In osmunda fiber and tree fern they may be given a complete fertilizer every two weeks. In bark they should be fed at every watering, with one of the fertilizers prepared for bark, having a high nitrogen content.

Training roots. If you have but few plants, you can control their habit of sending their heavy roots in all directions. Roots that have extended to some distance from the plant can be brought back toward the pot and finally trained to go into the medium. Newly-growing roots can also be trained into the pot. Wet the root thoroughly to make it flexible, and then tie a sling of string around the root and the plant stem. Pull it in the direction you wish it to go until it resists the pull. Let it alone for a few days, and then every now and then, tighten the string. Finally, it will be in a position for you to maneuver the tip into the potting medium. Growers with many plants will probably not have time to do this; so when they water or use fertilizer solution, they should wet the aerial roots as well.

Vanda from seed. Vandas may be readily grown from seed, using the methods recommended for Phalaenopsis. The wide variety represented in the genus gives an opportunity for a wealth of hybrids. Inter-generic crosses with other members of this tribe add to the possibilities. Growers in Hawaii and in the Orient have led the way with tremendous numbers of hybrids, fascinating in their combination of colors and shapes. The interest is spreading to other parts of the world.

The Species

Of the large number of species, fewer than half are well known. Some that are rather rare are now being used in hybridization. The outstanding species are popular with amateurs, as are the many hybrids.

Vanda amesiana. This is a smaller plant than some of the others, with semi-terete leaves. It bears sprays of fragrant flowers which range from white to rose-purple on foot-long stems. It occurs in Burma and Thailand at elevations of 5000 feet and flowers in mid-winter.

Vanda coerulea. This is the famous blue Vanda, much loved for its own sake as well as for its contributions to hybrids. It varies from clear cobalt to both paler and deeper shades of blue. Its dense sprays carry ten to twenty flowers which are each three to four inches across. The sepals and petals are nearly equal and overlap each other, giving the effect of a round, flat, compact flower. The little lip is three-lobed, the front lobe a rich blue. The flowers last about a month when kept cool. This strap-leaf species occurs under sunny, cool conditions at high elevations in northern India and Burma. It flowers anytime from fall through winter and spring and it can be grown either in a cool spot in a Cattleya house where it can have plenty of light or with cool orchids. *Vanda coerulea* crossed with *Vanda sanderiana* produced one of the best known of all hybrids, the large, flat, blue Vanda Rothschildiana.

Vanda concolor. Rather rare in collections, this strap-leaf species is a tetraploid which has been used somewhat in hybridization. Its yellow-brown flowers are borne about seven to ten to a stem. The plant occurs in China and flowers in the summer.

Vanda dearei. The fragrant, long lasting flowers are creamy white with a yellow lip, qualities that endear them to growers although the species is not as striking as some. The cross *Vanda dearei* × *Vanda sanderiana* produced Vanda Ellen Noa, one of the outstanding strap-leaf hybrids. *Vanda dearei*, a strap-leaf species, occurs in the Sunda Islands, Borneo, and Java and flowers in the summer.

Vanda hookeriana. A tall, terete-leaf species, its cylindrical leaves channeled on the upper surface and pointed. Each stem bears five or six flowers which are about two and one-half inches across. The sepals are white flushed with purple, the petals, which are larger and wavy, are white flushed and spotted with purple. The side lobes of the lip are amethyst with pale lines, the middle lobe, which is broad and spreading, is white stained with deep purple. This species is very common in Malaya and also occurs in Borneo and Sumatra. It should best be grown out-of-doors in bright sun. The flowers appear in the fall. The plant has contributed its huge lip to the hybrid Vanda Miss Joaquim, which is grown in fields in Hawaii and imported into this country in large quantities.

Vanda kimballiana. A semi-terete species requiring cool conditions. The plants are slender, and rarely grow taller than fifteen inches. The lovely flowers are pure white except for the lip, the middle lobe of which is deep rose, marked with deeper veins; the side lobes are yellow. The base of the lip forms a spur about an inch long. The plant grows on the faces of cliffs, exposed to the sun, in the high altitudes of Burma and flowers in late summer or early fall.

Vanda lamellata. A dwarf strap-leaf species with slender recurved leaves. It bears many-flowered stems of light yellow blooms that are stained with brown and measure about two inches across. There is a more brightly colored variety, var. *boxalli,* that is more commonly grown and is used in hybridization. It occurs in the Philippines and flowers in the winter.

Vanda luzonica. This striking species has two-inch flowers borne in generous numbers on sprays up to fifteen inches long. They are white with crimson markings and a bright red lip. The plant is rather short, growing about two feet high, with strap-shaped leaves which are fifteen inches long. It occurs in the Philippines and flowers in the spring. This species has been used a great deal in hybridization and contributes its coloring to its progeny.

Vanda merrillii. Although it was discovered only fairly recently, this species is already becoming popular. Its small creamy flowers are

stained with red to red-brown and have a shiny waxy texture. The lip has side lobes of white with purple dots, and a fiddle-shaped mid-lobe streaked and stained with red. It is a strap-leaf species which occurs in the Philippines and flowers spring and summer.

Vanda sanderiana. This is one of the most beautiful orchids known. Because of its beauty, size, and shape it has been used most frequently in hybridization. It is a magnificent broad, flat flower, with rounded parts. The lateral sepals are especially large and are the most striking feature of the flower. The coloring is a fusion of hues. The dorsal sepals and the petals shade from white to rose. The lateral sepals are yellow-green suffused with reddish brown and marked with a network of brown. The little lip is dull crimson, with a squarish middle lobe and side lobes that form a little cup under the tip of the column. The color variations in this species are quite remarkable, some tending to purple, others to red. It is a strap-leaf species which occurs in the Philippines and flowers in the fall. *Vanda sanderiana* contributes its broad, flat, rounded shape to its

Fig. 74 Vanda Rothschildiana, the spectacular blue hybrid that has been the ancestor of so many wonderful hybrids. (Courtesy of Jones and Scully, Inc.)

hybrids, one reason why it is so frequently used. Its hybrids are likely to have the reticulation (network) of deeper color which is one of its charms. In Vanda Rothschildiana this reticulation is of a deep blue. The influence of its shape is clearly seen in two of its recent hybrids —Vanda Nellie Morley and Vanda Ellen Noa.

Vanda spathulata. A tetraploid with tall spikes of golden yellow flowers, this tall plant has strap-shaped leaves that are only three inches long. Both leaves and flower stems are spotted with red. The flowers are small, only an inch or so across, and have a lip of darker yellow marked with red-brown. It is a native of India and Ceylon that is being used in hybridization.

Vanda sumatrana. Although not commonly grown, this species is being used in hybridization. It is similar to *Vanda dearei* in general aspect, with shiny greenish-brown flowers. The plant occurs in Sumatra and flowers in the winter.

Vanda teres. This very lovely species has played a great role in introducing Vandas to

Fig. 75 *Vanda teres,* a terete leaved species. (Courtesy of H. A. Dunn)

this country. Its flowers are large, with broad wavy parts. The petals and sepals are similar in size; the sepals are white tinged with rose and the petals are a rich deep rose. The lip has large, yellow side lobes that fold over the column, and a triangular outer lobe that is rose, veined and spotted with yellow, spreading at its outer end and split in the center. The plant occurs in Burma and flowers from May to September. The hybrid Vanda Miss Joaquim, *Vanda hookeriana* × *Vanda teres,* was the first hybrid to be widely distributed. *Vanda teres* is a terete-leaved species, which is very popularly grown, although it may be too light-demanding for parts of this country.

Vanda tessellata. This is the correct name for the species better known as *Vanda roxburghii.* It is the one upon which the genus was founded in 1820 by Dr. Brown, who adopted the name given it in Bengal, "Vanda," as the name of the genus. It is a medium sized plant with strap-shaped leaves and a spike of six to eight greenish-yellow flowers. The wavy sepals and petals are white on the back, reticulated with olive-brown on the front. The long middle lobe of the lip is violet. This native of Bengal flowers from May to August. It has been used in hybridization.

Vanda tricolor. A well known species which has thick, waxy or leathery flowers, heavily spotted with bright red-brown on a yellow ground. The flowers are white to cream colored on the back. The middle lobe of the lip is lyre-shaped, rich purple, and decorated with elevated lines. The flowers are fragrant and long lasting. The variety *suavis,* sometimes treated as a distinct species, has sepals and petals of white, spotted and barred with reddish purple. The front lobe of the lip is pale rosy purple, the side lobes deep purple. Both are tall, strong plants with strap-shaped leaves. They are native to Java and flower variably.

■ HYBRIDIZATION IN VANDA

Hybridization in Vanda is beset by special problems that arise from mixed hybrids made between species of different leaf types. Hybrids within each leaf type group are, with rare exceptions, entirely fertile, except that any triploids produced are by their nature quite sterile. Inter-group hybrids can be made by crossing a terete species with a strap-leaf species, or by crossing a terete hybrid with a strap-leaf hybrid, but most of the resulting hybrids are almost entirely sterile.

The basic haploid chromosome number in Vanda is 19 and (except for the tetraploid species) the species all have a diploid number of 38. In the inter-group hybrids, the 19 chromosomes from the terete species will not pair at reduction division with the 19 chromosomes from the strap-leaf species, and hence, because the distribution of chromosomes is very erratic, sterility results. Production of any viable seed by such hybrids is usually the result of non-reduced gametes. The situation is most unfortunate because the semi-terete hybrids are very lovely, and one can imagine the wondrous hybrids that would result if they could be used freely as parents. When two striking exceptions to the sterility of the semi-terete hybrids occurred in Hawaii, W. B. Storey and H. Kamemoto, by dint of a great deal of work with the microscope, worked out a fascinating genetic detective story.

Vanda Mevr. L. Velthuis (V. Miss Joaquim × V. *sanderiana*) is a semi-terete diploid hy-

Fig. 76 Vanda Mevr. L. Velthuis, a diploid semi-terete hybrid, whose genetics is described in these pages.

(Courtesy of Jones and Scully, Inc.)

brid and would be expected to be quite sterile. One individual plant of V. Mevr. L. Velthuis crossed with *V. coerulea* gave a small hybrid progeny, V. Nora Potter. V. Nora Potter immediately became famous, in the first place, because they are very handsome; in the second place, because it was most unusual for a hybrid such as V. Mevr. L. Velthuis to be a successful parent; and in the third place, because the Nora Potters were discovered to be pentaploid. The question of how two diploid parents could give rise to a pentaploid progeny was worked out by W. B. Storey from a study of the formation of sex cells in V. Mevr. L. Velthuis. He discovered that it produced giant 4n gametes, sex cells that contained 76 chromosomes. These, united with the 19 chromosomes from *V. coerulea*, gave the 95 chromosomes of the pentaploid V. Nora Potter.

V. Emma van Deventer is a semi-terete hybrid between *V. teres* and *V. tricolor*. Since the parents were diploid, it was assumed that the offspring V. Emma van Deventer were also diploid. Several plants of Emma van Deventer, owned by different people, were crossed with plants of *V. sanderiana*. At best a few seedlings might have been expected, but in each case seed formation was abundant and thousands of vigorous seedlings were raised. The unusual fertility was astonishing. The cross was named V. Nellie Morley, and the plants proved to be triploid in each of the progeny, and all were

quite uniform. It was thought that the triploidy had resulted from non-reduced 2n gametes from V. Emma van Deventer. Another cross between V. Emma van Deventer and *V. sanderiana* produced a pentaploid progeny, and this inspired H. Kamemoto to investigate the parents of both types of offspring. He found that the pentaploid progeny was produced in the same manner as the pentaploid progeny from V. Mevr. L. Velthuis; in this case a diploid Emma van Deventer had given rise to giant 4n gametes. Chromosome counts on the Emma van Deventers that had given the triploid offspring proved them to be, not diploid as had been thought, but tetraploids. The discovery of their tetraploid nature explained their unusual fertility, for tetraploids form reproductive cells with ease. The 2n gametes that had given rise to their triploid offspring were then known to be normally reduced (from the 4n cells of the parents) rather than to have been non-reduced gametes of a 2n parent.

Tetraploids of the type of V. Emma van Deventer are called "amphi-diploids," for they contain the full diploid number of chromosomes from two unlike parents. The significance of this is that whereas the plant would be sterile, or nearly sterile, with 19 chromosomes from the terete parent and 19 from the strap-leaf parent, it has been made fertile by the doubling of these chromosomes. Each set of 19 terete chromosomes now has another set to pair

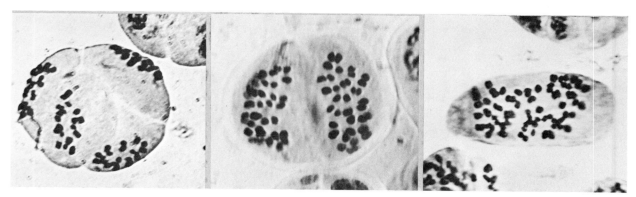

Fig. 77 Variation in the formation of reproductive cells in Vanda, which leads to differences in ploidy. Left, a quartet of normally reduced haploid cells, containing 19 chromosomes. Center, a pair of nonreduced diploid cells, containing 38 chromosomes. Right, a giant tetraploid cell with 76 chromosomes, formed by doubling of the diploid number. (Courtesy of H. Kamemoto).

with, and the 19 chromosomes from the strap-leaf parent also have a set to pair with. It is not known how this amphi-diploidy, usually a rare event, occurred in several plants from the same seed pod.

The ability of some additional semi-terete hybrids to give progeny in the two ways just described is testified by the recent findings of both triploid and pentaploid progenies. Thus the sterility barrier is being broken by the ability of individual plants to produce non-reduced gametes and occasionally to double their own chromosome number. Hybrids which give but very few viable seed may still be most useful if their polyploid offspring can in turn be used as parents. There are still large numbers of semi-terete hybrids that appear to be completely sterile. If they could be made to double their chromosomes, they, too, would become fertile. Here is a way in which colchicine might be useful (see Chapter 8), if a proper technique could be worked out.

AERIDES

Aerides, the type genus of the tribe, is very much like Vanda in plant characters and cultural requirements. It offers drooping sprays of delicately beautiful flowers.

Aerides feildingii. The nickname of this species is "fox brush" orchid, and although the flower spray is a fat cylinder about the size of a fox tail, the name in no way does justice to the flowers. About a hundred (or more) dainty, one-inch flowers are borne on the stem, each a bit of perfection that has to be looked at closely. They are saucer shaped with an open pointed lip, solid pink in color, or with a bit of white at the edges. They have a sparkling crystalline texture, and a dainty perfume. The plant occurs in Sikkim and Assam, and flowers in the spring and summer.

Aerides lawrenciae. These tall Philippine plants produce sprays of fifteen to twenty flowers, each about one and one-half inches across. The waxy flowers are greenish white, tipped with amethyst. The lip is closed at the tip like the tip of a Persian slipper, and the basal section together with the erect side lobes forms a pouch. The lip has a central strap that curves backward completely covering the column. The flowers, which are sweetly fragrant, appear during the late summer and early fall.

Aerides odoratum. This species is similar to *Aerides lawrenciae,* but it has a stronger fragrance and some differences in flower shape. The "horn" of the lip is more sharply curved, and the pouched portion is not as wide. The plant occurs in the Philippines, and flowers in late summer and early fall.

Aerides quinquevulnerum. Most common of the Philippine species, found growing on trees within twenty miles of the city of Manila. The flowers are white, each petal and sepal tipped with reddish purple, the "five wounds" from which it derives its name. There is a form common in the Islands of Mindoro which is burgundy colored, var. *purpuratum.* The flower spikes are quite long, many flowered, and a

Fig. 78 *Aerides odoratum,* whose piquant flowers are delightfully fragrant. (Courtesy of Montreal Botanical Garden)

Fig. 79 *Angraecum sesquipedale,* the lovely "star of Bethlehem." (Courtesy of Jones and Scully, Inc.)

plant may produce several at a time. Flowers during late summer.

ANGRAECUM

Native to tropical Africa, Madagascar and the Seychelle Islands. There are numerous species, but only a few are really known in cultivation in this country. The plants are similar to Vanda, and they may be grown with Cattleyas. However, the night temperature should not go below fifty-five degrees. The lip typically produces a long spur at its base.

Angraecum eburneum. A scoop shaped, shiny white lip and slender green sepals and petals, make this species from the Comoro and Seychelle Islands most attractive. The spur is but three inches long.

Angraecum sesquipedale. Waxy white, five-inch star-shaped flowers with spurs ten inches long are produced on generous sprays and create a handsome species. The long spur, and the close association of orchids with specific insects, caused Darwin to predict that there must be a moth with a proboscis long enough to obtain the nectar from the base of the spur and so perform the act of pollinating this species. Later, the Sphinx moth of Madagascar, home of *Angraecum sesquipedale,* was found to be the elusive species in question. Its Christmas flowering season has given *Angraecum sesquipedale* its nickname of "Star of Bethlehem."

Angraecum superbum. Another species from Madagascar, this is similar to *A. eburneum* in having a white lip and pale green sepals and petals, but it has a spur even longer than that of *A. sesquipedale*. The flowers are three inches across, and are very fragrant.

Other Members of the Aerides Tribe

Renanthera is a genus similar to Vanda, grown for its brightly colored flowers, which, though small, are produced in great numbers and make a striking display. Subtle variations of yellow marked with red, and red with orange, are the general color schemes of the species. The purpose of crossing this genus with Vanda is to introduce the deep red tones into the hybrids. The resulting hybrids have a wide variety of shapes which gives them a fascination all their own. Renanthera has four pollinia (in contrast to the two in Vanda, Phalaenopsis, Aerides, and Angraecum), and the lip is moveable. The plants are slender, with short fleshy leaves, and some reach such great height that they are almost too tall for the average greenhouse. They need exceptionally good light.

Fig. 80 *Angraecum eburneum,* one of the most widely grown of the genus. (Courtesy of Jones and Scully, Inc.)

Renanthera coccinea. This species grows six to ten feet high. The branched flower stem comes from an upper leaf axil, and bears a hundred or more flowers that are two inches wide and four inches long. The very slender petals and dorsal sepal are bright red marked with yellow. The lateral sepals are longer and wider, and are clear red. The tiny yellow lip is tipped with red. A native of Cochin China, it flowers in the fall.

Renanthera imshootiana. Similar to *Renanthera coccinea,* but growing only about two feet tall, this species produces a wealth of flowers on a freely-branching stem two feet long. The dorsal sepal and petals are short and slender, standing up above the broad lateral sepals and giving the flower the look of a butterfly. The dorsal sepal is dull yellow, the petals the same but dotted with red, and the lateral

Fig. 81 Opsisanda Juliet (*Vanda sanderiana* × *Vandopsis gigantea*). (Courtesy of Wm. Kirch)

sepals are cinnabar red on the upper surface, dull yellow beneath. The species is a native of Assam.

Renanthera lowii. Once called *Arachnanthe lowii,* this huge, spectacular plant grows very tall and produces flower stems six to ten feet long. Its heavy leaves are much longer than other members of the genus, being two to three feet in length. Of the forty to fifty flowers produced on the stem, the lower two are quite different from the rest. They are small and fleshy, tawny yellow with crimson spots, while the others are larger, less fleshy, with a pale yellow-green ground and irregular blotches of reddish brown, and a small yellow lip spotted with purple. The species comes from Borneo.

Renanthera matutina. This smaller species from Java has flowers of bright yellow shaded with crimson.

Renanthera monachica. The short leaves of this species are one-half inch thick and dark bluish green. The flower stem bears twenty-five or more flowers, one to one and one-half inches in diameter. They are bright orange with deep red spots. This native of the Philippines flowers in early spring.

Renanthera storei. Called the "fire orchid" in the Philippines, this species is quite similar to *Renanthera coccinea.* The dorsal sepal and petals are brick-red; the lower sepals are brilliant crimson marked with lighter tones. The lip is crimson with yellow bars and a white center. The flowers last for two months. This is perhaps the most widely used species in hybridization.

Arachnis is a genus also used in hybridization with Vanda. Its name means "spider-like." The genus was at one time designated as Arachnanthe, and later was included in Renanthera by some authorities. The genus Arachnis is not given as such in Bailey. Some of the species are now retained in Renanthera. Arachnis is characterized by four pollinia and by having the lip hinged to the base of the column and readily movable. The genus likes light, as much as or more than Vanda.

Arachnis flos-aeris. Native to the Philip-

Fig. 82 Renantanda Jack Warne (*Vanda sanderiana* × *Renanthera storei*). (Courtesy of Jones and Scully, Inc.)

pines, these plants grow eight to ten feet tall and produce short flower stems with about ten three- to four-inch flowers. They are yellow barred with purple-brown and have a musky scent. The flowers appear from July to March.

Arachnis moschifera. These striking cream or yellow-green flowers are spotted and barred with deep red or purple. They have the texture of enamel. The stems are slender and climbing. The flowering time is variable.

Vandopsis, a genus whose name means "like Vanda," resembles Vanda except that the lip has no spur. The plants are very robust and heavy. The members of the genus are frequently crossed with Vanda.

Vandopsis gigantea. Heavy pendulous plants produce flower stems ten to fifteen inches long with flowers three inches across. The flowers are golden yellow, blotched with cinnamon, and have a white lip. The species occurs in Burma.

Vandopsis lissochiloides. This is the most

Fig. 83 *Rhynchostylis densiflora* 'Rattana,' C.B.M.—A.O.S., an exceptionally fine example of the delight offered by many of the less well known members of the Aerides tribe. (Courtesy of Jones and Scully, Inc.)

familiar of the species, and is sometimes mistakenly called *V. batemannii*. The flower stem bears a dozen or more three-inch flowers which are yellowish, spotted with purple on the upper surface and reddish-purple underneath. The flowers are somewhat coarse in texture and last a long time. It occurs in the Philippines and flowers from spring through summer.

Saccolabium is a genus of delightful dwarf plants which produce dense sprays of charming little flowers. The lip is sac-like, as the name implies. They can be grown with Cattleyas, with plenty of water during the growing season, less during the winter. All of the species are brightly colored. *Saccolabium hendersonianum* has bright rose flowers, *Saccolabium cerinum* flowers that are red-orange, and *Saccolabium coeleste* flowers that are white tipped with blue.

Ascocentrum, once included in Saccolabium, has a delightful species, *Ascocentrum miniatum,* which is barely a foot tall and bears an upright stem of twenty to forty tiny bright orange flowers.

Other members of the Aerides tribe included by Bailey are Acampe, Camarotis, Cleisostoma, Listrostachys, Luisia, Mystacidium, Polyrrhiza, Rhynchostylis, Sarcanthus, and Sarcochilus, all of which have similarities to those already described, but are less often grown. To this list should be added the genus Anota, (formerly included both in Rhyncostylis and in Saccolabium), and the genus Trichoglottis.

Inter-generic Hybrids

Inter-generic hybrids in this tribe are numerous, and more will undoubtedly appear as time goes on. The combining names given to the bi-generic hybrids do not as readily show their origin as do those in the Cattleya tribe, although some ingenuity was used in creating them. They are as follows: Aeridopsis = Aerides × Phalaenopsis; Aeridovanda = Aerides × Vanda; Arachnopsis = Arachnis × Phalaenopsis; Aranda = Arachnis × Vanda; Aranthera = Arachnis × Renanthera; Ascocenda = Ascocentrum × Vanda; Luisanda = Luisia × Vanda; Opsisanda = Vandopsis × Vanda; Renantanda = Renanthera × Vanda; Renanthopsis = Renanthera × Phalaenopsis; Renanopsis = Renanthera × Vandopsis; Sarcothera = Sarcochilus × Renanthera; Tanakara = Aerides × Vanda × Phalaenopsis; Trichovanda = Trichoglottis × Vanda; Vandaenopsis = Phalaenopsis × Vanda.

13 | *The Cattleya Tribe*

THE Cattleyas and Laelias, the showy members of this tribe, have already been described, as have Brassavola and Sophronitis and the part they play in making the marvelous bi- and tri-generic hybrids. However, these handsome orchids should not be allowed to overshadow their lovely cousins.

EPIDENDRUM

The Epidendrums, a wide-spread genus of one thousand species, are loved by amateurs everywhere. They are easy to grow, and flower profusely, some producing their beautiful clusters of brightly colored flowers almost all year round. The flowers vary from one and a half inches, each a dainty miniature, to six inches in diameter. Many are worth growing for their fragrance alone.

They grow wild in tropical and subtropical America, from Florida south to Brazil. They are so abundant in parts of Central America that they could almost be classed with weeds. Yet when they are transplanted to our greenhouses, they match their true quality with that of their more exalted relatives. Epidendrums were among the first epiphytes to be imported into Europe. In fact, the first epiphytic orchid to flower in England was *Epidendrum cochleatum,* in 1787.

There is some variation among the widely distributed species as to cultural needs, but in general they do well in a Cattleya house, with night temperatures from fifty-five to sixty degrees. Some may like a spot that runs a little cool and others one that runs a bit warmer. Many do well in hanging positions, in baskets, or on slabs of tree fern, or fixed with a piece of osmunda fiber to a slab of log. They may be grown in osmunda fiber or bark, and the reed stem kinds may even be grown in a fluffy soil compost. These last are often grown in gardens in warm climates. They should be watered like Cattleyas.

Epidendrums can be divided into three general groups, according to the characteristics of the plants. In the group called Encyclium are placed those with true pseudobulbs, such as *Epidendrum atropurpureum, E. fragrans, E. prismatocarpum,* etc. The group Euepidendrum contains the tall growing, reed stem types such as *E. ibaguense, E. evectum,* etc. Plants with little or no thickening of the stem, such as *E. elegans,* are placed in a group called Barkeria.

The Species

Out of such a large genus it is possible to give here only a handful of species, which have been selected for their variety and popularity.

Epidendrum atropurpureum. This is one of the loveliest of the genus. The mahogany and green sepals and petals spread wide, the tip of each curving forward gracefully. The spreading lip is white with crimson stripes. Six to ten of these attractive, long-lasting flowers are borne on a long spray rising from the top of the short, oval pseudobulb. Ranges from Mexico to Venezuela. Flowers in late spring and early summer. A plant on a slab makes a magnificent display with its leads growing upward and a fan of flower spikes. The variety *randianum* (or *randii*) has the sepals and petals outlined in light green, and has a white lip centered with a purple-rayed blotch. The variety *roseum* has a bright rose-colored lip that forms a pleasing contrast to the dark sepals and petals.

Epidendrum ciliare. One of the best known, this species is loved for its easy-going habit. The plant looks like a Cattleya and grows about a foot tall. The slender, graceful flowers are about five inches across and are borne in clusters of three to seven. The sepals and petals are yellow-green, set off by a dainty, three-

Fig. 85 *Epidendrum fragrans* will flower in home, greenhouse, or out-of-doors in the summer. (Courtesy of H. A. Dunn and H. Griffin)

lobed, white lip, with a needle-like mid lobe and fringed side lobes. It grows abundantly in Mexico and flowers in the winter.

Epidendrum cochleatum. The shape of these attractive, upside-down flowers suggests an octopus. The slender, yellow-green sepals and petals stream down from the shell-like, green- and purple-striped lip. The flower stem elongates through a period of five to seven months, producing a succession of flowers, with four or five open at a time. The slender, conical pseudobulbs are five to eight inches tall, bearing a pair of leaves. They may be found from Florida to Colombia. The variety *triandrum* is one of Florida's native orchids. The species flowers from spring through fall.

Epidendrum difforme. A delightful small species, this one has slender stems and alternate pale green leaves. The waxy, fragrant, greenish-white one-and-a-half-inch flowers are borne directly at the top of the stem in clusters of three to five. The sepals and petals are slender, while the lip is spreading and wavy at the edge. The plants occur from Mexico south to the Panama and flower in summer or early fall. There are slight variations in the flowers and the plant sizes from region to region.

Epidendrum elegans. This is a cool-growing species with slender terete stems about a foot tall, topped by several leaves. The flower spike is a foot or more tall and bears a loose cluster of small, bright flowers. The colors range from

Fig. 84 *Epidendrum atropupureum,* one of the most striking of the genus. (Courtesy of H. A. Dunn and H. Griffin)

Laeliocattleya Gold Gleam. (Courtesy of Clint McDade and Sons)

Laeliocattleya Derna. (Courtesy of Clint McDade and Sons)

peach-pink to lilac. A member of the Barkeria section, this species occurs in Mexico and Guatemala and flowers in the winter.

Epidendrum fragrans. The flowers of this species are spicily scented and pretty but not very showy. They are similar in shape and size to *Epidendrum cochleatum* but are creamy white with a red peppermint-striped lip. Pseudobulbs are from four to five inches tall, bearing a short single leaf. Since the flower stem is short, the cluster of blooms nestles close to the leaf. The plants occur from Guatemala through the West Indies to north Brazil and flower in late summer and early fall.

Epidendrum ibaguense. This is the preferred name for the species familiarly known as *Epidendrum radicans.* The plant is vine-like, having a tall, slender stem with rather widely-spaced short leaves and long aerial roots. It should be trained to a support in the greenhouse. The tall and erect flower stem bears a dense cluster, actually a sphere-shaped head, of one-inch, brilliantly-colored flowers, ranging from red to orange to yellow. Each flower is a little jewel, having waxy little sepals and petals and a fringed lip. *Epidendrum ibaguense* crossed with a number of other reed type species has given an array of "reed-stem" hybrids. Selection has produced plants that are more compact and shorter than their parents, making them more suitable for small greenhouses. The flowers run through all the tones on the yellow to red section of the color circle, including peach, pink, red violet, brick red, etc. The best known of the reed-stem hybrids is Epidendrum O'brienianum, *E. ibaguense* × *E. evectum*, registered in 1888. The latter is a little known species which is nevertheless useful in hybridization. *Epidendrum ibaguense* occurs throughout Central and South America, growing in open weedy soil in dense masses and flowering throughout the year. The reed-stem species are very dominant for plant character and flower size and shape, which may be due to the fact that some are tetraploid.

Epidendrum lockhartoides. A delightful miniature resembling the genus Lockhartia in its braided appearance, this species is as deco-

rative when not in flower as when blooming. Six to eight tiny green flowers are borne on a short stem, each barely exceeding its bract and folding back upon it. The plants occur in Panama and flower in the fall. They like a bit more shade than others.

Epidendrum mariae. A very lovely species, it has two-inch pseudobulbs and leaves only four inches long. The flower stem is about eight inches tall and bears one to three large flowers. The petals and sepals are small, greenish-yellow, while the huge lip is spreading, with a deeply indented outer portion, white with green veins in the throat. It occurs in Mexico.

Epidendrum nemorale. This species will do best in a cool bright spot in the Cattleya house. The pear-shaped pseudobulbs bear erect leaves that are about a foot long. A two-foot-long spike bears ten to twenty densely clustered four-inch flowers. The flowers are pinkish

Fig. 86 *Epidendrum radiatum,* a waxy, creamy flower with candy striped lip. (Courtesy of Rod McLellan Co.)

Fig. 87 *Epidendrum vitellinum* makes a bright spot of orange-red in the greenhouse. (Courtesy of Rod McLellan Co.)

mauve with purple streaks. The plant occurs in Mexico.

Epidendrum prismatocarpum. One of the most showy of the genus, this species has large, airy clusters of two-inch, boldly-marked flowers. They are waxy, pale yellow-green, spotted with purple-black. The sepals and petals are slender, and the spear-shaped lip is slender and pointed, pale purple with a yellow tip and a white border. It occurs in Central America and flowers in the summer. Some plants are quite tall, other specimens smaller, the conical pseudobulbs being from three to six inches in height and the leaves a foot long.

Epidendrum radiatum. Similar to *E. cochleatum* and *E. fragrans* in plant character and flower shape. The flower is more round than *E. fragrans* and heavier in substance, with the lip less pointed and the striping of a deeper shade. Occurs from Mexico to Venezuela. Flowers variably.

Epidendrum schumannianum. The ex-

tremely long, thin stems of this species bear oval leaves for more than half their length. The flowers are produced on a branched stem, and are oddly colored, being purple on the underside and burnt sienna spotted with brown on the upper surfaces. The plants, which occur in Costa Rica and Panama, flower in late winter and early spring.

Epidendrum stamfordianum. This is a popular species, though it is a little hard to get started when shipped in from the wild. It produces its flower stalk from the base of the tall pseudobulb, instead of from the apex. The flowers are produced in generous numbers, and are fragrant. The sepals and petals are narrow, yellow spotted with red. The lip, which resembles a bird with its wings spread, is white to yellow. The plants are found from Mexico to Colombia and Venezuela.

Epidendrum tampense. A native of Florida, this is an attractive, though not showy, orchid. The small greenish flowers are borne on a slender stem. The little lip is tinted with purple. This is the little orchid that for a while was rather widely sold by non-orchid dealers as the

Fig. 88 *Epidendrum nemorale* gives dainty clusters of pinkish flowers. (Courtesy of Rod McLellan Co.)

Fig. 89 Epiphronitis Veitchii, one of the earliest bigeneric crosses, made in 1890. It is *E. ibaguense* (radicans) × *Sophronitis grandiflora*. (Courtesy of Rod Mc-Lellan Co.)

"butterfly orchid." It flowers any time of the year.

Epidendrum vitellinum. The small plant, with pseudobulbs barely two inches tall, bears two slender leaves six to nine inches long. The flower stem is about eighteen inches tall and carries a dozen or more one-and-a-half-inch flowers that are entirely orange-red. The variety *majus* is a heavier plant with larger, more brilliant flowers, and is the one usually imported. The species occurs in Mexico at high altitudes and likes a cool spot in the Cattleya house. It flowers in early fall.

Other Members of the Cattleya Tribe

Broughtonia is a genus native to the West Indies, containing two or three species sometimes included with Epidendrum. Best known is *Broughtonia sanguinea*, a little plant with pseudobulbs two inches long and leaves two to four inches long. It gives a cluster of one-inch, crimson to blood-red flowers which have slender sepals and nearly round petals and lip. It

likes somewhat warmer temperatures than Cattleyas, and can be grown in the warm greenhouse, or possibly hanging in a warm spot in the Cattleya house.

Cattleyopsis is very similar to Broughtonia except that it has eight pollinia while Broughtonia has four, and the leaves are toothed on the edges. *Cattleyopsis ortgesiana*, from Cuba, and *Cattleyopsis lindenii* from Cuba, the Bahamas, and Jamaica are both dwarf plants that have a real appeal.

Diacrium contains few species, one of which, *Diacrium bicornutum*, is superbly beautiful, and is called the "Virgin Orchid" because of its purity of form and grace. The flowers are sparkling white, the oval, pointed sepals and petals are about the same size. The little bifurcated lip is faintly dotted with purple. The flowers are borne on an erect stem which produces up to twenty buds successively. The plant is rather tall, with horn shaped pseudobulbs that are nine inches tall and have several leaves at their apex. The plant occurs in north-

Fig. 90 *Diacrium bicornutum*, a beautiful species, becoming rapidly better known. (Courtesy of H. F. Loomis)

Fig. 91 *Schomburgkia lueddemanii,* the ultimate in ruffles. (Courtesy of H. A. Dunn and H. Griffin)

long. The flower stem bears two to four one-inch flowers that are white with purple in the lip and which have six pollinia. Occurs in Brazil. Flowers variably.

Shomburgkia, a genus of about fifteen species, is often included in Laelia. *Schomburgkia lueddemanii* has tall flower sprays that bear large clusters of ten to twenty beautiful flowers each. The extremely wavy sepals and petals are brown. The three-lobed lip is purple, trimmed with yellow. It occurs from Panama to Venezuela and flowers in the summer.

We should note here that the genera Cattleyopsis, and Laeliopsis are given in addition to those included in the tribe by Bailey.

Inter-generic Crosses in the Cattleya Tribe

The bi- and tri-generic crosses between Cattleya, Laelia, Brassavola, and Sophronitis have already been described. In addition to these, many others have been made. Diacattleya and Dialaelia are crosses between Diacrium and Cattleya and Laelia, respectively. Epicattleya, Epidiacrium, Epilaelia, and Epiphronitis reveal their origin as crosses between Epidendrum and Cattleya, Diacrium, Laelia, and Sophronitis. Leptolaelia is the hybrid between Leptotes and Laelia. Liaopsis is the hybrid between Laelia and Laeliopsis. The ease with which the various genera may be crossed shows how closely related they are. An amateur might have a good bit of fun trying various combinations. The curent interest in the smaller flowered but distinctive hybrids made from the bifoliate Cattleyas has spiked a renewed interest in the possibilities offered by Epidendrums as parents, particularly the larger flowered kinds such as *E. atropurpureum, E. mariae* etc.

ern South America, Trinidad, and Tobago, and is often found on sea cliffs where it is bathed with salt spray. It flowers over a period of two months or more, usually during the summer.

Laeliopsis is quite similar to Cattleyopsis. *Laeliopsis domingensis* has four pollinia, and was once included in Cattleya. It is grown like Broughtonia and occurs in Haiti and the Dominican Republic.

Leptotes. *Leptotes bicolor* is the only species of its genus. It is a dwarf plant, with short terete stems only an inch long and a fleshy little leaf about three inches

14 | *The Cymbidium Tribe*

THE genus Cymbidium far surpasses the other genera in this tribe. The tribe grows natively from Japan to Australia, through China, India, Burma, Malaysia, and even in the Philippines. Yet within this tremendous area the various species are restricted to rather segregated geographical regions. Some inhabit the cool higher elevations; others dwell where it is warmer. Many have been revered since ancient times; others have been discovered more recently.

CYMBIDIUM

Cymbidiums are among the loveliest of orchids and the most useful. The familiar kinds have tall, arching sprays of waxy, delicately-colored flowers which make a wonderful display in shades of yellow, green, rose, and white —plain or subtly blended. The plants themselves are attractive for their grassy foliage. The keeping quality of Cymbidiums is unusual even among orchids, and the blooms last in perfection a minimum of six weeks and sometimes as long as three months.

The serene beauty of the flowers gives them a charm quite different from that of the showy, ruffled Cattleya or the curiously flagrant Paphi-opedilum. Their oval, pointed sepals and petals are of nearly equal size and shape and are colored similarly. The dorsal sepal often bends slightly forward over the lip. The lip is fleshy, with side lobes that stand erect beside the column, and a front lobe that bends down in tongue-like fashion. It is from the somewhat boat-shaped lip that the genus gets its name (*Cymbid*, Greek for boat). The lip is usually marked with a pattern of spots and lines, bears one or more ridges, and is sometimes downy. The column is nearly erect, often flushed with color, and frequently speckled or lined with the same shade that marks the lip. The species bear from one to thirty blooms on a spike.

Most of the Cymbidiums grown today are hybrids, and until now these have been almost entirely the cool-growing types bred from the species with large showy flowers, which range natively through high elevations in the Khasia Hills and the Himalayas. These hybrids flower well only in areas where they can have cool summer nights, nights below 60° and preferably around 55°. With ingenious handling, and especially with the help of cooling systems, some growers have been able to flower them where the nights are warmer.

It has been found that the delightful miniature Cymbidiums from China and Japan along with a few small flowered "pendulous" species will do well in warmer areas. This, along with the current interest in smaller flowers, has opened a new field in Cymbidium breeding. Not only is there opportunity for much variety and beauty in the creation of miniature hybrids, but there is a possibility, in crossing them with the large-flowered kinds, of broadening the temperature tolerance of the latter.

Cymbidiums are evergreen plants, with abundant fleshy roots. The pseudobulbs vary according to the species from robust spheres larger than your fist to a slender and barely apparent thickening of the stem, and are sheathed with the bases of the leaves. The leaves remain green for several years, and as they fall, their dried bases remain attached to the pseudobulb. The plants are compact and cover a circular area. The leaves are slender, of leathery texture, not particularly fleshy, and vary in length from about a foot in the smaller species to sometimes three feet in the larger ones. The species differ somewhat in the num-

Fig. 92 Cymbidium Peri 'Beefeater.' A very floriferous hybrid. (Courtesy of Armacost and Royston, Inc.)

ber of leaves per pseudobulb, from nine to fifteen being usual. New growths arise laterally from the base of mature pseudobulbs.

The flower spikes appear from June through October, according to the habit of the plant. Spikes that appear early may flower in the fall, while those that appear later may flower through the winter and spring. However, the development of the spikes and the time of opening of the flowers is not always thus conveniently associated. In some plants spike development, enlargement of the buds, and opening of the flowers proceed in a swift, continuous sequence. In others, although the spikes appear at about the same time, the growth through fall and winter is slow, so that the buds are not ready to open until late spring.

The spike is at first similar in appearance to a vegetative growth, but by the time it is three or four inches long its character becomes apparent. The spikes are rounded and their tips are sharply pointed. The stems are clothed in sheathing leaves that remain tightly clasped during their early development. As the spike lengthens, the tip which encloses the buds is fatter than the rest of the stem. When the spike has reached about half of its ultimate length, the buds emerge from the last sheathing leaf. The section bearing the buds elongates, giving space between the buds, and the buds enlarge until finally they are ready to open. Usually the buds at the base open first and the rest follow in succession. If a stem is cut after several flowers are open, and is kept in water in the house, the rest of the buds will open and attain really quite good color and substance, although the last few will probably not be up to the quality of the rest. Cymbidium is one of the few orchids that will do this. It is therefore unusually useful in cut flower arrangements. However, if you wish perfection in each flower, the spikes should be allowed to mature on the plant.

There are two types of growth and flowering habits. In one type flower spikes are produced from the immature pseudobulb. In the other the spikes come from the fully mature bulb. In the first type, new growth starts in late winter or early spring. This growth is not completely mature when, in late summer or early fall, it gives rise to flower spikes. It continues to grow and mature while the flower spikes are developing. In the second type, new growths are started during the summer, making their appearance shortly before flower spikes arise from the same pseudobulb. These are sometimes so close in development that one cannot tell which are the vegetative growths and which the spikes. However, the flower spikes soon outstrip the vegetative growths, which develop slowly through fall and winter. In the spring they take on a new spurt and grow rapidly so that by mid-summer they are fully mature and ready to start new vegetative growths. Soon thereafter, their flower spikes appear.

It is possible that some of the difficulties encountered in flowering Cymbidiums with regularity are due to a mixing of these basic habits in the hybrids. Plants in both categories (those which flower on the immature bulb and those which flower on the mature bulb) must have reached just the right stage of development by late summer in order for flower spikes to be triggered into development. As the end of flowering approaches, start the plants into rapid vegetative growth; step up fertilizing and watering, give all the sun you can, and let the night temperature run about 55°.

Cymbidiums have become so important, for commercial growers and the cut flower market as well as for amateurs, that people all over the country are determined to grow them. There is great need for exact information as to what initiates Cymbidium flowers. Research is being done, but is hampered by a number of things. Species Cymbidiums are not too numerous in this country, and when available are not obtainable in large numbers. Information gained from the study of species is basic and helps us understand the hybrids. But one cannot assume that because certain species behave in certain ways that other species will behave in the same way, or that hybrids containing them will do so. When research is done on hybrids, it is desirable that the plants studied should be identical, which means that they should be members of the same clone (divisions of the same origi-

Fig. 93 Vegetative growth and flower spike coming from pseudobulb at nearly the same time. Note how tightly pointed the flower spike is.

nal plant), which, again, limits the numbers of plants available. The accumulation of measured information is slow, and we still have to go pretty much by what has been learned by general experience. Added to these problems is the fact that certain plants just won't do what you expect of them. Certain of the modern hybrids, which by the flowering of the first seedlings look wonderful, may show themselves to be quite tricky, flowering just often enough to keep you hoping, or flowering for some people and not for others. Reluctant flowering may be caused by chromosomal aberrations, or it may be that certain individuals simply need a different combination of environmental factors.

■ GREENHOUSE CULTURE

Temperature. In general, we know that Cymbidiums flower with greater regularity in areas where the summer nights are cool, rarely up to or over 60°, close to 55°

for most of the time, and where they get good bright sun. They tolerate the higher daytime temperatures that go with bright sun, and although temperatures above 85° are not advantageous, with plenty of water and circulation of moist air they will tolerate 95° to 100° if not of too long duration. Cymbidiums do not burn as easily as the thicker leaved kinds. It was at one time thought that perhaps what Cymbidiums needed was a wide difference between day and night temperatures rather than a specifically cool night temperature. This has not proven out, however, for regardless of the day temperature and the spread between day and night temperatures, they actually flower better when the summer nights are close to 55°. Also, vegetative growth is better with cooler nights, the plants being more vigorous and the leaves tougher and stronger.

Flower spikes start forming during the summer and may appear on into the fall. Those spikes that appear last of all may have actually initiated buds earlier but have been slower in growing and therefore tardy in making their appearance. At any rate, the initiation of flower buds and the appearance of spikes in general seem to be brought about by the combination of low night temperatures and long bright days. Plants that fail to make spikes during this period rarely start spikes later on (in winter), undoubtedly inhibited by the short days of winter even though by then the night temperature is favorable for their formation.

If, during the summer (the period of long days) the plants can be furnished the necessary cool nights, flowering should take place. We have found that on our occasional warm nights (in Wyoming) we can lower the temperature by several degrees if we run the evaporative cooler. If the natural humidity in your area is such that an evaporative cooler would not reduce night temperature, we suggest instead using a refrigerative unit. Compact units of modest size are available for use in homes, motel units, etc., and one of these should reduce the night temperature in a small greenhouse. They are more expensive than evaporative coolers, and perhaps would run into too much money for a large greenhouse.

In order to allow the bright light necessary, less shading should be applied than to a Cattleya house. The greenhouse temperatures therefore tend to go very high. Although the plants can take short periods of high temperature, they will do better if the temperature can be kept under 85° for the most part. This is possible with extremely free ventilation, all the ventilators open, and someone on hand to damp down the walks and benches and mist the plants several times a day. Far more efficient and easier on both grower and plants is an evaporative or refrigerative cooler, or a pad and fan arrangement, or mist nozzles with fans to move the air upward.

Growers in moderately warm areas have had some success with Cymbidiums by putting them outdoors during the summer. The nights may be a few degrees cooler outdoors than in a greenhouse, and the freer air movement is a help. The plants are set on cinder or gravel beds, or are placed on low stands, either in a lath house, or under a roof of lath or plastic shading, or under a tall tree that will give some protection at noon. Cymbidiums that are grown outdoors all year long can take full summer sun. Greenhouse plants that have had nearly full sun and which are put outdoors early enough to become hardened to it may also be able to take full summer sun. There is no advantage in letting them burn, however. Be sure they get plenty of water and spray them for red spiders. They must be brought indoors before frost.

A trick that has been tried, but without consistent success, is treating the plants with ice water during the latter part of the summer. The plants are watered in late afternoon or early evening with water that has been cooled with ice, and some growers even pour ice cubes or crushed ice into the pots. The jubilant success of one summer does not necessarily show up the next. The general plaint is "ice water worked last summer but it didn't work this summer." A possible reason for its not always working is that the roots may be cooled so much that they are not able to absorb nutrients fast enough to supply the needs of the plants. Reports of spikes' dropping their buds would indicate poor nutrition. Chilling the roots while the air surrounding the leaves is still quite warm may upset the physiological balance of the plant.

The Missouri Botanical Garden some years ago worked out a system by which they were able to flower Cymbidiums very successfully in spite of the long hot St. Louis summer, with nights that are often above seventy degrees. The system was to do everything to bring the plants through the summer in good health (much air circulation, even to removing some of the roof glass, good light to keep the plants making food rapidly to make up for rapid use of food, plenty of fertilizer from April to October, copious amounts of water, which meant watering on every bright day, and additional cooling of the greenhouse by frequent damping down and misting of the plants which kept water evaporating from the plants and their surroundings), and then, when the nights became cooler in mid-August, giving the plants long days artificially. Lights were kept on from dusk to 10:30 or 11:30 P.M. until the middle of October, at which time the lights were kept on for gradually shorter intervals to simulate a shortening day, until they were discontinued in November. During this period of "long days and cool nights" a large percentage of their plants set flower spikes. In fact, their display of flowers equaled those seen in areas considered to be true "Cymbidium country."

During fall and winter temperature is less of a problem. The ideal night temperature is 50°, with a fluctuation to just one side or the other. Some growers confine the fluctuation between 50° and 55°, others prefer to keep it between 45° and 50°. Winter day temperatures are held close to 60° in dull weather, and allowed to rise to 65° on bright days. Too high temperature day or night can cause erratic opening of flowers or the dropping of buds. This brings up a problem dealing with early flowering. The aim of many growers is to beat the season, with flowers as early in the fall as possible. However, spikes that come very early and have the flower buds out of the last sheathing leaf by September, may drop their buds due to the high day temperatures still prevalent through that month. Such early flowering plants should be kept as cool as possible.

Light. During the summer Cymbidiums can take, and should have, a great deal of light, a minimum of 4000 foot candles, and up to 8000 foot candles where the temperature can be kept from going to dangerous extremes. If this cannot be furnished them in a greenhouse, even with methods to keep down the heat, it is better to move them outdoors. With the freer air movement out in the open, the plants can often take a higher light intensity than they can in a greenhouse. Plants that grow outside all year round can usually take full sun. As described above, greenhouse plants that have had a great deal of light indoors may be hard enough to take full sun outdoors provided they are moved out before hot weather sets in. If any burning shows up, move them to where they will receive partial shade during the middle of the day, or provide a lath or plastic screen roof that will admit seventy to eighty per cent of full sun.

During the winter the plants must still have good light, clear glass except possibly in areas with extremely bright winter sun, in order to develop the flower buds. Those which have flowers in shades of pink and red will have richer coloring if they develop in bright light. However, those which have green or yellow flowers should be given a bit of shade as they approach the opening stages, as these colors tend to fade in bright light. Remove the extra shade as soon as flowering is finished.

Potting. Selection of a compost for Cymbidiums is a matter of personal choice, the main requisite being that the compost hold water well and furnish free drainage. Types of compost used range from straight osmunda fiber (shredded), to straight bark, with various mixtures of materials in between. Composts consist of half osmunda and half fibrous loam; half osmunda and half dried oak leaves; one-third shredded osmunda, one-third loam, one-third sand; sandy loam mixed with shredded redwood fiber (Palco Pete) and dried oak leaves; bark mixed with sand, peat moss, and oak leaves. Some of the mixes turn out to be largely of fibrous content, others are more soil-like. Some growers package and sell their favorite Cymbidium mix. To various mixes some like to add hoof and horn or bone meal for the slow release of phosphorus, and uramite for the release of nitrogen.

Cymbidiums do not like to be disturbed too often, preferably not more often than every two or three years. Mature plants should therefore be given a pot large enough to accomodate a good many new growths. Often from one bulb two growths will come, and from each of these two more the next year. The plants will do better and give more flowers if they are carried on into ten- or twelve-inch pots instead of being divided frequently. A plant needs repotting when its pseudobulbs become crowded against the edge of its container. This will usually happen before the medium has become unfit for growing. If a plant is not doing well, however, remove it from the pot and determine the cause, and then put it in fresh compost.

Plants should be repotted immediately after each one has finished flowering. This will mean that some will be ready in March or April (a few earlier) and some not until May or June. The former will not yet have started new roots, which is ideal, but the latter, even though root tips may be active, should be potted if they need it. Try to disturb the new roots as little as possible. Plants that did not flower should be included with the early group for repotting.

A plant that is not to be divided can be moved into a new pot with very little disturbance. Prepare the new pot with a fair amount of crock for drainage and add a layer of potting medium over the crock. Remove the plant from its pot, shake off the old compost (or if osmunda, dig out as much of the core fiber as you can without tearing the roots), and trim off any dead roots. We usually do no root trim-

ming other than this, unless some roots are so long that they would be broken in the potting process. There are growers who prefer to trim the roots back to a four-inch stub.

Set the plant in the pot so that the level of the new compost will come about half an inch above the rounded base of the pseudobulbs and half an inch below the rim of the pot. Pour in enough of the potting material, previously dampened, to fill the pot to half its depth. Work it in among the roots with your fingers and thump the pot on the bench to settle it. Then procede to add compost and thump it in place until the pot is full. With your thumbs or a tamper, firm the surface around the inside edges of the pot. If osmunda is used, dampen the chunks first and then tear them apart so that the fiber is softly shredded. Stuff some of it into the central part of the root ball and among the roots, then set the plant in the pot and work the fiber into the space between roots and pot, finishing it with a potting stick. It should be firm, but not as hard as for Cattleyas.

In moving plants on into larger pots, it is well to remove any leafless backbulbs that are situated where they can be cut off without disturbing the green part of the plant. If the plant consists of a complete circle of green bulbs with a few backbulbs in the center, these had best be allowed to remain. When the plant has made its new growth toward one side, backbulbs can easily be removed from the other side. Sometimes when a large plant has had the backbulbs removed from one side it leaves a long narrow green section that is awkward to pot. This had best be divided to make two or more plants of better shape.

Dividing a Cymbidium is more of a challenge than dividing a Cattleya. The pseudobulbs grow so close together that often it is difficult to tell which one comes from which other one. The rhizome that connects them is rather short, and the bulbs must be pressed apart to reveal it. A one-lead division should consist of the lead bulb and at least the bulb behind it. However, since two leads so often come from each bulb, the smallest division it is wise to make often consists of two leads and the bulb from which they arose. From the point of view of flower production, it is better to keep together five or six bulbs. Smaller divisions often do not flower the first year.

After removing the plant from its pot, turn it around in your hands to study it. Press the bulbs apart a bit to see how the bulbs are connected, and gently wiggle or twist a group here and there to see which ones are held together. This will help you plan where to make the divisions. Some growers feel that it is safer to break the bulbs apart so as to avoid the possible spread of infection from cutting tools. However, the rhizome is woody and hand-breaking sometimes tears good buds away from the base of the pseudobulbs. If you prefer to use a knife or pruning shears, flame the tool before going on to each new plant. Each break or cut should be treated to prevent the entrance of fungi or bacteria. Swab it with a strong solution of fungicide or a slurry of Tersan. Dividing a plant of necessity causes many roots to be broken. Trim broken roots back to four-inch stubs. Then pot the divisions as described above.

Two diseases of Cymbidium often are not revealed until potting time. Since leafless pseudobulbs are sheathed with leaf bases, and since these bulbs often remain on the plant for some time, it is often not suspected that they may be internally rotted. However, if pseudobulbs lose their leaves too soon, resulting in a plant that has leaves only on the youngest bulbs, or if the bulbs are soft, infection may be present. Cut through the rhizome between the back-bulbs. Infection is shown by brown, dark purple, or black tissue. Discard any bulbs that are infected. Continue to cut forward (flaming the knife between cuts) until clean white or cream-colored tissue is found. The infection spreads from bulb to bulb through the rhizome so that if it is found in the rhizome the chances are that it has already entered the next bulb. The bulbs become rotted inside, which kills the leaves. New growths from infected bulbs often show watery areas on the leaves, and, of course, the leaves soon die. A bacterial soft

Fig. 94 Upper, when dividing a Cymbidium, press the pseudobulbs apart to determine the "lines" of growth. Lower, strip the old leaf bases away from the back-bulbs. Insert base of pseudobulb in a sand-peat moss mix (or other mix), or use polyethylene bags as described in text.

rot causes the brown to purple watery decay of the pseudobulb. A fungus, *Pythium ultimum,* produces the jet black color in the pseudobulb which soon shrivels and becomes "mummified." Plants from which infected areas have been removed should be soaked for twenty-four hours in Wilson's Anti-damp or in some other fungicide, and then dried bare-root for ten days. If infection recurs after potting it is best to perform surgery again and re-treat, but if it persists the plant should be discarded.

Care of newly potted plants. Growers differ on this subject. Some put the newly potted plant directly on a regular watering schedule; others prefer to water only lightly until new root growth is evident and then start heavier watering, and this last seems to work best for me. Cut roots seem to heal better when kept on the dry side (the compost just damp), and

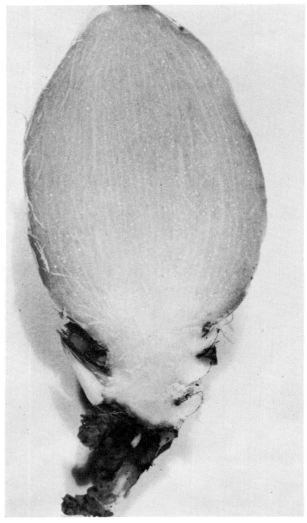

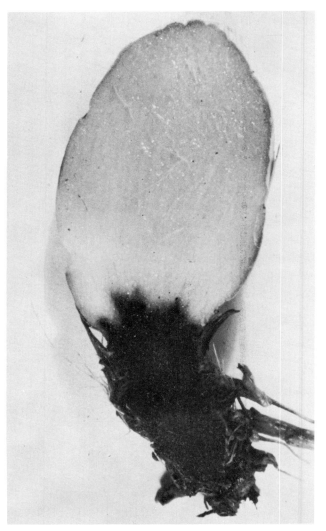

Fig. 95 A black or purple discoloration of rhizome or pseudobulb indicates a rot. Left, a healthy pseudobulb, Right, a diseased one, cut in half to show internal tis- sues. Note the healthy white buds at the base of the one at left, and the blackened killed buds on that at the right.

the formation of branch roots is encouraged. A mist spray of the foliage on bright days helps to prevent water loss and makes up for lessened activity of the roots after potting. Whether the plants should be given extra shade during the recovery period depends on day temperatures. Those which are repotted early in the season may not need extra shade, while those repotted later may benefit from it for a few weeks. Do not start giving fertilizer until root action develops.

Starting backbulbs. Backbulbs may be started right away, or, as some prefer, they may be allowed to dry for ten days or so first. In the latter case, set the backbulbs from each plant in a separate paper bag with a label (a cardboard box will also serve) leaving them open to the air and in a dry place. They can be started in a polyethylene bag, in which a bit of damp potting medium has been placed. Set the bag on the bench between pots of plants, where they will be shaded by the foliage and kept in an upright position. If the bulbs fall over the new growths will assume awkward angles. The bulbs may also be started in pots or flats, in a mixture of fine bark and peat moss, or either of these with sand. The new growths will start their own roots when they have reached a length of three inches or so. Those bulbs already in pots can be carried on in them, but those in polyethylene bags or flats should be potted as soon as roots reach a length of about an inch. New growths on backbulbs will come along faster if they are kept a little warmer for a while, with nights of about 58°. This can be accomplished by putting them in the Cattleya house, for example. But if you do not have a warm spot for them, they will still make growth.

Watering. Except for the period right after potting, Cymbidiums should not be allowed to dry out. Depending on the medium you use, water frequently enough to keep the medium quite moist. In bright hot weather, with the luxuriant foliage transpiring water rapidly, you may have to water every day. Large plants that fill the pot will use water more rapidly than newly potted ones. During the cool days of winter, watering will not need to be as frequent.

Humidity and ventilation. Cymbidiums need good ventilation and air movement. The relative humidity should be around 50% as an average. If you do not have humidifying equipment, help the plants through the heat of the day by giving them a mist spray over the foliage, and by damping down the ground. The relative humidity may be kept higher during the growing season than when the plants are in flower. Flowers are susceptible to *Botrytis* spotting under too damp conditions, especially if there is not good air circulation. Fresh air brought into the greenhouse, either by open ventilators or by fans, greatly helps to keep plants and flowers clean and healthy. Ventilators may be left open all night in summer.

Fertilizing. There are almost as many systems of fertilizing Cymbidiums as there are compost mixes. For plants growing in a mix containing a good bit of organic material, or in osmunda fiber, a 10-10-10 fertilizer used about every other watering is sufficient. However, for plants grown in bark or a mix that is largely bark, a high nitrogen fertilizer is necessary with every watering. When organic materials such as bone meal, leaf mold etc. are added, the materials which these release need not be duplicated in a chemical fertilizer applied with the watering. For instance, if uramite has been added to bark before potting, it is not necessary to use a high nitrogen fertilizer; rather, a balanced fertilizer should then be used.

Many growers fertilize only from spring through early fall, some the year round. Some use the same fertilizer throughout the year, while others cut down on the nitrogen content from August on. Some growers fertilize from spring to August, give no fertilizer while the spikes are setting, and resume fertilizer after the spikes are well started. If fertilizers are used during fall and winter, the concentration should be reduced or the frequency cut down because the plants do not need as much during short days and cool temperatures as they do during the long and warmer days of summer. Fertilizer used during winter should not have an excessively high nitrogen content.

■ **GARDEN CULTURE**

In regions where the temperature does not fall below twenty-six degrees, Cymbidiums may be grown out-of-doors. Large trees will furnish noon shade with a little sunlight filtering through, or a lath house may be used in lieu of trees. The laths should run north and south so that the sun will cast moving shadows, and the space between laths adjusted according to the intensity of the sun in your area. Where day temperatures are moderate or where the sun is not too intense the plants may be able to take full sun. When the thermometer shows signs of falling below twenty-six degrees, the plants should be covered for frost protection.

The plants may be grown in beds, with soil prepared in a ditch one foot deep and one foot wide. In the ditch put a layer of leaf mold six inches deep, and then a layer of horticultural peat to an equal depth. This is tramped down, and a layer of sandy soil added on top. Then, the compost is thoroughly mixed by turning it over two or three times with a shovel. Moisten the compost and wait a day or two before planting.

Remove the plants from their containers, and carefully loosen up the ball of fibre or compost. If it is possible to do so without injuring the roots, spread them out about three inches below the surface, cover them with pure peat, and put some peat directly around the pseudo-bulbs. Then fill in with the compost. If the roots are too tightly tangled, set the loosened ball in the trench and fill the compost in around it. Water lightly until new growth starts, giving frequent syringings of the foliage. When the plants are established, they may be watered rather abundantly.

Cymbidiums are attractive grown among rocks along with other plants, where their location is carefully prepared with sufficient compost.

■ SEEDLINGS

Cymbidium seed is obtained by hand pollination and sown in flasks after the method described for Cattleyas. It sticks to the sides of the tube of disinfecting solution, but may be handled either by keeping it agitated when a dropper is used, or by picking it up with a platinum loop. The seed is somewhat slow to germinate, but the seedlings grow well.

When the seedlings are removed from the flasks, they may be put either into five-inch community pots, or, better, in flats. Pure osmunda fiber is satisfactory for their growth, as are the composts described earlier. The community pots should be kept in a covered box, or the flat covered with a pane of glass, to furnish them the close, damp atmosphere conducive to rapid growth. At this stage they benefit from a night temperature of 58° to 60°. When the plants are three or four inches tall they may be moved from the community pot into three-inch pots. If those in flats still have

Fig. 96 Development of seedlings. Left, from flask to three-inch pot. Right, a seedling in five-inch pot,

developing its first flower spike.

room to grow, they may be left there for a while longer.

Seedlings may be shifted to larger pots as the need requires without disturbing the ball around the roots. They grow rapidly, and often flower at five years of age, though the naturally slower ones may take seven or eight years.

Cymbidium seedlings are reasonably priced and are a good buy for the amateur. Since it takes backbulb propagations two or three years to reach flowering size, two- or three-year-old seedlings will actually flower about as soon. Unless you have a particular interest in obtaining propagations from certain plants, the young seedlings will give the greatest satisfaction.

The Species

Of the sixty or more species of Cymbidiums, only ten or so have gained importance from a cultural point of view, and only a few of these have played a really important role in the making of our present day large showy hybrids. Even these appear less and less in cultivation as their place is taken by the superior hybrids. In addition to the large flowered species there are a number with smaller flowers, some most generous in the numbers they produce, which may increase in importance and popularity because of their tolerance for warmer temperatures. Lastly, there are the charming miniature species, many of which may also be grown under warmer conditions.

The Species:
Large Flowered, Mostly Cool Growing

Cym. eburneum. This species seems to be rather hard to grow, and is now rarely cultivated. But it has had a great influence on hybrids, in fact it was one of the parents (with *Cym. lowianum*) of the first Cymbidium hybrid, made in 1889, the famous Cym. Eburneolowianum. The broad flower parts of *Cym. eburneum,* its round shape, and delightful fragrance have come down through a long line of hybrids, largely through mating other species with the primary hybrid Cym. Eburneolowianum. Its flowers are rosy-white, or pure white, with a creamy lip, dotted with rose-purple and having a yellow ridge down the center. The flowers are three to four inches across, usually only one to a stem. The plant is rather weak growing, with slender pseudobulbs and leaves one to two feet long. It grows in the Khasia Hills at elevations of 5000-6000 feet and flowers in late winter and early spring.

Cym. erythrostylum. So called because of its red column, this species has flowers that are white with a few rose colored dots at the base of the petals and sepals. The creamy lip is heavily lined with red-violet. The petals are held forward, meeting at the top edges, and give the appearance of a hood over the lip. This hooded aspect is often inherited by hybrids that include this species. The early flowering habit of this species is one of the characteristics sought in its hybrids. The plant is small, with pseudobulbs one and a half to two inches tall, and leaves ten to fifteen inches long. The arching flower spike bears four to eight flowers. It occurs in Annam, and flowers in the fall and winter.

Cym. giganteum. In spite of its large, fragrant flowers and early flowering habit, this species is not used as much now as it was at one time. It does not have the good keeping qualities that we now expect, and its hybrids are often dull in color. It is found in the ancestry of many hybrids, however, to some of which it has contributed its yellow-green color. It occurs in Nepal, and flowers in fall and winter.

Cym. grandiflorum. These handsome plants are distinguished by having the base of each leaf expanded into a ribbed sheath, striped yellow and green. Their growth is tufted, the pseudobulbs scarcely thickened. The fragrant flowers reach five inches in diameter, and occur five to fifteen on a curving spray that originates from the base of the newly formed pseudobulbs. The petals and sepals are clear green, and the large lip is pale yellow spotted with red-purple. In using this species in breeding, growers have had to eliminate its only poor feature, that of frequently dropping its flower buds before they open. Sometimes the buds sit on the stem for weeks apparently ready to open, only to turn pink and fall off. The hybrids we now have flower satisfactorily, and many of them trace their green color to *Cym. grandiflorum*. The species grows natively in Nepal, Sikkim, and Bhotan.

Cym. l'ansoni. This species was once thought to be a variety either of *Cym. lowianum* or *Cym. tracyanum*, but its distinct differences make it a valid species. Its striking flowers have yellow sepals and petals, heavily lined with purple-brown, and the large spotted lip is pale in contrast. Its most outstanding hybrid is Cym. Ceres (*Cym. l'ansoni* × *Cym. insigne*) which ranges from pink to red and which, in turn, has been a most successful parent. Although it occurs in upper Burma, only a few plants have ever been found.

Cym. insigne. One of the most valuable of the species, it is prized for its vigor, its compact growth, and its tall, upright spikes of twelve to twenty flowers. The spikes grow three to four feet tall. The flowers range in color from white (var. *album*) and near white, to rose-lilac, with rosy dots at the base of the sepals and petals. They are three to four inches in diameter. The lip is rounded, dotted with rose, and has a yellow keel. Both the white and colored forms have been used in making many fine hybrids, which have since been combined in various ways to give a wide variety. Two of the important hybrids are the tetraploids Cym. Alexanderi 'Westonbirt' (Cym. Eburneo-lowianum × *Cym. insigne*), and Cym. Pauwelsii 'Compte d'Hemptinne' (*Cym. lowianum* × *Cym. insigne*). *Cym. insigne* was discovered comparatively recently, in 1901. This species occurs in Annam and flowers in early spring.

Cym. lowianum. This is another handsome and much used species. The plants are large, with pseudobulbs up to nine inches tall and leaves two to three feet long. The flower spike arches gracefully, and bears fifteen to thirty-five large flowers. It has many varieties that are almost as desirable as its hybrids. The flowers keep for two months or more, and this desirable quality, along with its floriferousness,

has been handed down to its progeny. The flowers are greenish-yellow with faint red or brownish veins. The rather pale yellow lip is downy and has a V-shaped red-brown blotch on the front lobe. One of its often-used varieties, var. *concolor*, has clear yellow-green petals and sepals, and its lip is marked with a light orange-buff patch. It occurs in Burma. Flowers from late winter to early summer.

Cym. parishii. This rather rare species resembles *Cym. eburneum*, except that the pseudobulbs and leaves are larger, and the spike bears three to six flowers instead of one or two. The fragrant, white flowers are four inches in diameter, with the lip decorated with large purple spots. The parent of the many hybrids made from this species was the variety 'Sanderae,' distinguished by much more color in the lip, and broader and more pointed petals and sepals. It has been combined with many of the other fine species. It grows natively in Annam, and it flowers in the summer.

Cym. schroederi. This species is found in the ancestry of many hybrids, but does not add much to them in quality. Therefore it has not continued in use. It has greenish yellow flowers and a lip marked with dull red blotches. It occurs in Annam.

Cym. tracyanum. This species has contributed its early flowering season to its descendants. The yellow-green flowers are fragrant and occur five to twenty-five on a spray. The plants are vigorous and are grown with ease. It is said that, while the species is often used out-of-doors, its flowers keep better in the damper conditions of a greenhouse. The flowers are yellow-green, marked with bright red, and have a yellow lip also marked with red. The plant occurs in Burma and Siam. Flowers are produced in the fall.

The Species: Small Flowered, Pendant Spikes, Warm Growing

The plants in this group are smaller in general than in the previous one, and the flower spikes, instead of arching upward from the pseudobulb, travel across the potting medium and down over the edge of the pot. With one

Cymbidium Jocosity. (Courtesy of Armacost and Royston, Inc.)

Cymbidium Babylon 'Castle Hill' FCC/RHS. (Courtesy of Dos Pueblos Orchid Company)

exception, they like intermediate or warm temperatures, and may be grown in bark or a loose Cymbidium mix. They like plenty of sun. They are not common in cultivation as yet, but will probably be more readily available as time goes on. Some of them may be grown out-of-doors in such places as Florida and Hawaii. In a greenhouse be careful not to over-water them, and to pot them high to give their spikes a chance to grow out over the surface of the medium.

Cym. devonianum. The flower spike of this odd plant will burrow down through the potting medium if not trained over the edge. It is said to have an unpleasant odor, which may not carry on to its hybrids. The dense flower spike carries over twenty olive to tawny flowers that have a rosy lip decorated with a dark purple spot on each side. A number of hybrids have been made with this species. The leaves are broad and fleshy and taper to a narrow base or petiole. It occurs in northern India,

Fig. 97 Left, *Cymbidium devonianum*. Right, *Cymbidium tigrinum*. (Courtesy of Fred A. Stewart, Inc.)

Cym. aloifolium. These straw-colored or tawny flowers have a yellow lip with brown markings. They are borne on a pendant spike, and are about one and one-half to two inches across. The plant, which occurs in Burma, blooms in winter and spring.

Cym. atropurpureum. A dozen or more heavy little flowers are borne on a drooping spike about a foot long. The sepals and petals are maroon-purple with a velvety sheen, and the lip is white. The plant, which is epiphytic, occurs at elevations of 500 to 3000 feet in mountainous areas of Malaya, and the Philippine Islands. It flowers in late spring and early summer.

needs cool temperatures, and flowers in the spring.

Cym. finlaysonianum. These large plants give many two-inch flowers that are borne on a pendant spike that reaches two to four feet in length. It grows natively along with *Cym. atropurpureum,* and is also epiphytic. The flowers are dull yellow with a central stripe of reddish-brown, and are fragrant in the morning. It flowers in the spring and summer. The plant grows easily in warm areas.

Cym. pendulum. The plant has stiff, upright leaves and a short pendant flower spike. The pretty little flowers are light yellow trimmed with purple, and have a purple lip with yellow lines. This species is native to northern India. It flowers variably.

The Species: Miniatures

The species *Cym. pumilum* and *Cym. tigrinum* have been known in England and in this country for some time, and have been used to make a number of hybrids. Although other species had been described by botanists in Europe and elsewhere, not many became well known in cultivation in this country. We are particularly indebted to orchid lovers of Japan for making us aware of the charms of the miniatures native to Japan and China, which the Japanese people cherish for their beautiful foliage as well as for their flowers. A few other species, long known also to growers in their native countries, are now making their way to our shores.

Fortunately for growers in this country, all of the miniature species and their hybrids (at least those made so far) can be grown along with Cattleyas, although a few require a warm spot in a Cattleya house. A few are epiphytic, identified by their velamen-covered roots. These do well in bark, while the others will do well either in bark or in a Cymbidium mix. Japanese growers apparently keep their plants somewhat cool during the winter, with night temperatures between forty and fifty degrees, growing them warmer in the summer and with "half-sun." Whether they would do better in our greenhouses if kept this cool during the winter we do not know, because they seem to do very well with Cattleya temperatures all year round.

Cym. canaliculatum. This is an epiphytic plant which gives dense spikes of attractive little flowers in a wide range of colors, including brown, green, yellow, magenta, and maroon. The variety 'Sparkesii,' is the favorite, with its deep maroon petals and sepals and its pink lip with red dots. The plant occurs in Australia. It flowers in the spring.

Cym. ensifolium. (Called *Kenran* in Japan, meaning "Sword Cymbidium.") The small flowers, many to the spike, are fragrant, yellow-green, and have a white lip blotched with dull red. The blossoms appear in the fall. The plant occurs in China and, rather rarely, in Japan.

Cym. faberi. The Japanese call this species *Ikkei-kyuka,* which means "many flowers on a scape." There are three color forms—reddish, greenish, and white. The plant needs plenty of water, especially during the growing season, and will do well with a bit less light than some other species. It is a native of China. It flowers in late spring and early summer.

Cym. forrestii. In Japan this species is known as *Shina-Shunran* or "Chinese spring orchid." The very fragrant flowers are green tinged with red and are borne singly on short stems. The plant occurs in China and flowers in the spring.

Cym. gyokuchin. The name is derived from *Gyochin,* meaning "young fish in the water." It was described in an ancient Chinese book on orchids and was imported into Japan over a century ago. The sepals and petals are pure yellow-green, and the lip is pure white. Less fine varieties have touches of red. Some have the foliage striped or mottled with white or yellow. The plant, which occurs in China and Formosa, flowers in the fall.

Cym. kanran. ("Winter orchid.") The spikes of this species carry many fragrant little flowers, which vary from green to red. The deep green foliage is glossy, and in some varieties the margins of the leaves are white. Occurs in Japan and Formosa. Flowers in late fall and winter. Cannot take too strong light.

Cym. hoosai. This species has up to fifteen fragrant flowers to a spike. Two forms occur. Those from China are called *Shina-hoosai,* and are such a dark purplish red that they are often called the "black Cymbidium." Those from Formosa are called *Taiwan-hoosai,* and are of a paler color. Both flower in the early spring.

Cym. pumilum. This very floriferous little plant bears thirty flowers to a spike. The blossoms are purplish red with a white lip dotted with red. Many of the plants have variegated foliage. They like a cool spot in the Cattleya house, although the hybrids can be grown somewhat warmer. The species is native to China and flowers in early summer.

The famous Cym. Minuet is *Cym. pumilum* × *Cym. insigne*.

Cym. tigrinum. A truly dwarf species, the pseudobulbs are about an inch tall and leaves four inches long, although the flowers are rather large sometimes reaching three inches in diameter. Two or three blooms occur to a stem. The sepals and petals are green tinged or spotted with brown, and the large lip is white or cream colored marked with red-purple. The plant, which occurs in Burma and Thailand and flowers in the fall, is frequently used in hybridization.

Cym. virescens. In its native Japan this species is called *Shunran*, "Spring Orchid." The

in hybridization has become legendary. Many, many crosses have been made with Alexanderi 'Westonbirt' as a parent. The best of the progeny, selected for their size, shape, and substance have been in turn crossed with each other, and back again to Alexanderi 'Westonbirt.' Thus has developed a long line of Alexanderi 'Westonbirt' hybrids. It was not known until fairly recently that Alexanderi 'Westonbirt' was a tetraploid, having 80 chromosomes (four times the haploid number of 20, and thus designated as 4n). In addition, many of the selected individuals from among its progeny have also proven to be tetraploid. Where crosses are made with both

Fig. 98 Left, *Cymbidium pumilum album*, a true miniature (Courtesy of Yoshio Nagano). Center, *Cymbidium devonianum*, with pendulous flower spike (Courtesy of Fred A. Stewart, Inc.). Right, Cymbidium Flirtation 'Princess Royal,' a hybrid between *Cym. pumilum* and Cym. Zebra (Courtesy of Fred A. Stewart, Inc.).

little plants have grass-like leaves about six inches long, often margined with yellow or white. The flowers are green with tinges of red, and are borne singly on short stems. They do not open fully. The species is spring flowering.

Cymbidium Hybrids

The destiny of the large-flowered Cymbidium was determined by the discovery of Cym. Alexanderi 'Westonbirt' (Cym. Eburneolowianum × Cym. *insigne* 'Westonbirt') registered by H. G. Alexander in 1922. This lovely large white Cymbidium was so successful in transmitting its size, shape, and substance to its progeny that it became the most popular parent in Cymbidium history, and its value

parents tetraploid, progeny that are almost entirely tetraploid are possible.

The dominance exhibited by Alexander 'Westonbirt' includes a strong influence on the color of the progeny. This influence causes a paling of the expected color, regardless of how brilliant the other parent may be, so that the offspring are almost entirely white, cream, or pale pink. This does not detract from the beauty of the hybrids themselves, for they are wonderful large flowers. From this line of hybrids have come the best of the white Cymbidiums, as well as many that are of delicately lovely coloring; but it has meant that other breeding lines have had to be developed in order to achieve more color. Cym. Pauwelsii

'Compte d'Hemptinne' (*Cym. insigne* × *Cym. lowianum*), a buff-pink tetraploid registered in 1911, is now being used with great success as a parent. It imparts good size and substance and, when used with brightly colored hybrids, does not dim the colors. Apparently, when used with Alexanderi 'Westonbirt' hybrids, its presence allows succeeding generations to be more brightly colored and to show a wide range of colors.

A number of tetraploid hybrids stemming from these two great progenitors are themselves proving to be excellent parents. Some may in time become as valuable as their older counterparts. The four which we shall name are all English crosses, proven by count to be tetraploids, and have shown their worth in recent crosses. (While these individuals are known to be tetraploids, this does not mean that all the other individuals in these crosses are tetraploids. A good many more have been found to be, and the chances are that some crosses may be entirely tetraploid, but only a count can prove it.*)

Balkis 'Silver Orb,' Balkis 'Luath,' and Balkis 'Perfection,' from the cross registered in 1934 by Lionel de Rothschild, Exbury: Alexanderi 'Westonbirt' × Rosanna 'Pinkie.' The colors are white and blush pink.

Babylon 'Castle Hill' and Babylon 'Carpentier,' from the cross registered in 1942 by H. G. Alexander: Olympus 'Rex' × Pauwelsii 'Compte d'Hemptinne.' They are rich pink in coloring.

Rosanna 'Pinkie' and Rosanna 'Warringal,' from the cross registered in 1927 by H. G. Alexander: Alexanderi 'Westonbirt' × Kittiwake. These are blush pink.

Nam Khan, from the cross registered by Lionel de Rothschild in 1941: Pauwelsii 'Compte d'Hemptinne' × Rosanna 'Pinkie.' The colors range from pink to yellowish pink.

Growers who have obtained divisions of these plants, as well as other fine members of these crosses, are using them to great advantage. Some of their progeny may in the next

* D. E. Wimber, G. A. L. Mehlquist, and E. W. Wells have made over 300 chromosome counts in Cymbidiums.

decade equal or outshine them, if that is possible. Results of breeding the above plants have shown them capable of allowing other colors to come through.

The breeding of tetraploids should not overshadow the variety of diploid hybrids. Many of the diploids rival the tetraploids in quality, and many outshine tetraploids in brilliance and variety of colors, if not in size. In general, the diploids produce more flowers to the spike. The majority of good greens, yellows, and reds are diploids. Growers are constantly on the alert for the spontaneous appearance of tetraploid plants in these colors. These might arise from the accidental non-reduction of reproductive cells, allowing a 2n sperm cell to fetilize a 2n egg cell. If such plants should occur, and should be capable of transmitting their color to all of their progeny, they would be invaluable. Growers are crossing many of the diploid greens, yellows, and reds with Balkis, Babylon, Rosanna and Nam Khan (and their offspring) to produce triploids (3n). In the triploid progeny, a variety of colors come out, but a percentage have the desired color of the diploid combined with the better size of the tetraploid. Some of the diploid hybrids being used for this purpose are Cym. Apollo 'Exbury' (yellow); Cym. Saigon and Cym. Flare (red); and Cym. Blue Smoke and Cym. Vale of Kashmir (green). In purchasing seedlings from such crosses, one should know in advance that they will not be uniform in coloring—for instance, a cross with a green diploid will give only a percentage of greens out of a variety of colors. With the swing to wider variety in sizes, (as evidenced by hybridizing the smaller-flowered species) a diploid with brilliant color or a subtle combination of colors, which is also graced by nice form and heavy substance, should be admired for its own intrinsic qualities. With Cymbidiums, as with Cattleyas, we have passed the stage at which everything has to be big to be of value.

In conjunction with the polyploid breeding of Cymbidiums, there occasionally occur pentaploids (5n) and plants with odd numbers of chromosomes, aneuploids. The pentaploids are said not to be superior to tetraploids and triploids in quality of flowers and plant characters. The aneuploids may be abnormal in some way, either in plant growth or in the flowers themselves. It is possible that reluctance to flower or failure to flower may be caused in some cases, but not all, by the presence of extra chromosomes which may upset the physiological balance of the plant. A certain amount of sterility is encountered among the aneuploids as well as among hybrids between unlike species, for example, crosses between miniature and large species.

An interesting observation has been made on the number of flowers produced to a spike in the primary hybrids of the Himalayan species. You might expect that if you crossed a species that usually produced one bloom with one that produced twenty-five, the resulting hybrid would give something close to the mean (average) between these two, or thirteen. But that is not the way it happens. Actually, a hybrid between a species that gives one and a species that gives twenty-five will itself produce about five or six flowers to a spike. Mathematically, five is the geometrical mean between one and twenty-five, arrived at by multiplying one by twenty-five and taking the square root of the product. Studies of various crosses have shown that Cymbidiums follow this general rule, and the rule may be used to predict the number of flowers you will get in any primary hybrid. As inheritance becomes more complicated in advanced hybrids, it is not possible to trace this feature through the maze of habits represented in any one plant. This rule may not hold true in hybrids between the Himalayan species and the small-flowered ones. In

Cym. Jean Brummit (*Cym. devonianum* × *Cym. eburneum*), the number of flowers per spike comes close to the number produced by *Cym. devonianum*.

Other Members of the Cymbidium Tribe

Cyperorchis is a genus closely related to Cymbidium, and native also to the Khasia Hills and the Himalayas. It has very few species. The flowers differ from Cymbidium in having narrower sepals and petals, which remain closed for nearly their entire length, spreading apart only at the tips. The flowers are small and are borne close together on the stem.

Grammangis differs from Cymbidium in that the leaves arise from the apex of the tall pseudobulb. About four species are known, and these are native to Madagascar and Java. The genus is seldom cultivated.

Grammatophyllum is a genus noted chiefly for one member which is a giant among orchids. This is *Grammatophyllum speciosum*, which has pseudobulbs 6 to 10 feet tall, to which the leaves add even greater height. One specimen in cultivation grew to a height of 18 feet, and produced as many as fifty flower spikes simultaneously, each of which carried 70 to 100 flowers. The 6-inch flowers are clear yellow, spotted with purple. Obviously this is not a species to be grown in a small greenhouse. *Grammatophyllum fenzlianum* is not as large a plant but produces flower spikes 5 feet long bearing sixty flowers each. They are green or yellow-green, spotted with brown. Unfortunately neither of these is a frequent bloomer, but one plant in flower must indeed be a glorious show.

15 | *The Cypripedium Tribe*

THE Cypripedium tribe consists of four terrestrial genera, one genus native to the north temperate zone, one to southern Asia, and two to South America. The first two genera are well known, and both are called Cypripedium in common usage. However, the name Cypripedium accurately belongs only to the ladyslippers of the north temperate zone, found in the woods of North America. The Asiatic genus is Paphiopedilum, and this name will be used here. The South American genera are Phragmipedium (which is sometimes given as Phragmopedilum), and Selenipedium.

The Paphiopedilums (Asiatic) are the ones cultivated by amateur and commercial growers, and nicknamed the "Cyps." Included in this genus are some of the most striking of all orchids. In florist shops they compete for admiration with Cattleyas and Cymbidiums and are becoming increasingly popular. They have been favorites of English growers for generations. Their marvelous range of colors—from yellow, green, brown, red, and purple, to white—is often subtly combined in single flowers. Phragmipedium and Selenipedium are genera interesting to collectors, although not widely grown. The true Cypripediums are known by all who love and study wild flowers and may be grown with special care in our gardens.

The flowers of the Cypripedium tribe are distinct, differing markedly from those of other tribes. The most appealing floral part is the lip, which is shaped like a pouch or slipper and which suggested their name (Cyprus, sacred to Venus, and *pes, pedis,* Latin for foot). Conspicuous, too, is the dorsal sepal standing guard above the lip, often broad and brilliantly marked. The petals extend laterally and are slender in proportion to the dorsal sepal. The other two sepals are fused together and lie behind the pouch. Usually they are hidden in a front view of the flower, but when they are enlarged, they add one more touch of beauty.

It would seem that these structures would be enough to distinguish the tribe. But botanically speaking, the number of fertile anthers is more important. All members of the Cypripedium tribe have two fertile anthers, whereas other tribes have only one. A third anther, which is sterile, is modified to form the conspicuous shield-like body called the staminode, which projects forward from the column and covers the reproductive parts. (See Fig. 99.)

The members of the Cypripedium tribe lack pseudobulbs and so are not equipped for storing water. There is a short stem from which grow the leaves. After the leaves have formed on a new growth, the flowering stem rises from the tip of the stem, between the leaves.

PAPHIOPEDILUM

This genus of handsome Asiatics has an almost lurid beauty. The heavy-textured flowers are unexcelled in keeping quality and may be enjoyed either on the plant or cut for a month or more. Some few remain fresh for as long as three months. The species vary in their flowering season so that blooms may be had at any time during the year. One of their chief attractions is their ease of culture. They are a good choice for amateurs who do not have a greenhouse, for a pot or two will grow beautifully on a window sill or in a Wardian case. The species are inexpensive, and a few dollars will buy many years of pleasure. The hybrids are more costly, particularly the more recent ones.

The fifty or so species are native to tropical Asia, Malaya, and the near-by islands. Some are found at relatively high altitudes in the mountain chains, where rainfall is abundant and temperatures are cool. Here they grow on accumulations of decaying vegetation, on ledges, or in crevices of limestone rocks, partially shaded by overhanging cliffs or trees. Other species occur at lower elevations where the temperatures are higher.

Temperature. Culturally, the cool- and warm-growing ones may be distinguished by their foliage. Those with plain green leaves require a night temperature of between 50° and 55°. Actually, the temperature need not be held as low as 50°, as long as it usually remains close to 55°. The day temperature should be kept between 65° and 72° in the winter, and it would be ideal if the summer day temperature could be kept not over 75°. However, the cool species, like most orchids, will accept and tolerate summer temperatures above this,

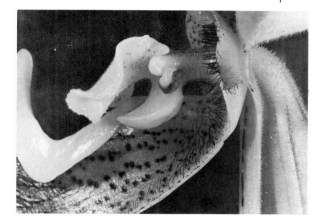

Fig. 99 Reproductive parts of a Paphiopedilum. The petal has been removed and half of the lip cut away. The column has three parts. The structure at the top is the staminode, a shield that covers the other parts. The foot-like structure that swings down into the lip is the stigma, the under-surface of which receives the pollen. There are two anthers, one on each side just above the stigma. The pollen grains are contained in a soft sticky wax, exposed on the lower surface of the anther.

but will do their best if they do not often exceed 85°. In order to protect the cool Paphiopedilums where the heat of summer is prolonged, some growers put the plants out-of-doors in the shade of large trees. The pots may be set on cinder beds or on benches to assure drainage. They should be elevated to keep slugs and cutworms from reaching them.

The warm-growing species are those with mottled foliage, and hybrids between the plain and mottled foliage kinds come in this category. They prefer a night temperature that does not go below 60°, but which, on the other hand, may go above this in the summer. They may be grown comfortably with Cattleya, with day temperatures that suit Cattleya and its companions.

Both the cool- and warm-growing kinds can be accommodated in a Cattleya house, as a matter of fact, if the former can be given a spot that runs a bit on the cool side. Shade will have to be adjusted for them as described below.

The good keeping qualities of the Paphiopedilums make it possible to have them for most holidays. Occasionally however it is desirable to slow down the opening of the blooms for a certain purpose. When the stem has reached its full length and the buds are almost fully developed, the temperature may be lowered a few degrees. Flowering is thereby slightly delayed. The temperature must not be lowered too soon or the stems will remain short and the plant will not be as handsome in bloom. Slightly lowered temperatures will allow the flowers to last longer, so that many growers, in order to keep a group of flowers as long as possible, keep the temperature a few degrees cooler after the plants have come into full bloom.

Potting. Paphiopedilums thrive when potted in soft, brown osmunda fiber. Some growers prefer a mixture of three parts osmunda to one of live sphagnum moss, but it is difficult to keep the sphagnum alive. Others are now successfully using bark, preferably

a seedling grade, or one in which the largest size pieces are one-half inch. A mixture of eighty per cent bark and twenty per cent dried crushed oak leaves is also popular, as are bark mixed with tree fern and plain tree fern. The choice of a compost is a personal thing. The chief essential in any compost is that it should have free drainage, because the roots, although never allowed to become dry, do not thrive in a sodden compost.

The plants are best repotted soon after flowering, at which time they may be divided into groups of not less than three growths. Remove all dead leaves and roots and all decayed compost. After adding crock for drainage, hold the plant at such a depth for potting that the base of the plant will be about one-half inch deep in the medium. If the plant is set too high the new roots will not thrive, and if too deep, the base of the plant may rot. If osmunda is used, pot firmly but not as hard as

Fig. 100 Left, the new growth appears from within a leaf axil of the mature growth. Right, the fuzzy root tips grow down among the pieces of crock in the bottom of the pot. These roots must not be allowed to become dry.

for Cattleyas. Mixed compost should be firmly tamped. After potting water only enough to keep the compost damp until new root growth begins. In the meantime, give the plants a light mist spray once a day—just enough to dampen the outer portions of the leaves and not so heavily as to allow water to collect in the leaf axils. Water standing in the leaf axils encourages bacterial infection. (See page 271.) The plants will become re-established in about three months.

Water. Since growth is continuous in this genus, and because the plants have no pseudobulbs, the potting medium should not be allowed to dry out. The frequency of watering depends so much on environmental conditions and on the type of medium used that it is difficult to give any set schedule. During bright weather two waterings a week may be sufficient, with longer intervals between waterings in dull weather. Misting the plants is usually not necessary except in very hot weather. Always water thoroughly so that water runs out of the bottom to flush out excess salts, for accumulation of salts is injurious to the roots.

Light. Paphiopedilums do best in diminished light. During the winter, when days are short and the light slants from the south, they need between 1000 and 1500 foot candles. As the days lengthen into spring, shading should be applied to cut the amount of light gradually down to 800 or 900 foot candles. In areas where summer heat is great, this may even be reduced to 700 foot candles. However, let the plants themselves be the guide. The foliage of the plain leaved species should be a good green; yellow-green shows they have too much light. The mottled-leaved species can be an even richer green.

Humidity. These plants require the same humidity as do Cattleyas. Good air circulation is a must. Excessive moisture on the leaves encourages disease.

Fertilizers. Paphiopedilum is perhaps more resentful of over-feeding than any other kind

Fig. 101 Water standing in the heart of the growths encourages a bacterial rot that can spread quickly through the plant. Note the blackened areas of the leaves in the center.

of orchid. If the salt content of the growing medium is too high, root growth is reduced or, in extreme cases, eliminated. In osmunda fiber no extra nutrients are required. This is one thing that makes osmunda fiber such an excellent medium for this genus; all you have to do to get fine root and top growth is to water properly. In mixed composts an occasional feeding with a 10-10-10 fertilizer may be beneficial, perhaps no more than once a month, with the pots thoroughly watered with plain water in between times. In straight fir bark, a 30-10-10 fertilizer is essential, given every other watering. Again, flush the pots thoroughly in between times. If root growth is lessened in any case where fertilizer is given, try reducing the frequency, perhaps giving an additional application of plain water in between times.

Propagation. Paphiopedilum is easily propagated by division, with three growths to a division. However, while this increases the number of plants of a kind, it does not usually increase the number of flowers from a group of plants. Plants may be allowed to become large specimens with many leads, which are extremely handsome. They actually need division only when the growths have extended out so far from the center of the plant that the center is empty of leaves. In such cases, the growing sections of the plant often separate themselves naturally, falling away from the old dead portion of the rhizome. When dividing a plant it is best to break the rhizome with your fingers rather than cut it. Just give the rhizome a quick twist to break it.

Growing Paphiopedilum from seed is not so easy as it is with other kinds. Part of the difficulty lies in a reluctance of the seed itself to germinate, and part in breeding the plants. Experts in growing Paphiopedilum from seed have used many and varied formulae for germination. The problems and methods are discussed below.

The Species

The genus is divided into three sections according to certain features of the flowers.

Section I has flowers nearly round, made so by the large, round petals. All have mottled leaves and require somewhat warmer temperatures than the plain-leaved species.

Section II has elongated, slender petals, and a plain pouch with the top not eared. All have plain green leaves and require cool treatment.

Section III has the pouch eared or notched on the posterior edges. Plants with both mottled and plain leaves are represented.

Section I

Paphiopedilum bellatulum. This species is attractive for its foliage as well as for its charming flowers. The leaves are up to ten inches long and are three and one-half inches wide. They are deep green, mottled with lighter

green on the upper surface, purplish underneath. The flower is round, shaped like a deep saucer, with the almost egg-shaped lip backed by the broad petals. They are white to pale yellow marked with purple spots, which run nearly into lines on the dorsal sepal, and which are smaller on the lip. The species occurs in China and flowers in the summer.

Paphiopedilum delenatii. This beautiful little plant has oval leaves that are dark green mottled with light green above, light green mottled with red-violet underneath. The rounded flowers have an oval, pointed dorsal sepal that is velvety on the back and margins, white flushed with rose, and round white petals. The spherical lip is white and rose, lightly flushed with lavender. Occurs in Indo-China. Flowers in late winter and early spring.

Paphiopedilum godefroyae. This small species has leaves six inches long by one and one-half inches wide. They are mottled green on the upper surface, and green spotted with brown-purple underneath. The short flower stem bears one or two white or pale yellow flowers that are lightly spotted with magenta. The petals are oval and point downward. The species occurs in Cochin-China and flowers in the summer.

Paphiopedilum concolor. The plants are about the same size as *P. godefroyae,* with leaves mottled green on their upper surface and spotted with deep crimson below. The flowers are yellow, spotted with purple. The dorsal sepal is concave and almost round, and the broad petals point downward. The paler lip is nearly cylindric and somewhat flattened on the sides. The species grows in Moulmein. It blossoms in the fall.

Paphiopedilum niveum. The plants are about the same size as the two preceding species, with the foliage strikingly colored, green mottled with gray-green above and brilliant purple underneath. The flowers are white with a scattering of purple dots, and the dorsal sepal is red on the back. The edges of the flower are prettily waved. This species occurs naturally in the Loncavi and Tambilan Islands. The flowers appear in the spring.

Section II

Paphiopedilum praestans. The striking flowers are large and brightly colored. The two-inch tall dorsal sepal is whitish, decorated with sharp lines of purple. The spirally twisted petals are yellowish, veined with brown, and are about five inches long. They have hair-bearing warts on their margins. The lip is rather long, somewhat flattened on the sides, and is shiny yellow, suffused with red. A native of New Guinea, it flowers in August.

Paphiopedilum rothschildianum. A handsome species, the plants have two-foot long, green leaves, and a spike that may bear several flowers. The flowers are stunningly colored. The dorsal and lateral sepals are yellow striped with black-purple. The fused lateral sepals in this species are larger than in many others and give the effect of a mirror image of the dorsal. The long, slender petals extend five inches and are pale green, spotted with purple, distinctly lined or nerved with dark green. The long lip is purple, veined with a darker shade and yellow toward the top. It stands sharply forward. A native of Borneo and Sumatra, it flowers in the winter.

Paphiopedilum sanderianum. This is a remarkable species. The petals are one and one-half feet long, twisted, pale yellow, barred and spotted with purple. The dorsal sepal is narrow and pointed, yellow-green with brown stripes. The long, projecting lip is brown-purple and yellow. It occurs in the Malay Archipelago, and flowers in early spring.

Paphiopedilum stonei. Three to five stunning flowers are borne on a stem. The dorsal sepal is white, trimmed with two or three crimson streaks and the lateral sepals almost equal it in size. The twisted petals are five to six inches long, tawny with crimson spots for two-thirds of the length, and solid crimson at the end. The lip is rose, reticulated with crimson; the upper sides fold in and are white. This species is from Borneo and flowers in the fall.

Section III

Paphiopedilum argus. This species has distinctive, medium-sized flowers. The dorsal sepal is oval and pointed, white striped with green, or sometimes with both green and purple. Occasionally it is spotted with blackish purple at its base. The wavy petals have a white ground with green veins for two-thirds of their length, and clear purple tips. Blackish warts decorate the inner surface of the petals. The lip is brownish purple, green underneath, and the narrow, infolded lobes are light purple spotted with a deeper shade. The foliage is mottled. Native to Luzon, it flowers in April.

Paphiopedilum barbatum. An attractive species whose deep purple tones often approach red. The nearly round dorsal sepal is folded at the midvein. It is white, green at the base, stained and striped with purple. The petals, which bear blackish warts on their upper edges, are brownish green at the base changing to purple at the tip. The lip is deep brownish purple. The foliage is mottled. It occurs in the Malay Peninsula and usually flowers in the summer.

Paphiopedilum callosum. Beautiful, large flowers, noted for their huge dorsal sepal, which may be three inches across. It is folded at the midvein and somewhat wavy at the top, white, with alternately long and short veins changing from purple at the base to green above. The petals are pale green with purple tips and have a sprinkling of blacklish warts on the upper margin. The brownish purple lip is green beneath. The foliage is mottled. A native of Siam, it flowers in the spring.

Paphiopedilum charlesworthii. This is a charming species with mottled foliage and medium-sized flowers. The large and spreading dorsal sepal is white, suffused and spotted with rose-purple. The petals are yellow-green, reticulated with brown, and the lip is rosy-purple. It occurs in Bengal. The blossoms appear in the fall.

Paphiopedilum dayanum. An attractive species with mottled foliage it produces slender flowers on a long stem. The dorsal sepal is prettily shaped, with the lower sides folded back and the upper edges folded forward to form a point at the top. It is white with green veins. The long, slender petals are greenish brown changing to rose purple. The slender lip is somewhat pointed at the tip, brownish purple, veined with green. The plants are native to Borneo. Flowers appear in May and June.

Paphiopedilum exul. The lightly marbled foliage is bordered with white. The yellow-green dorsal sepal has a white margin and brown spots. The petals and lip are yellow with faint brown markings. This species occurs in Siam.

Paphiopedilum fairieanum. Small plants with light green leaves have attractive, medium-sized flowers. The nearly round dorsal sepal is large in proportion to the size of the flower, with an undulating margin. It is greenish white, reticulated with violet. The upward-curving petals are yellow to white, streaked with purple, bearing tufts of hairs on their wavy margins. The smallish lip is green and white. It occurs in Assam and flowers in the fall.

Paphiopedilum hirsutissimum. Large, dark colored, hairy flowers make this a striking species. The roundish dorsal sepal is heavily marked with black-purple and bordered with green. The petals are slender near their base, wider toward the end, and somewhat twisted. They are mottled with deep purple on a green ground near the base, becoming bright purple at the tip. The deep green lip is tinged with purple. The foliage is plain green. The plant is native to Assam. It flowers in the spring.

Paphiopedilum insigne. This is the easiest to grow and one of the most popular of the genus. It appears everywhere, in collections and in the florist's show window. Perhaps its most attractive feature is the shiny appearance of the flowers; they almost look as if they had been varnished. The broad, oval dorsal sepal has the top turned slightly forward. The central part is apple green, spotted with purple along the darker green veins, and the upper part is white. The wavy petals are pale yellow-green, veined with brown. The lip is also yellow-green, suffused with brown. The species occurs in Nepal and Assam. It produces flowers in the winter. *Paphiopedilum insigne* has many

named varieties, of which the variety 'Harefield Hall' has proved to be outstanding both in itself and as a parent of hybrids. This form is larger than the type, and recent studies have shown it to be a natural triploid (having three times the usual haploid number of chromosomes). The standard chromosome number of Paphiopedilum is twenty-six in the vegetative cell, thirteen in the reproductive cells. 'Harefield Hall' has thirty-nine, or three times thirteen.

Paphiopedilum lawrenceanum. This handsome species has mottled yellow-green foliage and large flowers. The beautiful dorsal sepal is nearly round, white with deep purple, flame-shaped veins reaching nearly to the tip. The straight, veined petals are green with purple tips, and both margins carry black warts. The lip is dull purple, tinged with brown and green. It occurs in Borneo and flowers from April to July.

Paphiopedilum lowii. Quite an unusual species, it produces three to six dainty flowers on a long nodding stem. The leaves are light green. The flower parts are slender. The oar-shaped petals are yellow with black spots toward the base, violet at the outer ends. The dorsal sepal is slender at its base, spreading at the top, yellow-green, veined with brownish purple. The lip is brown. This native of Borneo could equally well be included in Section II. It tends to be epiphytic rather than terrestrial, and needs especially good aeration. The blossoms appear in the summer.

Paphiopedilum spicerianum. These medium-sized flowers are distinguished for the large dorsal sepal which is markedly wider than it is tall, yet is folded in a turret-like manner. The foliage is dark green. The dorsal sepal is white, with a simple crimson-purple band down the center. Its basal region is green, spotted with red. The petals have wavy margins and are pale green spotted and striped with purple. The lip is rather long, dull purple marked with green. One of the important ancestors of our modern hybrids, it occurs in Assam. The plants are in blossom from October to December.

Paphiopedilum venustum. This species has rather short leaves which are marbled with gray-green on the upper surface, and mottled with dull purple underneath. The flowers, which are produced singly on a tall stem, have a heart-shaped dorsal sepal that is white with dark green veins. The petals have the basal part green with dark warts, and the outer portion dull brownish-purple. The pale yellow lip is tinted with rose, veined and netted with brown. The plants are native to Northeast India, and blossom in late winter and spring.

Paphiopedilum villosum. Large, glossy, hairy flowers are produced on rather large plants whose leaves are green above, purple spotted beneath. The dorsal sepal is brownish purple with a green tip. The longish petals are wavy, yellowish brown with a prominent central band of purple. The lip is brownish yellow. *Paphiopedilum villosum* var. *Boxallii* is sometimes given as a separate species. In this the dorsal sepal is marked in the center with numerous black spots. Var. *Boxallii* has been a frequent parent of hybrids. Flowers in January and February. This species, which occurs in Moulmein, has also been found growing as an epiphyte.

■ GROWING PAPHIOPEDILUM FROM SEED

When a group of species as distinct and as beautiful as the Paphiopedilums displays itself before you, you cannot down the urge to make hybrids with them. Growers have long worked to blend the best features of several into new combinations, and there are today some stunning hybrids. But the casual observer cannot know the patient work and the many disappointments that lie behind the flower he sees.

The first Paphiopedilum hybrid was made in 1869, a cross between *Paph. barbatum* and *Paph. villosum.* Since then, many successful hybrids have appeared, of which one of the most famous is Paph. Maudiae, the so-called green orchid. Its parentage is *Paph. callosum* var. *Sanderae* × *Paph. lawrenceanum* var. *Hyeanum.*

A number of difficulties exist in the breeding of Paphiopedilum hybrids. A great deal of effort has gone into the making of crosses in this genus, with less relative success than with other genera. Many of the beautiful hybrids shown today are almost sole survivors of the matings that made them. In the first place, the hybrids are frequently partially or entirely sterile, according to their genetic make-up. This means that often only a small amount of viable seed is produced. In the second place, Paphiopedilum seed is hard to germinate, so that much good seed never results in seedlings.

This does not mean that an amateur cannot breed Paphiopedilums, for he may hit on a combination that gives a fair amount of good seed. But even if he achieves only a few plants for his effort, he will be rewarded by a justifiable thrill at success under such challenging circumstances.

The pollen of Paphiopedilums does not keep as well as most pollen. Hence it should be used shortly after it has been removed from the two anthers. A toothpick can be used to transfer the granular pollen directly to the stigma.

A seed pod matures in approximately nine to eleven months, occasionally in a shorter or longer time. The technique used for sowing the flasks is essentially the same as that described for Cattleya. Calcium hypochlorite solution is usually used as the disinfecting agent. The coat of Paphiopedilum seed is unusually hard and moreover is protected by hairs which make it more difficult to wet with a disinfecting agent. Some workers add a drop or two of a wetting agent, such as Santomerse, to the 140 c.c. of hypochlorite solution to aid its penetration. The exposure to the disinfecting solution is ten to twenty minutes.

A good growing medium is Knudson's "C" solution, with the addition of .05 gram of peptone to one liter of the agar-nutrient mixture. The *p*H should be adjusted to 6 to give the more nearly neutral conditions suited to Paphiopedilum. Daniel Hill offers a prepared medium for Paphiopedilum.

Often out of a large number of seed sown, only a scant few ever germinate. Paphiopedilum experts have germinated several hundred from a single pod, and an occasional amateur has been so fortunate. Contrast this, however, with the many thousands obtainable from almost any Cattleya cross. Sometimes seeds germinate after months or even years, but it is almost impossible to maintain the proper growing conditions over such long periods. It is, therefore, suggested that a generous amount of seed be sown in each flask.

The reluctant germination suggests the possibility of the presence of an inhibitor in the seed. Burgeff used a soaking technique which improved the percentage of germination. He allowed the seed to stand in sterile water for two weeks to two months before sowing it in the flasks. His growing medium differed slightly from Knudson's "C," and he kept the flasks in the dark until the embryos began to lengthen.

Using unripe seed is another method suggested to improve germination. The pod is removed from the plant just before it is ready to split open. Have the flasks ready to receive the seed. Dip the pod in a solution of one part of Clorox to nine of water. Then slit it open with a sterile knife, and transfer the seed directly to the flasks by means of a sterile platinum loop. If desired, the seed may first be removed to a tube of sterile water, and then sown either with a loop or a pipette (dropper). This method is known as the green pod method and is described on page 122.

Obviously, one method of getting better germination would be to obtain a higher percentage of good seed from the cross. And here is your chance to experiment. As will be seen below, chromosomal aberrations are the cause of a good bit of partial or complete sterility in Paphiopedilum. Abnormalities in the reproductive cells may cause any one of the following kinds of incompatibility. The pollen may fail to produce pollen tubes, or the tubes may not grow long enough to reach the ovary. If they reach the ovary, they may fail to penetrate the ovules. Perhaps the growth of the pollen tubes is so slow that the ovules degenerate before the tubes reach them. Even

after penetration of the ovules, the reproductive cells may not be able to unite. Sometimes, after the reproductive cells have united, an embryo fails to develop.

There is little you can do in a mechanical way about such incompatibilities as the last two mentioned. But research on other types of plants that have difficulty in setting seed suggest a few tricks to try on Paphiopedilums. As far as I know, they have not been tried on orchids. Supposing that the cross you particularly want to make has failed because of the undue length of time it takes the pollen tubes to reach the ovules, or suppose that seed is formed only in the apex by the first tubes to reach the ovary, the others being too slow in growing down. You might try bud pollination, which has been successful in some other cases. The flower to be pollinated is opened while still in the bud stage and the pollen placed on the stigma. The extra time gained may be just the critical difference between success and failure of the cross.

Another method to try is the application of a growth promoting substance to the ovary. Mix thoroughly one gram of naphthalene acetamide with ninety-nine grams of lanolin. Smear a small amount of this on the base of the ovary at the time of pollination. Its stimulating effect may enable seed to be formed where it might not otherwise develop.

■ INHERITANCE IN PAPHIOPEDILUM

Crosses between certain species have produced hybrids that have proved fairly fertile, and these have been fruitful in the production of other hybrids. Crosses between certain other species have often given hybrids that are almost or entirely sterile. With great patience, breeders have obtained some offspring from the nearly sterile hybrids, as few as a dozen seedlings at times. Thus out of the tremendous numbers of hybrids given in Sanders' "Complete List of Orchid Hybrids" a great many represent crosses from which but few plants were raised. A quick perusal of Sanders' listings gives a very striking introduction to the problems that have been involved in breeding. Under the names of some hybrids there appear long lists of other hybrids made with these parents. Under the names of others but one or two further crosses appear, indicating that these were not fruitful parents. Some of the hybrid names never again appear in the lists, indicating either that these were sterile or were not desirable enough to have been used. A few of the sterile hybrids have come down to us through vegetative propagation, or even by repetition of the crosses that produced them, because they were such lovely things. An example is P. Maudiae, an unsatisfactory parent but a very popular plant.

The problems in breeding stem partly from the range of chromosome numbers among the species, and partly from incompatibility even among some species with the same chromosome number. Among the chromosome numbers there are represented 26, 28, 30, 32, 34, 36, 40, 42, and the gametes from these species would contain 13, 14, 15, 16, 17, 18, 20, and 21. The natural triploid, *P. insigne* 'Harefield Hall' has 39 chromosomes, and can produce gametes of 13 and 26 chromosomes.

Species which have 26 chromosomes are: *bellatulum, charlesworthii, delenatii, druryi, exul, fairrieanum, hirsutissimum, insigne, niveum, stonei, villosum,* and *villosum* var. *Boxallii.* Increasing in chromosome numbers we have *rothschildianum* with either 26 or 28; *praestans* with 28; *spicerianum* with 30, occasionally 28; *callosum* with 32 (and a number of other species, not described in this chapter, with 32); *dayanum* with 34; *lawrenceanum* with 36 and occasionally 40; and *venustum* with 42.

The greatest numbers of modern hybrids have come from the species *insigne, villosum, villosum* var. *Boxallii,* and *spicerianum,* with *bellatulum* also entering into the line. Although *spicerianum* has 30 chromosomes, 4 more than the others, which have 26, these species are quite compatible. Aneuploidy naturally has resulted among the hybrids. Many polyploids also have appeared, having arisen from non-

reduced gametes or by a doubling of the chromosome number in some other way during the process of seed formation (see Chapter 8). R. E. Duncan reported the following ranges of chromosome numbers among hybrids: diploid and near-diploid, 26, 27, 28, 29, and 30; triploid and near-triploid, 39, 40, 41, and 42; tetraploid and near-tetraploid, 52, 53, 54, 55, and 56; and one near-pentaploid with 70. The usual reduction of fertility that accompanies polyploidy, and which is further reduced by aneuploidy, is, in the case of the Paphiopedilums, additionally reduced by low pollen fertility. Often pollen grains that appear to be normal fail to make tubes and thus cannot function. When we say, therefore, that hybrids from this group of species are fairly fertile, we mean that they are fertile by comparison with the far less fertile hybrids from other groups of species.

Analysis of the chromosome types (shape, size, etc.) of the various species has enabled cyto-geneticists to follow the behavior of these chromosomes in relation to each other when sets from different species are present in the hybrids, and to see what happens to them during reduction division. Failure to pair, is, of course, the chief reason for the production of many non-functional reproductive cells. However, it was found that in the primary hybrids among *insigne, villosum,* and *spicerianum* the assortment of chromosomes frequently resulted in distribution of a basic set to the reproductive cells, which then could be functional. Chromosome counts on the progeny from these primary hybrids revealed that reproductive cells with thirteen and fourteen chromosomes had indeed functioned. Such analyses were made upon P. Leeanum (*insigne* × *spicerianum*) and P. Lathamianum (*villosum* × *spicerianum*), primary hybrids that were the start of the modern hybrids, and which appear many times in the breeding lines. The contribution of the extra chromosome by gametes bearing fourteen allows succeeding generations to build up their chromosome number by adding an extra chromosome here and there, accounting for the aneuploid numbers found among the hybrids.

When non-reduced gametes function, these may also carry an extra chromosome or two to the polyploid offspring.

As is true in all species, there is a great amount of variation in color and form to be found among the members of the Paphiopedilum species. For instance, in a species which has characteristic spotting, there are forms which are heavily spotted and forms which are spotted only lightly and some not at all. In species that have characteristic red or purple coloring there are rare forms without the red or purple coloring; these are green or pure white. Unfortunately, both the green and white forms are called "albino," and in reading about these forms one must know whether reference is had to "green albinos" or "white albinos." A new term is badly needed here.

Inheritance of color in Paphiopedilum is not clearly worked out, but it is a very difficult field. C. C. Hurst, who worked out the white inheritance in Cattleya (see Chapter 8) found that the green and white types in Paphiopedilum both seem to follow a pattern similar to that of the white Cattleyas. Apparently the red and purple pigment depend on the presence of the dominant C and R genes, and pure green or white can show up only when either or both pairs of these genes is recessive. Included in this group of so-called albinos is the yellow *P. insigne* var. *Sanderae,* which seems to behave similarly.

Certain features of the species, the color patterns in dorsal sepal and petals, the shape of the parts, etc., are perhaps incompletely dominant. Traces of a feature from this species and that are found in hybrid individuals, often combined with, or superimposed upon, other features. Such fine blendings occur in some of the modern hybrids that it would be difficult to say which feature came from which species. However, these features show up more strongly in some individuals in any cross, and in almost any group of Paphiopedilum hybrids one can at a glance pick out flowers that strongly exhibit the characteristics of one ancestor or another.

Mrs. L. Sherman Adams carried out a de-tailed study of *Paphiopedilum insigne, villosum, spicerianum,* and *bellatulum*—the four species most influential in the formation of the modern hybrids. By modern hybrids we mean the round, compact type chosen as the ideal for Paphiopedilum, and sought in the breeding work being done at present. Mrs. Adams included in her study the influence of these species in their earlier hybrids and in a modern hybrid descended from this group. Her findings were presented in a series of nine articles in the American Orchid Society Bulletin from January to September, 1954. The modern hybrid chosen was Clementine Churchill (Festivity × Lewis Crampton). This cross involved the repeated use of the species, both directly and by means of their earlier hybrids, to a total of something like 76 crosses before the final Clementine Churchill was reached. In this array, *insigne* is represented 34 times, *villosum* 5 times, *villosum* var. *Boxallii* 23 times, *spicerianum* 25 times, and *bellatulum* once.

We felt it would be of value to see how the characters of the various species showed up in individual flowers of Clementine Churchill, and prevailed upon Mrs. Adams to select examples for us from her huge collection of koda-chromes. Costs prevent giving these in color, but much can be seen in the black and whites.

In the accompanying display, Figure 102, each of the four species is given along with two members of the hybrid which show its influence. The flower to the immediate right of the species in each case is one which more nearly approaches the type of the earlier hybrids, which might be considered intermediate in form between the species, and the "modern" type shown at the far right. This cross is in itself almost a survey of the history of hybridization in Paphiopedilum.

A, B, and C, of Fig. 102, trace the influence of *villosum*. A is *villosum* 'Cornell #11,' characterized by a tall slender dorsal sepal, curved back at its lower sides. The marking on the dorsal sepal consists of a network of reddish lines, laid on a green ground which extends somewhat beyond the network of lines. The sepal is edged by a fine border of white, not

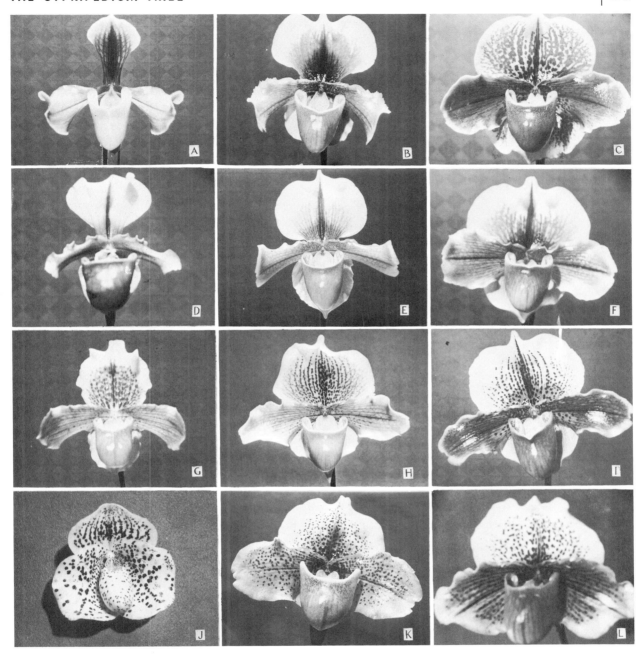

Fig. 102 Series showing the influence of the four species that make up the hybrid Clementine Churchill. A, *Paph. villosum*, B and C, members of the hybrid in which its influence is shown. D, *Paph. spicerianum*; E and F, individuals of the hybrid in which its influence is strong. G. *Paph. insigne*, H and I, flowers which show its influence. J, *Paph. bellatulum*, K and L, individuals which show its influence. In each case the flower to the immediate right of the species is a type that approaches the earlier hybrid style, more full than the species, but not so round and compact as the type preferred at present. The flowers at the far right more nearly approach the ideal "modern" type. (From kodachromes, courtesy of Mrs. L. Sherman Adams)

apparent in this picture. The petals widen out from a narrower base, curving forward in a pronounced fashion, and are broadly waved at the edge. They are bi-color, having the upper half red and the lower half green, the two halves divided by a prominent dark line, and they have a distinct notch at the tip. The pouch is long and narrow, flaring at the top and with long lobes. B, Clementine Churchill #7, shows the *villosum* influence in the markings of the dorsal sepal. The green ground has been lost through the influence of *spicerianum*, so that the markings show up as clear red. The petals have the *villosum* stance, flared outer ends, and dark mid-vein, but show the finer marginal waving of *spicerianum* and *insigne*. With the suppression of green in the flower, the petals have become almost solid red. The pouch shows the flaring of the upper portion and the long lobes of *villosum*. C is Clementine Churchill #61. The dorsal sepal shows a combination of influences. The coloring is exhibited as broken lines or coalesced spots, the influence of the *insigne* pattern upon the *villosum* pattern, while the dark center line comes from *spicerianum*. The petals are broad and flat as in *insigne*, with the *insigne* markings and marginal waving, but they have the notch at the tip that comes from *villosum*. This notch is apparent in almost all of the flowers shown on this page. The pouch, while broadened by the influence of the other species, still has something of the flared shape of *villosum*.

D, E, and F trace the influence of *spicerianum*. D is *spicerianum* 'Babson' with its tall, white dorsal sepal, much broader than it looks because it folds sharply on each side. It has a strong center line of red, and a faint area of green at its base. The petals are rather short and narrow, finely ruffled on the upper edge, and curved slightly forward. The pouch is somewhat blunt. E shows Clementine Churchill #62, which is strongly *spicerianum* both in shape and in the dark center line. The basal markings of the dorsal sepal have been increased somewhat by *villosum*, and spread from green at the base to red at the tips. The petals are a combination of *insigne* and *spicer-*

ianum, with a bit of *villosum* in the dark center line and notch. The pouch is more like that of *villosum* than of *spicerianum*. F is Clementine Churchill # 27, in which the dorsal sepal is still strongly *spicerianum* but with more of the *villosum* markings. The petals approach *insigne* quite strongly, but still have something of *spicerianum* and *villosum*. In coloring the petals have reverted to the bi-color type of *villosum*. The pouch is quite close to *spicerianum*.

G, H, and I show *insigne* and flowers in which its influence is strong. G is *insigne*, characterized by a flat rounded dorsal sepal which has two folds at the tip. It has a green central portion and a broad white border. Within the green ground it is marked by raised spots of reddish brown, arranged over obscure lines. The petals are flat and almost straight, with a slight ruffling at the edges, and a few spots arranged on reticulated lines. The pouch is round, slightly pinched in toward the top and with short lobes. H is Clementine Churchill #108, in which the general pattern and coloring of *insigne* are quite pronounced. The spotting of the dorsal sepal is more refined, and spreads a little closer to the border. The petals are very close to *insigne*, and, while the pouch is a bit more flared, it comes closer to *insigne* than to any of the others. I is Clementine Churchill #70, in which the overall aspect is again very much like that of *insigne*. The concentration of spots in the center of the dorsal sepal suggests the center line of *spicerianum*, and the pouch is quite like *villosum*.

J, K, and L show *bellatulum* and its influence. J is *bellatulum*, with its extremely rounded parts, covered with spots that show a hint of a pattern only in the dorsal sepal. It is entirely white except for the spots, which are purple. The little pouch is long and almost closed. Although this species appeared but once in the long and involved history of this cross, it is interesting to see that there are a number of Clementine Churchills that show its influence strongly. K is Clementine Churchill #115, which has the overall spotting of *bellatulum* in addition to the squat dorsal sepal and the short, broad petals. The pouch shape is not carried over here. L is Clementine Churchill #39, showing even more of the *bellatulum* influence, even to the long, rounded pouch. The petals, however, although much rounded, are spotted on a pattern of lines reminiscent of *insigne*. Neither K or L has the all-white ground of *bellatulum*, both having red and green in the petals and pouch.

PHRAGMIPEDIUM AND SELENIPEDIUM

Phragmipedium, one of the South American genera of the Cypripedium tribe, has about eleven species. It differs from Paphiopedilum in that the dorsal sepal is more or less like the petals, and the edges of the lip are infolded giving it a more slipper-like appearance. An important botanical difference is that the flowers are deciduous. They may be grown with plenty of heat and moisture from March to November, shaded from the direct rays of the sun. Osmunda fiber with a little leaf mold mixed in is a good compost, and it should be allowed to rise above the rim of the pot. The pot should have good drainage. After potting, keep on the dry side until growth starts.

Phragmipedium caudatum. Rather stiff, upright leaves, and flower stems one to two feet tall. Remarkable for its long, ribbon-like petals which grow to a length of three feet. The petals are yellow shaded with brown and tinted with crimson toward the tips. The dorsal sepal is slender and wavy, about six inches long, pale yellow veined with green. The species occurs in Peru.

Phragmipedium sargentianum. The leaves are tufted, six to eight inches long, with golden margins. The flower stem bears two or three blooms. The oval dorsal sepal is pale yellow with red veins. The petals are slightly longer, twisted at the ends, yellow with red margins and veins. The lip is rather long, also yellow marked with red. The plant occurs in Brazil.

Selenipedium, the other South American genus of the Cypripedium tribe, is so similar to Phragmipedium that it is included by many botanists in the latter genus. Some of the species given under Phragmipedium may therefore sometimes be found classified as Selenipedium. Selenipediums are often too large to be adaptable to small greenhouses, for example, *Selen. chica* of Panama reaches twelve to fifteen feet in height.

CYPRIPEDIUM

These are the moccasin-flowers or ladyslippers of our woods and moist meadows. They may be transplanted to our gardens if the new locality is made to imitate their native spot. There are about thirty species. Like the other members of the tribe, these are becoming less numerous with the passing years. Man probably has something to do with this, by using for himself the sunny areas where the plants would do best, so that they are forced to exist in the woods. They are sun-loving plants and do not grow so well in heavy shade. Lovers of these plants ask that instead of removing the wild clumps to your garden, plants be purchased from nurseries. The latter may even do better for you, for they will have been adapted to garden conditions.

These native Cypripediums require plenty of moisture. A dam built around their bed will help to retain water. They do best with some shade at noon.

Cypripedium acaule. Pink moccasin-flower. The single flower grows on a rather tall stem. The color is usually pale pink with deeper veining, but deep pink with light veins and pure white are also found. The lip is closed except for a slit in front. This species requires an acid soil and is the most difficult to grow. Often it lasts for a year or two and then dies out. It should be aided by the addition to the soil of such acid material as pine needles. It grows naturally from Newfoundland to North Carolina, and west to the Great Lakes region. The blossoms appear in May and June.

Cypripedium californicum. Tall plants produce leaves alternately on the stem. From six to twelve flowers occur about an inch apart on the stem. They are small, with green sepals and petals and a white lip. The species is native to California.

Cypripedium candidum. The green flowers have a pretty lip that is white, striped inside with purple. The plant is found in New York, Pennsylvania, Minnesota, Missouri, and Kentucky.

Cypripedium montanum. This handsome, fragrant species grows rather tall. One to three flowers are produced on a stem. The petals are wavy-twisted, dull brown, and the lip is whitish veined with purple. It is found from California to Washington.

Cypripedium parviflorum. The beautiful yellow ladyslipper, one of the most handsome of the species and the easiest to grow. The whole flower is bright yellow, with narrow, somewhat wavy petals and a wider dorsal sepal. In culture it requires a porous neutral soil, with plenty of moisture and some shade. It can be found almost everywhere from Kansas eastward.

Cypripedium pubescens. This species is also given as a variety of *Cyp. parviflorum.* Its flowers are similar but a little larger. The roots and rhizomes have some medicinal properties.

Cypripedium reginae, or *Cypripedium spectabile,* is truly named the "Queen" ladyslipper. It is tall and robust and produces a wealth of large flowers. The white sepals and petals are set off by the rosy shades of the lip. It requires a sunny spot in the garden and moist, neutral soil. The plant occurs from Maine to the Middle West and flowers in June.

16 | *The Dendrobium Tribe*

THE Dendrobium tribe includes the marvelous genus Dendrobium and a few genera of definitely lesser importance. The name is derived from *dendro,* tree, and *bios,* life.

DENDROBIUM

Dendrobiums, which have been loved by amateurs for a hundred years, are enjoying perhaps their greatest degree of popularity right now. From their native lands, where they have always been appreciated, they have been brought first to Europe, and more recently to Hawaii and to the mainland states. We are now benefiting from the loving care and interest bestowed upon them by the growers who have made them a specialty, and who have not only nurtured the species but have created a fascinating succession of hybrids. The Hawaiian growers, especially in recent years, have done intriguing things with the Dendrobiums, as they have with the Vandas and their relatives.

The very size of the genus Dendrobium, with its 1000 species, promises variety, both in size and character of the plants and of the flowers and the manner in which they are produced. There are kinds which give erect or arching sprays of five to twenty flowers, kinds which give drooping sprays of a dozen to a hundred blooms, and still others in which almost the entire length of the pseudobulb bears clusters of two or three flowers at each node so that it becomes a cascade of flowers. The individual flowers are often small, but all are perky or dainty, often of a glistening crystalline texture or velvety softness. The colors are rich, ranging from rose and violet tones, occasionally almost to red, to the most brilliant of yellow and gold. Some species are white.

The plants range in size from miniatures with little wiry or squat pseudobulbs, to a large group of robust species with pseudobulbs from a foot to three feet in height, and on up to kinds that have stems six to eight feet long. Among these are some whose stems bear three to five leaves at the top nodes only, and others whose stems are leafy for almost their entire length. There are deciduous species which lose their leaves the first or second year, and evergreen species which keep their leaves for three or four years. Except for a few in which the stems are truly pseudobulbous, most of them have rather slender, jointed stems that resemble canes. All are epiphytic and all make

Fig. 103 Apparently made of pure sunshine, the sparkling flowers of *Dendrobium densiflorum* are of crystalline texture with a soft fringe around the deeper yellow lip.

new growths each year from a rhizome. The growths come close together so that a plant with many stems springs from rather a small basal area.

The flowers are characterized by a "chin" or mentum formed by the joining of the lateral sepals to the foot of the column. In some the base of the fused sepals forms a short spur covering the mentum. The dorsal sepal and the petals are free. The lip narrows at its base to a stalk that is attached to the base of the column foot. The side lobes of the lip usually enfold the short column, while the outer lobe is spreading, pointed or rounded, sometimes fringed. The flowers last for two to three weeks.

The genus ranges wild over western Asia and the Pacific Islands, from the Himalayas through Burma to the Malayan regions, Australia, New Zealand, New Guinea, China, Japan, and the Philippines. The variety of climatic conditions gives a variety of plant habits, and their cultural needs vary accordingly. Some grow where there is a warm season accompanied by heavy rains, followed by a season of cooler temperatures and little rain. Some come from regions that stay the same temperatures the year round, but where the rainfall is less heavy for part of the year. In some areas the rainfall stays about the same but the temperature cools off for part of the year. In other areas there is little change from "winter" to "summer." Because of such diversity of native habitat, the species have to be given somewhat individual treatment in a greenhouse. The reputation the Dendrobiums have earned, of being somewhat tricky to flower, is perhaps justified, because they need to have everything just right for them. However, the reason one may not flower may be simply that it wants less water after its growths are mature, while another would flower if it were put in a cooler place in the fall.

We shall try to group the species according to sets of conditions that seem most generally suitable. All Dendrobiums like good light, some requiring about the same amount as Cattleyas, others even more. All thrive with good air circulation. If, from among the groups as we shall list them, some species do not flower for you, try changing the conditions a bit. Move them to a brighter spot, or to one that runs a bit warmer or cooler than the rest of the greenhouse. You can judge the right amount of light by watching the development of the stems and leaves. If they are weak and thin, put the plant in a brighter spot and watch it plump up and spread its leaves during the next few weeks. After the growth is mature, some species need what is loosely spoken of as a "rest," a time during which its active growth is checked to harden the new growth and prepare the plant for flower production. This involves for some a combination of cooler temperatures and less water, for others merely cooler temperatures without a reduction of water, and for still others merely reduction of water while the temperature remains the same.

Group 1. Grow plants in this group with Cattleya temperatures, move to cool temperature and restrict watering after growths mature. *Dend. nobile, chrysanthum,* and *wardianum.* These are deciduous species. *Dend. nobile* does not lose its leaves until the second year, and it is these growths which produce flowers the second winter. *Dend. chrysanthum* and *wardianum* lose their leaves the first winter, before or during flowering. All three should be watered and fertilized generously while growing, have good light (*nobile* may not need quite as much as the other two), and temperatures 55° to 60° at night. In the fall, move them to a cool bright greenhouse with a night temperature of 50° (as for Cymbidiums). Cut down the frequency of watering, giving just enough to keep plants from shrivelling and cease fertilizing through the winter. After flower buds are well formed, resume normal watering until flowering is finished, and then keep on the dry side until new growths are well started. At this time move back to Cattleya temperatures and resume regular watering and fertilizing. If these species are not given "cool-dry" treatment in the fall, vegetative growths will form where flower buds should appear. These vegetative growths may be removed and potted separately when they start their own roots. Hybrids between *Dend. nobile* and species of Groups 1 and 2 require the "cool-dry" treatment also.

Group 2. Grow with Cattleyas all year round, but keep on the dry side after growths are made up in the fall. *Dend. anosmum, findlayanum, heterocarpum, parishii,* and *pierardii.* These also are deciduous species. They require a night temperature of 55° to 60° all year round. While the growth is developing and until it is mature, water generously and give ample fertilizer, plenty of light, and good air movement. In the fall, as the last leaf appears, restrict the watering (no fertilizer) to just enough to keep the plants from shrivelling, until flower buds have formed. Then water moderately through flowering and until the new growth (which sometimes starts at flow-

ering time) is well along. After the new growth sends out its own roots, resume more generous watering and start fertilizing again. If *Dend. findlayanum* does not flower for you after the first attempt, try keeping it closer to 55° the next winter. If *Dend. anosmum* does not flower, try it in a spot where the temperature does not go below 60° during the winter.

Group 3. Grow at Cattleya temperatures, move to cool greenhouse for the winter, but do not restrict watering. *Dend. aggregatum, chrysotoxum, densiflorum, farmeri, fimbriatum, moschatum,* and *thyrsiflorum.* These are evergreen and should not be allowed to dry out at any time of the year. From the time growth starts and until it is mature in the fall, keep them with Cattleyas, with the usual good light, water frequently enough to keep the medium moist, and fertilize as for other species. *Dend. moschatum* may like just a little shade in a bright Cattleya house, while the others may be able to take even more light than Cattleyas. Syringe the foliage frequently to control red spiders (and spray with a miticide as well) for they find these plants very attractive. In the fall, move to a place where they can be given nights of 50° but continue to water often enough to prevent drying. After flowering and until new growth starts the plants should be kept cool. After new growth starts, move them back to the Cattleya temperature range.

Group 4. Grow moderately cool, with winter nights close to 55°, not over 60°, summer nights close to 60° and summer days not extremely hot. Handle like Cattleyas as to water and light except give a short dry period after growth is made up. *Dend. dearei, formosum, lyonii, infundibulum, macrophyllum, sanderae, schuetzei.* These are evergreen species. They grow well with Cattleyas where Cattleyas are grown under moderately cool circumstances, but may not do well in the warmest parts of the United States, unless the grower has means for keeping down the temperatures.

Group 5. While this group does not like excessive heat and humidity, it prefers a little

Fig. 104 Two of the large flowered Dendrobiums. Upper, Dendrobium Millie Sander (*Dend. dearei* × *Dend. formosum*) is an example of the dearei type of hybrid. Note the long spur formed by the base of the petals. (Courtesy of Wm. Kirch) Lower, *Dendrobium phalaenopsis*, a cross between selected strains.

more heat than Group 4. Thus this group can be grown with Cattleyas almost anywhere, in a spot where the night temperature runs closer to 60°. If possible give them a bit more light than Cattleyas, with free air movement. *Dend. gouldii, stratiotes, taurinum, undulatum, veratrifolium.* These are evergreen species. Some growers grow all of them without a rest period. Others give a short period of lessened water to *Dend. taurinum, undulatum,* and *veratrifolium* as growth matures. If any of these species

seems not to be growing as vigorously as it should, or if the buds drop after they are well formed, put the plant in a spot where the night temperature does not go below 60°. The cultural conditions given here are suitable for hybrids between this group and *Dend. phalaenopsis, biggibum,* and *superbiens,* described below.

Group 6. Grow with night temperatures that run between 60° and 65°. *Dend. biggibum, phalaenopsis,* and *superbiens.* These are evergreen species. *Dend. phalaenopsis* and *superbiens* require restricted watering after growth is made up and until the flower spikes start, normal watering during flowering, and restricted watering again until new growth is well along. New growth sometimes does not start until late summer. During the time of restricted watering syringe the foliage frequently to keep the plant plump. *Dend. biggibum* does not require a drying off period, or at best it needs only a very brief one. These three species are frequently used in hybridization with those of Group 5. The hybrids in which *Dend. phalaenopsis* figures prominently are often referred to as "Dendrobium Phalaenopsis hybrids." A curious thing about these hybrids is that some of them are much more tolerant of shade than the species and will do well under conditions suitable for Phalaenopsis, that is, with about half the amount of light required by Cattleyas. Plants have performed nicely for me in an orchid case in the living room, although they have not reached the large size they can achieve in a greenhouse. These same plants grow poorly in our Cattleya house in which the night temperature rarely reaches 60° in the winter, remaining close to 55°.

■ GENERAL CULTURE

Potting and dividing. Dendrobiums may be grown in osmunda, a good medium because it gives their fine, wiry roots a firm foothold and tends to hold the sometimes top-heavy plants in place very well. They may also be grown in bark if they are carefully staked. Some growers like to plant them on tree fern logs or slabs, from which they do not have to be removed for a number of years. Some of the deciduous species develop very long stems which cannot hold themselves upright and which therefore grow in a pendant manner. These are best grown in baskets of osmunda or tree fern fiber, or on tree fern logs, or on slabs to which a chunk of osmunda fiber is first wired. Such containers are hung from the top of the greenhouse to give the stems room and light. A few, such as *Dend. chrysanthum* which would drag the tips of its stems on the floor of the average small greenhouse, may be tied along one side of the greenhouse with a loop of string about every two feet of their length.

Dendrobiums may be divided like other sympodial plants. It is best to wait until the new growths have started. Re-potting and dividing should be done just as new roots show or just before they make their appearance. The evergreen species should be divided to retain three or four older stems along with the new lead. In some kinds the old stems flower for several successive years. In the deciduous species, after a stem has flowered it begins to shrivel and is then no longer of use to the plant. These shrivelled stems should be cut off. Be sure that you do not remove them until they have flowered, or their chance to flower is past (*Dend. nobile*, for instance, flowers on growths made the previous year, that is, the flowers come the second winter rather than the winter after the growth is made). Divisions consist of the new growth and the stem from which it arises. The old stem may be removed after it has flowered and the new growth is well along.

As with other orchids, there is no need to divide a plant as long as it is doing well and gives a nice show with several leads flowering at once. The deciduous species are often grown to plants with dozens of leads in one container. It is even possible to plant several divisions in the same container to give a spectacular showing.

Small plantlets that develop along the older stems of both evergreen and deciduous species may be separated from the stem as soon as their own roots start. When put in their own pots, these grow rapidly, sometimes flowering the first year. Old stems, after flowering, may be cut into sections between the nodes and placed on damp sphagnum moss (or a fine bark and sand mix) in order to encourage plantlets to develop.

In general, Dendrobiums do not need as large pots for their size as do many kinds. Their roots are fine and wiry, and they do not grow to any great length. However, plants with many leads will need larger pots than those with one or two leads. A four or five inch pot should accommodate a plant with four or five leads. After potting, wait for roots from the new leads before watering regularly. In the meantime spray the foliage and the surface of the potting medium, using a fine mist.

Dendrobiums from seed. Dendrobium seed germinates readily and the seedlings grow rapidly. The largest numbers of hybrids come from *Dend. nobile* and its relatives (Groups 1

Fig. 105 A young plant growing on the pseudobulb that produced the season's flowers. The plantlet may be removed and potted by itself.

and 2), and *Dend. phalaenopsis* and its relatives with the ceratobium section, Groups 5 and 6. Another group of hybrids stems from intercrossing *Dend. dearei, formosum, infundibulum, sanderae,* and *schuetzii.* We should like to point out that the "cultural" groups as we set them up are not meant to follow the lines of botanical relationships, although for the most part they coincidentally do. The genus is divided botanically into sections and sub-sections too numerous to give here. Hybrids in general have been made within the botanical groups. In other words, it has been found that species that are structurally related breed together more readily than species from groups less closely alike. However, there are instances where crosses have been successfully made between species in different botanical sections and sub-sections. For example, *Dend. macrophyllum* has been crossed with several members of the group to which *Dend. phalaenopsis* belongs; *Dend. dearei* has been crossed with Dend. farmeri, from a different section; and *Dend. sanderae* with *Dend. nobile,* again from a different section. Perhaps more such crosses will be tried in the future.

The Species

Dendrobium aggregatum. This charming dwarf species has little chunky four-jointed pseudobulbs bearing a single leaf. The flowers are very round, opening full and flat, with a squarish lip that is downy in the center. They are a delicate orange-yellow to pinkish-yellow, from ten to thirty on a drooping rounded spray. The plants occur in northern India, Burma, and southern China. They flower in the spring.

Dendrobium anosmum. This plant is also known as *Dend. superbum,* which is actually the name of one of its varieties. Richly colored, three-inch flowers of deep magenta with the heart shaped lip shading into purple at its base. They are produced in pairs from the upper nodes of the three-foot stems. The variety *superbum* has larger flowers and stems that reach five feet; its flowers are fragrant. The species is native to the warm regions in the Philippines. The flowers appear in the spring.

Dendrobium biggibum. Rather slender stems, eighteen inches in height, bear four to eight leaves at their upper nodes. The two inch flowers are rich magenta, trimmed with a white crest in the center of the notched lip. The flower spray carries a dozen or more blooms, and rises from one of the upper leaf axils. The plants occur in the warm areas of Australia and New Guinea. They flower in winter or spring.

Dendrobium chrysanthum. Golden-yellow flowers are produced in clusters of six or so from the nodes toward the end of the extremely long (six to eight foot) stem. The flowers are waxy and have two maroon spots on the lip. As the stems elongate, the lower leaves begin to fall, until finally all the leaves are shed at the time of flowering. This native of Nepal and Burma flowers from late fall to winter.

Dendrobium chrysotoxum. The ribbed, cylindrical or spindle-shaped stems are about fifteen inches tall and bear six or eight leaves. The golden yellow flowers are borne in many-flowered erect or drooping sprays from the upper nodes of the stem. They are two inches in diameter, and have a round fringed lip that has a deep orange-yellow spot and red lines in the throat. The species occurs in Burma. It flowers in early spring.

Dendrobium dearei. Pure white flowers with a greenish throat, about two inches in diameter, are borne on sprays that come from the upper nodes of the stems. Each spray has seven to fifteen blooms. The flowers are characterized by a rather long spur and very round flaring petals. The leafy stems grow from a foot to three feet tall. This species forms the starting point for a long line of white "dearei type" hybrids. It is native to the Philippines. The blossoms appear in the summer.

Dendrobium densiflorum. This species makes a stunning display with its drooping balloon- or lantern-shaped sprays of sunny yellow flowers, fifty to a hundred completely encircling the stem. The flowers are about an inch and a half across (sometimes a bit larger), golden yellow with an orange lip, of a sparkling crystalline texture, and with a finely toothed edge to the petals and lip. The plants are sturdy, with stems about fifteen inches tall, somewhat four-angled and a bit knobby at the nodes. The leaves are satiny, rather thick, becoming leathery with age. The plant is native to Nepal and Assam and it flowers in the spring.

Dendrobium farmeri. Similar to *Dend. chrysotoxum* but paler in color, this plant has stems that are four-angled and bear two to four leaves. The rounded flowers are about two inches across and have a downy lip. They are borne on loose sprays that droop from an upper node. The species occurs in Sikkim, Nepal, and Burma. It flowers in the spring and summer.

Dendrobium fimbriatum. Best known for its variety *oculatum,* this species is one of the most striking of the "drooping spray, yellow-flowered" types. The sprays are a little smaller than they are in *Dend. densiflorum,* carrying about a dozen to twenty flowers. The golden flowers are round, with a round fringed lip that has a deep maroon spot or "eye" in its central portion. The crystalline texture makes them actually sparkle. The stems are about two feet tall, with closely spaced fairly thin leaves clothing almost their entire length. *Dend. fimbriatum* itself (not var. *oculatum*) is a taller plant whose flowers have an orange eye instead of the maroon spot. Occurs in Nepal and Burma. The flowers come from two- and three-year-old stems, in late spring.

Dendrobium findlayanum. Daintily colored flowers are produced in pairs in the late summer from the several nodes near the end of the stems. The petals and sepals are white, tinted with lilac, and the heart-shaped lip is white tipped with pink, yellow in the center. The slender, curved stems have swollen nodes and grow two to three feet long. The species is a native of Burma.

Dendrobium formosum. One of the finest of the white Dendrobiums, this species has flowers three to four inches across and a variety *giganteum* that has five-inch flowers. The long lasting flowers, which appear in the fall, are deceptively delicate looking, pure white ex-

cept for a yellow spot on the lip. They are produced in clusters of three to five from the upper nodes of rather stout, short, hairy pseudobulbs. The species occurs in Burma.

Dendrobium gouldii. A member of a group whose petals are slender and twisted, flaring upward like a pair of horns, this group is called "ceratobium" or, affectionately, the "antelope" orchids. A wealth of yellow blooms are borne on erect sprays from the upper nodes of three-foot leafy stems. The species occurs in New Guinea, and flowers in the fall.

Dendrobium heterocarpum. This is the correct name for the species also known as *Dend. aureum.* Fragrant, creamy yellow flowers, whose brighter lip narrows to a pointed tongue and is streaked with purple, are borne in two's and three's from the nodes of the previous year's growths (sometimes also from three year old growths). The flowers, which are about two inches across appear in late winter. Stems are erect, yellow, and grow about eighteen inches tall. The species grows natively from the Himalayas to the Philippines.

Dendrobium infundibulum. The three-inch white flowers of this species have lip markings varying from red to yellow, quite similar to *Dend. formosum.* The plant occurs in Burma and flowers variably.

Dendrobium lyonii. This delightful species is distinctive in shape and coloring. The wide-spreading sepals and petals are slender and pointed, whitish with greenish yellow or pink tips and burgundy colored bases. The lip is also slender and pointed, whitish, with the throat and side lobes maroon-red. Twenty or more of these three-inch flowers are borne on a long drooping airy spray in the summer. The plants have very squat four-angled pseudobulbs, topped by two long leathery leaves. This species is native to the Philippines.

Dendrobium macrophyllum. As the name suggests, this species has unusually large leaves, borne at the top nodes of two-foot ridged stems. The sprays are erect and carry a dozen or fifteen attractive flowers. The oval pointed sepals are hairy on the outside, pale yellow-green, and larger than the white petals.

Fig. 106 Upper left, *Dendrobium nobile,* flowering in mid-winter close to the frosted glass in a cool house. Its velvety flowers come from the leafless canes of the previous year. Upper right, *Dendrobium fimbriatum* var. *oculatum,* has bright yellow flowers set off by a deep maroon center. (Courtesy of Jack Sweet). Lower, The miniature *Dendrobium aggregatum* produces a tremendous array for so small a plant. (Courtesy of Wm. Kirch)

The large lip, its outer lobe long and recurved, is striped with purple. The species occurs in New Guinea, and neighboring islands.

Dendrobium moschatum. These plants vary in size from those that reach three feet to some that grow to six feet tall. The lovely and unusual flowers are three inches across, with sepals and petals of pale yellow tipped with rose. The lip is slipper-shaped, downy, with five lines of fringe in the center, and is yellow except for two bright spots of maroon surrounded by orange. The flowers are produced in the winter, sometimes later, on sprays from the uppermost nodes of the previous year's growths. The plants are native to India and Burma.

Dendrobium nobile. This delightful species has over eighty named varieties. It was the most widely known of all Dendrobiums, together with its hybrids, until the *Dend. phalaenopsis* hybrids came along to challenge but not replace them. The charming, brightly-colored blossoms are produced in nodding groups of three or so from the nodes along the two-year-old stems. The flowers are three inches in diameter, with sepals and petals white tipped with rosy purple; the rounded lip is velvety, purple in the throat and bordered with white. The winter or spring flowers are long-lasting and lend themselves, as do so many others, to dainty corsages. This species occurs at high elevations in India.

Dendrobium parishii. Reminiscent of *Dend. nobile,* with its flowers borne at the nodes along the fifteen inch stems, these are amethyst purple, with two maroon spots in the throat of the downy lip. The plants occur in Moulmein and flower in spring and summer.

Dendrobium pierardii. Drooping stems that grow from three to five feet long produce an incredible wealth of flowers in pairs at the nodes. The blossoms are two inches in diameter, pale pink with the yellow lip striped with purple. New growths appear in early summer at about the same time as the flowers. The plant is native to India.

Dendrobium phalaenopsis. A beautifully colored species with many handsome varieties,

Fig. 107 *Dendrobium gouldei,* vigor and generosity in flowering characterize this member of the ceratobium, "antelope horn," group of species. (Courtesy of Wm. Kirch)

its flowers appear in the late spring and are borne in dainty arching sprays from the upper nodes of both old and new growths. The stems are from eighteen inches to over two feet tall. The sepals are white flushed with rose, the more rounded petals are mauve veined with a deeper shade. The side lobes of the lip are deep maroon-purple, while the slender pointed middle lobe is pale purple with deeper veins. This species is considered to be a superior variety of *Dend. biggibum,* but there are certain structural differences in the flowers that persuade many to keep it as a separate species. Among the outstanding varieties of *Dend. phalaenopsis* which have entered much into hybridization are: *Dend. phalaenopsis* variety *alba* and variety *hololeucum,* both white; *Dend. phalaenopsis* 'Schroderianum,' which is very richly colored; and a long line of selected "strains" chosen for their particular markings, richness of color, or outstanding form. Many of the strains and varieties have been inter-

Fig. 108 *Dendrobium phalaenopsis* flowers from both old and new growths, giving an array of flowers in rich, soft hues. Shown here is the selected strain 'delicata.' (Courtesy of Jones and Scully, Inc.)

crossed to produce lovely things, but these are, of course, not true hybrids. Fascinating hybrids have been made with the "antelope" species, of the botanical section ceratobium. The species occurs in Australia.

Dendrobium sanderae. A very lovely species, similar in some ways to *Dend. dearei*, it has white, showy flowers, about three and a half inches in diameter. The petals are broad and flaring, and the lip has a wide, spreading outer lobe. The throat is purple, with a few purple stripes extending from the center. There is a variety *parviflorum*, more generally seen in cultivation, which has the flowers a bit smaller but in which the throat is much darker. The flowers appear in the spring in clusters of six to twelve from the upper nodes of the two foot stems. The species occurs in the mountains of northern Luzon.

Dendrobium schuetzii. Another of the *dearei* type, this is a smaller plant. The foot tall stems are very slender at the base. The large white flowers appear in the fall and are borne in clusters of four or so. They last for many weeks. The plant is native to the Philippines.

Dendrobium stratiotes. This is one of the attractive "antelope" Dendrobiums. Both sepals and petals are twisted or wavy, the long petals standing up like a pair of horns. The sepals are creamy white, the petals pale yellow-green. The lip is white, streaked with purple. It occurs in Indonesia and New Guinea and flowers in the fall.

Dendrobium superbiens. A striking species, whose crimson-purple flowers have the sepals and petals bordered with white. The broad lip is reflexed and wavy. The two-inch flowers are borne fifteen or more on arching-erect sprays from the top nodes of the three foot stems. Occurs in Australia. Flowers in late summer or fall.

Dendrobium taurinum. A strikingly colored member of the "antelope" group. The recurved sepals are pink, while the longer petals, which resemble the horns of a bull, are reddish brown tinged with purple. The massive lip is rosy marked with raised reddish brown lines, ruffled at its edge. The plant occurs in the Philippines and flowers in the fall. It needs more copious watering than other members of the group.

Dendrobium thyrsiflorum. Very close to *Dend. densiflorum,* and probably a variety of it, its flowers are identical in shape and size. They are borne in the same lantern-shaped spray and also have the sparkling, crystalline texture. The sepals and petals are white and the lip is deep orange. The plant occurs in Moulmein and Burma and flowers in the winter or spring.

Dendrobium undulatum. The flowers of this species are dull yellow, more or less spotted with purple, with extremely twisted sepals and petals. The lip is bright yellow dotted with purple and decorated with five white keels. This species and *Dend. taurinum* are about the same size, with three- to four-foot stems, and flower sprays two feet long. *Dend. undulatum* is native to Australia and New Guinea.

Dendrobium veratrifolium. A much larger plant than the other "antelope" species, this one has stems to five feet and flower sprays two and a half feet long bearing many more flowers. Its size and vigor are the characteristics it contributes to hybrids made with various of the other "antelope" species. Its flowers do not have the extreme twisting shown by some; in fact, the oar-shaped petals are not twisted at all but they do stand up tall between the sepals. The lip is broad and open. The flowers are variable in color, mostly white with the lip marked with branching veins of purple. The species occurs in New Guinea.

Dendrobium wardianum. The flowers of this species are slightly larger than in *Dend. nobile.* They are waxy and white, with the sepals, petals, and lip all tipped with amethyst. The yellow throat is marked with two bright, clear cut spots of purple. The three-foot stems are pendant and, in the spring, bear pairs of the three-inch flowers for almost their whole length. The plant occurs in Assam and Burma.

Other Members of the Dendrobium Tribe

Authorities differ on the matter of what other genera are closely related to Dendrobium. Bailey gives Inobulbon and Sarcopodium. Others include Pseuderia, Cadetia, Eria, Porpax, and Cryptochilus. All, with the exception of Eria, are little known. Eria is widespread in the Philippines, where it is enjoyed for its small plants and tiny sprays of flowers.

17 | *Odontoglossum Tribe*

An ARTIST with words might contrive a new adjective to describe the wonders of this tribe of epiphytes. The adjective would have to suggest feathers and pixies, butterflies and pansies, filigree work and the classical ballet. Woven through it would be a feeling of golden sunlight and cool, frosty nights. And when its syllables were cleverly fitted together, it would mean Odontoglossum, Oncidium, and Miltonia, the three important members of the six belonging to this tribe.

Odontoglossums and Miltonias were widely grown in nineteenth century England, in the house, the garden, and the greenhouse. A writer of the times described a plant that grew wonderfully in the sitting-room of his home, where it was covered with frost on winter nights and had no heat until the fire was lighted for tea. Sprays of Odontoglossums were made into bouquets for "lady musicians" and were used in arrangements for decorations. Single blossoms were considered quite the best boutonnieres for gentlemen. While other kinds of orchids were admired and even grown in quantity, the Odontoglossums and Miltonias were really the popular orchids of the day.

Oncidium, the third important member of this tribe, offers variety scarcely to be matched elsewhere in the orchid family. An amateur could easily become an Oncidium fancier, for possession of a few of the species provokes a curiosity to know the other elfin forms of the genus. Legend has it that it was *Oncidium papilio* that started the craze of amateur orchid growing.

The genera belonging to the Odontoglossum tribe are so closely related that some botanists consider it merely one large and varied genus. The genera may be freely crossed with one another. So many natural hybrids have been found that the job of marking these from distinct species is far from finished. Whether the tribe is considered one genus or several, certain characters separate the types from each other, and the generic division is helpful in classifying the hundreds of species.

The tribe inhabits tropical America, from Mexico to Bolivia, and climbs from the hot, coastal regions to the cool, misty heights of the Andes. The species from lower elevations can be grown anywhere. Those from the intermediate elevations are a little more restricted, but many of them can be accommodated in greenhouses where Cattleyas do well. The cool kinds, from the highest altitudes, especially the "crispum" type of Odontoglossums, require conditions not found in many places in this country. The Pacific Northwest offers conditions closest to their needs, and with special handling they can be grown in other areas where cool days as well as cool nights exist during the summer. The introduction of the evaporative cooler to offset our summer heat has widened the possibilities for growing members of this tribe, particularly the border-line species in the groups from intermediate elevations, and it may also make it possible for many growers to experiment with the "crispum" type Odontoglossums.

MILTONIA

Miltonia is affectionately called the "pansy orchid," and their charms are indeed similar to those of the much beloved pansy. Their flowers open flat, with the same frank expression, and their rounded parts are as softly colored. The blossoms are held gracefully on slender stems that appear from the base of mature pseudobulbs and reach a length of from six to eighteen inches. A plant with a number of flower sprays resembles a hand-arranged bouquet, with its pretty, light green foliage forming a background for a compact array of flowers. The pseudobulbs are small, oval-compressed, and smooth; each bears two or more narrow leaves at the apex and a few small ones sheathing the base.

It has taken a good bit of experimentation to learn how to grow Miltonias in this country. It is now known that they will thrive with night temperatures of 55° to 60°, but that they do not like the nights to be warmer than this

Fig. 109 Miltonia Charlesworthii, a lovely hybrid which stems from the species *Miltonia vexillaria* and *Miltonia roezlii*. (Courtesy of Frederick T. Bonham)

even in the summer. As to day temperature, they do best when it does not exceed 80°. Higher day temperatures deplete the plants, unless they prevail just for short periods, giving the plants cooler weather in between times. The sections of the United States where Miltonias can be grown are therefore somewhat limited to those which normally have cool summer nights and where any hot daytime temperatures can be modified with an evaporative cooler. These would perhaps be the northern states, parts of the West Coast, and regions of higher elevation. Attempts are being made to breed hybrids more tolerant of heat.

Potting. Osmunda fiber or tree fern fiber are preferred by many growers, although a seedling grade of fir bark (one-eighth to one-quarter inch) is being used successfully. Drainage must be extremely good, and small pots are used. Rather than risk overpotting, most growers repot every year. Potting should be done during a cool season, either just as the new growths start in the spring, or in the fall.

Light. The species from Colombia and Panama require about the same amount of light as Cypripediums, 1000 to 1500 foot candles in the summer, a bit more perhaps in the winter when the air is cooler. The Brazilian species like about the same amount of light as Cattleyas. It is possible to grow both kinds, and their hybrids, in the same greenhouse with the light adjusted by shading according to their individual needs.

Temperature. The day temperature should preferably not exceed 80° and the night temperature they like best is between 55° and 60°.

Water. Miltonias should not be allowed to become dry. They use more water during warm weather, and care in watering during the summer is essential in order to bring them through the season in good shape.

Humidity. Miltonias must have ample humidity, best furnished by sprayers and fans, or other means of providing moving damp air. A relative humidity of about sixty per cent is best, fluctuating between fifty and seventy percent.

Fertilizer. In osmunda fiber, an application of a 10-10-10 fertilizer not more often than once a month seems best. Some growers fertilize only every two months. None is given during the winter where skies are dull, but an occasional application may be given where there is good winter sun. Fertilizing in fir bark should be more frequent, every other watering with a 30-10-10 formula, reduced a bit in winter.

Propagation. Miltonias will do better if not divided too often. Let them grow into plants with many leads and then divide them into clumps of a number of pseudobulbs. Division should be just before new growth starts. They are grown from seed in the same manner as other orchids. There are numerous lovely hybrids in both the Colombian and Brazilian groups, and many crosses between Miltonia, Odontoglossum, Oncidium, and Cochlioda.

The Species

Miltonia candida. The striking species from Brazil produces generous numbers of flower spikes, each with six to ten blooms. The flowers, which appear in the fall, are about two and one-half inches across, yellow marked with large red-brown blotches. The large oval lip is white tinged with yellow and has a wavy margin. The pseudobulbs arise at intervals of about an inch along the rhizome, and the foliage is characteristically yellowish.

Miltonia clowesii. This species resembles the preceding one and has the same yellow-green foliage. The flowers are a bit larger and are of a shade approaching orange. The lip is fiddle-shaped, white, with a violet base. It is also a native of Brazil and flowers in September and October.

Miltonia phalaenopsis. Less robust than some, this species has pale green, grass-like foliage. The short flower spikes produce one to three beautiful flowers, which have daintily pointed white sepals and petals, and a spreading lip that is white streaked with crimson. It comes from Colombia and flowers in the spring.

Miltonia regnelli. Three to five flat subtly tinted flowers are borne on a short stem. The sepals and petals are white, suffused with rose toward the base. The heart shaped lip is light rose, streaked with a deeper shade and having a white margin. The variety *purpurpea* has darker coloring. The plant is native to Brazil.

Miltonia roezlii. This lovely species is often found in the lineage of hybrids. The foliage is pale green and the pseudobulbs are tightly clustered. Two to four large flat flowers are borne on each spike. The sepals and petals are white, the latter having a purple band at the base. The large lip is two lobed, white with a tinge of purple. It becomes yellow at the base, where two little horns project backward on each side of the column. The species requires especially free ventilation, and plenty of moderated light. It occurs in Colombia and Panama and often flowers twice a year, winter and spring. The popular hybrid Miltonia Bleuana is a cross between *Miltonia roezlii* and *Miltonia vexillaria.*

Miltonia spectabilis. This was the first Miltonia introduced into culture, and comes from Brazil. It is indeed a spectacle when in flower, for large, sturdy plants may bear as many as fifty flowers, each on a separate stem, and all opening at once. The flowers, which occur in the fall, are large, white or cream colored, with a large, wavy lip that is rose-purple veined with a darker shade. The pseudobulbs are an inch apart, and the foliage is yellow-green.

Miltonia vexillaria. This species has the largest flowers of the genus and is the most popular. It is also the most frequently used in hybridization. The plants are sturdy, easily grown, and generous in the numbers of blooms produced. The richly colored flowers are four inches or more in diameter, and occur two to seven on a spike. A single pseudobulb may give rise to several spikes. The small sepals and petals are bright rose in color, sometimes with a white margin. The huge, bilobed lip is the

Fig. 110 *Miltonia roezlii,* whose velvety texture and soft markings give it a special appeal.

striking feature of the flower and the character desired in its hybrids. It, too, is a rich shade of rose, shading to white at the base, and streaked with yellow and red. Two small horns project from the base of the lip on either side of the column. The plant has pale green foliage, occurs in Colombia, and flowers in spring and summer.

ODONTOGLOSSUM

Some of the loveliest orchids known to man belong to the genus Odontoglossum. They range through Central America and parts of South America, mostly in mountainous regions, having their culmination in the high Andes Mountains. A few species which are little known reach elevations up to 12,000 feet, the "crispum" group lives around 8000 to 9000 feet, and still others range on down to 3000 feet. Even though some of them dwell at elevations comparable to those occupied by Cattleyas, they are not as tolerant of our warm summer nights and days, and are better grown as cool orchids, or grown where summer temperatures are quite moderate.

Those that live at the higher altitudes are

Fig. 111 A "crispum type" bigeneric hybrid, Odontonia Epha, which, through several ancestral hybrids, combines the species *Odontoglossum crispum* and *harryanum* and the species *Miltonia vexillaria* and *roezlii*. The flower is white with bright red markings. (Courtesy of Gordon M. Hoyt)

too touchy as to temperature for most of us to try. These are the "cold" species, or the "crispum" group as they are also called, after the most important species, *Odontoglossum crispum*. They require an ideal night temperature of 45° in the winter, 50° in the summer, with the day temperature not exceeding 60°. Hybrids in this group are a little more tolerant of warmer temperatures, but their culture is still restricted to areas where summer days and nights are cool and damp, such as parts of Europe and our Pacific Northwest, or other areas having a similarly fortunate climate. Air conditioning (refrigeration) may make it possible to grow this group where the temperature would normally be too warm, but the expense might be such that few amateurs would wish to indulge in it. The species included in this group are *Odontoglossum crispum, luteo-purpureum,* and *odoratum*. Along with the cool temperatures, this group needs a soft damp atmosphere, and, while they cannot take strong light, the light must not be cut below an amount necessary to make good growth and to mature the pseudobulbs.

A better group for the amateur is the cool group, or what we might call the "medium cool" group. Even these do not all lend them-

selves to summer conditions in the south and some parts of the mid-west, but evaporative coolers make it possible to grow them where it used to be considered impossible. Some of them can easily be grown with Cymbidiums, with about half of the amount of light demanded by Cymbidiums. Some will make themselves at home with Cattleyas, provided the nights stay close to or under 60° in the summer. Those that we suggest you try along with Cymbidiums are *Odontoglossum bictoniense, cirrhosum, harryanum, insleayi, nobile, rossii,* and *uro-skinneri*. Kinds to grow along with Cattleyas are *Odontoglossum cariniferum, grande, pendulum, pulchellum,* and *schlieperianum*. A species which is more tolerant of warmth and does well with Cattleyas in warm regions is *O. pendulum*.

The smooth, bright green pseudobulbs of the Odontoglossums are oval to round, usually compressed to a sharp edge at the sides. They bear one to two fleshy leaves at the apex, and often have small sheathing leaves at the base. The remarkably varied flowers have sepals and petals that are free and spreading, but an occasional exception has the sepals somewhat united. The base of the lip is parallel to the column, with its outer lobe spreading downward. This habit of the lip is one of the ways by which Odontoglossum is distinguishd from Oncidium, where the lip is never parallel to the column. The graceful flower stems arise from the base of the newly starting growth in some species, from the mature growth in others.

Potting. Osmunda, tree fern, or bark can be used. Pot to allow two or three years' growth, as it is not necessary to repot until the material has become broken down. Fertilizer may be given occasionally in osmunda, regularly in bark.

Light. *O. grande* and *schlieperianum* require the same amount of light as Cattleyas; *O. cariniferum, pulchellum,* and *pendulum* need just a bit less. Those which we have suggested to be grown with Cymbidiums will need more shade than the latter, but enough light to keep their foliage a light green.

Water. All require abundant water during the growing season, with good drainage so as not to allow the medium to stay sopping wet. The cold and cool kinds should not be allowed to become dry during the winter, although, of course, they will use less water than they do when growing. The kinds which tolerate warmer temperatures can be allowed to approach dryness between waterings, as can Cattleyas. Growers who are successful with *Odontoglossum grande* in climates warmer than ideal find that it does better for them if allowed to become dry between waterings during the winter.

Humidity. Kinds grown with Cattleyas need not be given a higher relative humidity than ordinarily maintained in the greenhouse. The cool growing kinds benefit from a mist spray on bright days. The cold types need a higher relative humidity, around 70% if possible, with care to keep the air in circulation to prevent disease. Good air circulation is, with all kinds, contributory to good health.

Temperature. For the cold group, nights of 45° to 50° and days preferably close to 60° winter and summer. Days can go to 70° when unavoidable, but everything should be done to keep the temperature from going above that level. For the cool kinds, nights close to 50°, days preferably not over 80°, ideally around 70°. For the rest, nights 55° to 60°, not much over 60° even in summer, days not over 85° except for unusual spells.

Propagation. Most Odontoglossums can be easily propagated by division. A few, however, do not respond well. They are readily grown from seed. The flasks of young seedlings must be carefully protected against heat. They mature more quickly than many other genera, in about half the time required for Cattleyas.

The Species

Odontoglossum bictoniense. This was the first Odontoglossum to survive the voyage to England and has been popular through the years. It bears three-foot sprays of small yellow-green flowers with a white or rose colored lip. Occurs in Guatemala and flowers in the fall.

Odontoglossum cariniferum. Greenish red flowers, bordered with light green, have a white lip which makes the two-inch flowers quite distinctive. The spring blossoms are borne on stems three or four feet tall, each of which has short branches with four or five flowers. The sepals and petals are narrow, pointed, not wavy, the edges infolded somewhat and having a keel on the back. The lip is spreading at the outer edge, narrowing to a claw directly under the column. This species occurs in Costa Rica, Panama, and Venezuela.

Odontoglossum cirrhosum. Narrow sepals that taper to slender tails, and a column that bears two cirri at its tip distinguish this attractive species. The sepals and petals are white spotted with maroon, as is the short recurved lip. The base of the lip bears a crest with two long teeth in front, and is yellow with radiating lines. This species, which comes from Ecuador, flowers in the spring.

Odontoglossum crispum. Connoisseurs often name this species the most beautiful of all orchids. Its lacy two and one-half foot sprays are crowded with flowers, each two and one-half to three inches across. The sepals and petals are pointed, daintily ruffled, with their borders toothed or notched. They are white, sometimes tinged with rose, and may be spotted with crimson or brown. The flower is centered by a speckled lip that is fringed with teeth, and whose borders are even more finely notched than the petals. This species is extremely variable, and more than a hundred varieties have been named. It occurs in Colombia, at an elevation of 9,000 feet. Flowers at any time of the year.

Odontoglossum grande. Large, brilliantly marked flowers make this one of the most widely grown species. The flowers are from five to nine inches across; from four to seven occur on a spike from September to December. The sepals are long and rather slender, yellow, barred with chestnut brown. The

Fig. 112 *Odontoglossum grande*, the yellow and brown "tiger'" orchid. (Courtesy of Rod McLellan Co.)

wider, wavy petals are brown at the base and yellow at the outer end. The generously rounded lip is white or cream colored, spotted with brown. The waxy flowers last for two weeks or so, and are very decorative. The species occurs in Guatemala, and has been nicknamed the "tiger orchid."

Odontoglossum harryanum. The variegated coloring of this species together with its striking shape make it the valued parent of many hybrids. Four or five three-inch flowers occur to a stem. The wavy sepals and petals are brown with irregular bands of yellow-green. The large shield-shaped lip is flat and wavy, its lower half white, changing to yellow, and its basal part brown, veined with purple. Seven serrated crests decorate its base. This native of Colombia flowers in the fall.

Odontoglossum insleayi. This species has flowers that resemble those of *Odontoglossum grande*, but which are smaller, reaching four inches in diameter. The sepals and petals are yellow, spotted with brown, and the lip is orange-yellow spotted with red-brown. It

occurs in Mexico and flowers from October to December.

Odontoglossum luteo-purpureum. This striking and varied species from Colombia, produces flowers in horizontal sprays. The wavy, oblong sepals are brownish-purple with a yellow margin. The petals are toothed, spotted with purple-brown. The deeply scalloped yellow lip is fringed and is spotted with purple or rose. The flowers appear in winter and spring.

Odontoglossum nobile. This species is a good substitute for those who cannot grow *Odontoglossum crispum*, but who can furnish quite cool conditions. The long flower spikes carry up to a hundred blooms, each three inches in diameter. The sepals and petals are usually white, sometimes faintly tinged with rose. The kidney-shaped lip is white with a few crimson spots. A native of Colombia, the plants usually flower in the spring.

Odontoglossum odoratum. The flowers of this species are small, but produced in great numbers on branching sprays in winter and spring. They are golden yellow, marked with red-brown, and the wavy narrow lip is covered with down. It occurs in Mexico.

Odontoglossum pendulum. This is the preferred name for the species familiarly known as *Odontoglossum citrosmum*. The drooping sprays carry thick clusters of rounded flowers in pastel hues. The sepals and petals are white to rose, and the extended lip is violet and spreads into two lobes at its apex. The species occurs in Guatemala and flowers in late spring.

Odontoglossum pulchellum. This species is easy to grow and flowers readily. Slender sprays carry six or seven small, waxy, rounded white flowers, each one and one-half to two inches in diameter. Their fragrance suggests lily-of-the-valley. This native of Guatemala flowers in the spring.

Odontoglossum rossii. One of the loveliest of the genus, this species has short flower stems that bear only two to five blooms, each three inches in diameter. The lack of numbers is compensated for by the beauty of the individual flowers and by their good keeping quality. The sepals are pointed, cream colored to greenish yellow, and barred with dark brown. The blunt, somewhat curled petals are white with a few brown spots at their base. The large, round, wavy lip is pure white. It occurs in Mexico and flowers in the winter.

Odontoglossum schlieperianum. Another species that resembles a small *Odontoglossum grande.* This one has three-inch flowers whose yellow-green ground color is carried into the lip. The markings vary from orange to brown. Its summer flowering season and the generous number of flowers (eight to fifteen to a spike), make it a worthwhile addition to a collection. This is a native of Costa Rica.

Odontoglossum uro-skinnerii. Ten to thirty flowers of striking coloring are produced on long spikes in the spring. The sepals and petals are green, marked with chestnut-brown, and the large, heart-shaped lip is rose, mottled with white. This species occurs in Guatemala.

ONCIDIUM

Whatever nature's mood may have been when she created the other orchids, surely it was fanciful when she designed the Oncidiums. She seems to have caught dancing rays of light, flickering patterns of sun and shadow, little fairy forms not seen by man, and made them into friendly, whimsical, thoroughly delightful little flowers. They are meant to be enjoyed with smiles and chuckles. Still generous after endowing so much beauty elsewhere, she seems to have poured out her warmth in the showers of gold given us by this genus.

At least three hundred species of Oncidiums have been discovered. The description of a mere handful is only a tantalizing glimpse of the whole genus. Favorites among the species are easy to find, and no two fanciers will list the same ones as deserving of attention.

The genus can be found throughout tropical America, from Florida and the West Indies, through Central America to the southern part of Brazil. As with the Odontoglossums, some are found in low, hot regions, others in the cool upper altitudes. They are more amena-ble to changes in temperature, however, and most of them will adjust themselves to a moderate greenhouse condition. This makes it easy for the average amateur to include a few Oncidiums with almost anything else he grows. As cut flowers, the possibilities they offer are limited only by the imagination of the person working with them. Their filigree-like sprays are charmingly decorative when used alone or as a foil for other flowers. Dainty arrangements for the hair or stunning corsages can be made with groups or with single blossoms.

This genus of epiphytes includes great variety. The pseudobulbs are rounded and flattened at the edges, similar to those of Odontoglossum, but some species are without

Fig. 113 *Odontoglossum pendulum,* also known as *Odont. citrosmum,* one of the easiest to grow. (Courtesy of H. D. Sawyer)

pseudobulbs. The foliage is usually clear green, but is sometimes mottled. The leaves are usually fleshy, oval and pointed, with a single prominent mid-vein; but species occur with thinner, many-veined leaves, and some with terete (cylindrical) foliage. The flower sprays are long, sometimes drooping, often erect. The blossoms may be large and showy, or small and dainty. The unvarying feature that distinguishes the Oncidiums from the Odontoglossums is that in Oncidium the base of the lip is never parallel to the column, but forms a right angle to it. The column is short and winged.

Potting. Oncidiums do well in straight osmunda or in fir bark. Large, robust plants need larger pots for their size than do small plants. Those that produce drooping sprays may be grown in baskets or hanging pots. Those that have tall erect sprays need plenty of head room. They need to be repotted only when the medium has broken down.

Temperature. Most of the genus will grow nicely with Cattleyas, requiring about the same temperature range and light conditions. If a plant or two does not flower under these conditions, try either giving it cooler nights or hanging it up to give it somewhat warmer temperatures. A little experimenting will enable you to grow almost all of them satisfactorily.

Light. Oncidiums have the same light requirements as the Cattleyas.

Humidity. The humidity conditions necessary for this species are the same as for Cattleyas.

Watering. The plants require abundant water during the growing and flowering season, somewhat less at other times.

Fertilizer. The strength of fertilizers and frequency of application are as for Cattleyas.

Propagation. Oncidiums respond easily to vegetative propagation, dividing the plants into clumps of three or more pseudobulbs, just before new growth starts. They are also readily grown from seed.

The Species

Oncidium altissimum. This species is often called the giant of the genus. The robust plants produce flower sprays that sometimes reach twelve feet in length, but usually grow close to six feet. They are gracefully arched or drooping and bear many small blooms. The small sepals and petals are pale yellow spotted with olive-brown, and the larger lip is a brighter yellow with a brown band. This native of the West Indies flowers in August.

Oncidium ampliatum. Magnificent panicles, attractively branched and arched, reach a length of three feet. The attractive little flowers are clear yellow, spotted with red toward the base of the small sepals and petals. The round flat lip is cream colored on the undersides. The round, flattened, ridged pseudobulbs look like turtles. The species occurs from Guatemala to Colombia and flowers from March to June.

Oncidium ansiferum. Plants with tall, broad, flat, cardboard-thin pseudobulbs bear sprays of delicate looking but long-lasting flowers in the summer. The flowers are in tones of yellow-green, faintly spotted with red. The side lobes of the spreading lip are large and hold themselves horizontally, looking like an extra pair of petals. This species occurs in Costa Rica and Panama.

Oncidium cabagre. Almost a miniature, this species has leaves which barely exceed six inches. The dainty little yellow and brown flowers are produced on stems about two feet long. Occurs in Panama and flowers in the summer.

Oncidium cheirophorum. This delightful miniature has little rounded pseudobulbs which are one inch tall and which bear two short leaves. They are bright green the first year and become speckled with purple as they age. The flowers, which grow in sprays about

Fig. 114 *Oncidium cheirophorum,* a delightful miniature. The plant is but five inches tall, and the dense little flower sprays are from six to eight inches tall. (Courtesy of Rod McLellan Co.)

six inches long, are very dense and are a bright, clear yellow. The plant spreads rapidly to fill its pot and makes a charming show. It is a native of Colombia.

Oncidium excavatum. A hundred or more gold and brown blossoms are produced on each three- to five-foot panicle in the fall. Each flower is one and one-half inches across. Occurs in Peru.

Oncidium flexuosum. A small member of the popular group of "dancing doll" orchids. Because of the much reduced sepals and petals and the voluminous lip, this group resembles a miniature ballet. The tiny, one-inch flowers of this species occur in dainty showers on a loose, airy panicle atop a tall stem. The sepals and petals are yellow, barred with brown, and

the broad, full lip is yellow with a few red spots. It grows and flowers with great freedom and, because of its small size, is welcome in little greenhouses. This native of Brazil flowers at various seasons.

Oncidium incurvum. This small species, which does best when grown a little cooler than the average, produces many dainty, gracefully branched panicles of rosy-purple and white flowers. It comes from Mexico and flowers in late summer and fall.

Oncidium kramerianum. The "butterfly orchid," which description it shares with its more famous relative, *Oncidium papilio,* does not grow with the abandon usual to the genus, but it rewards careful attention with a succession of single spectacular butterfly flowers. The petals and the dorsal sepal are drawn out to look like antennae. The lateral sepals are broad, golden yellow spotted with brown; and the large, round, ruffled lip is yellow with the finely toothed border decorated by a band of brown spots. The flowers appear one after another at the tip of a tall jointed stem. The foliage of the plant is green, mottled with brown. This Central American species has a variable flowering season.

Oncidium lanceanum. An odd combination of colors makes this a very striking species. The showy flowers are two to three inches across. The sepals and petals are blunt and fleshy, yellow, spotted with chocolate brown or crimson. The spreading lip stands in contrast to the rest of the flower with its rose outer portion and violet base. The robust plants have no pseudobulbs; and the wide, fleshy leaves are mottled with brown. The rather short, stout, erect flower stems bear a generous number of blooms in the summer. The species is native to British Guiana.

Oncidium leucochilum. Very large, tall plants have stunning flowers, two or more inches across, on a generous spray. The petals and sepals are green, heavily blotched with reddish brown, against which the white lip makes a striking contrast. This species comes from Central America, and blooms variably.

Oncidium obryzatum. Another "almost

Fig. 115 Upper left, *Oncidium kramerianum*, a spectacular butterfly in yellow and reddish brown, akin to *Oncidium papillio*. (Courtesy of H. A. Dunn and H. Griffin) Upper right, *Oncidium lanceanum*, a stunning species with large, heavy flowers of chocolate and yellow with a pink lip. (Courtesy of Jones and Scully, Inc.) Lower, *Oncidium ampliatum*, one of the airy "dancing doll" species (Courtesy of H. A. Dunn and H. Griffin)

miniature" Oncidium, these plants are especially vigorous and may outgrow the miniature dimensions. This Central American species is a delightful addition to a collection. Its half-inch brownish flowers appear on dainty sprays in the fall.

Oncidium ornithorrhyncum. The long specific name means "bird beak," and the drooping, tightly clustered sprays resemble a flock of birds. The rather small plants are easily grown and flower freely. The tiny, fragrant flowers are colored in shades of soft rosy purple. The species, which likes to be grown a little on the cool side, occurs in Mexico and flowers in fall and winter.

Oncidium papilio. This butterfly orchid is said to be responsible for the orchid craze that has swept the world. It is much like *Oncidium kramerianum,* described above, but flowers more freely. It was shown at an exhibition of the Royal Horticultural Society soon after its introduction to England in 1823. Here its striking appearance so intrigued the Duke of Devonshire that he was inspired to start an orchid collection of his own. Thus was the fashion for private collections started among wealthy Englishmen. *Oncidium papilio* has longer antennae than *O. kramerianum,* and the lateral sepals and lip are banded, rather than spotted, with brown. The upper sections of the jointed flower stem are flattened like the parts of a crab's leg. Flowers appear one at a time in succession from both old and new stems, throughout most of the year. The species is a native of the West Indies. See drawing page 4.

Oncidium pumilum. This is a miniature species, scarcely six inches tall, without pseudobulbs, and whose tiny flower spray is less than the height of the leaves. In the spring, the minute blossoms, each one-eighth inch across, grow in tight little clusters along the stem. The sepals and petals are rounded, and the lip has three deep scallops. The species, which comes from Brazil, is a beautiful "botanical" that would be a valuable addition to a small-scale collection.

Oncidium pusillum. A miniature without

pseudobulbs, this species has a perfect fan of small fleshy leaves. The single flowers produced on short stems in the spring, are huge in comparison to the size of the plant. Rather a challenge to grow because it is more tender than some, the plant is delightful to own. It occurs in Central America.

Oncidium sphacelatum. Plants that are two feet tall produce branched flower sprays three to four feet tall, holding 250 or more flowers each. The airy ballet is dressed in butter-yellow, the upper part of the flower sprinkled with brown, and the lip with a few large brown spots. The species abounds in the West Indies and Honduras and flowers in the spring.

Oncidium splendidum. These stunning flowers are blends of green, brown, and yellow gold. The greenish upper part is heavily barred with brown, against which stands the large pure yellow lip, decorated with a long white crest. The three-inch flowers are of heavy substance, and a single bloom makes a striking lapel pin. A flowering plant is a handsome sight, with its thirty-inch, branched flower stem crowded with blooms. The plant itself is spectacular, with its broad, extremely fleshy, reddish leaves attached to short stubby pseudobulbs. This species, native to Guatemala and Mexico, is often given as a variety of *O. tigrinum,* below, and is cultivated commercially to some extent. It flowers in the spring.

Oncidium tigrinum. The startling flowers of this species are among the most showy of the genus. They have the appearance of being made of two flowers wired together. The rather large sepals and petals are rich brown, barred with slender lines of yellow. The large, bright yellow lip is in complete contrast to this dark backing. The flowers are about two and one-half inches across, with rather few to a stem. The species occurs in Mexico and flowers in the winter.

Oncidium varicosum. One of the most beloved of the genus, the flower of this species is a "dancing doll" in a beautifully swirling skirt. Literally clouds of these sunny little flowers are borne in lacy, branching sprays. One to two hundred may occur on a single panicle. The

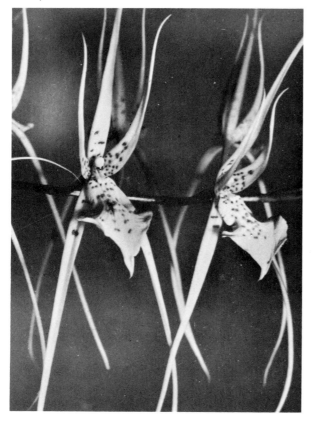

Fig. 116 *Brassia verrucosa.* Its spidery flowers are most eye-catching. (Courtesy of Mrs. James J. Waring)

upper part of the flower is yellow-bronze barred with brown. The lip is pure yellow, sometimes with a brown spot or band at its base, and a curiously toothed crest. The variety *Rogersii* is considered by some to be the best of all the Oncidiums. It is one that should be included in all Oncidium collections. This native of Brazil flowers in winter and spring.

Other Genera of the Odontoglossum Tribe

Brassia, a fourth member of this tribe, has spidery flowers which are most unusual and make an attractive showing in spite of their lack of richness of coloring. The sepals and petals are attenuated, giving the appearance of spider legs, and the lip is indeed shaped like the body of a spider. There are about thirty species, all easy to grow with a mixed collection of orchids. They require abundant water during the growing season, and must never be allowed to dry out.

Brassia verrucosa. The whole flower is seven or eight inches long with the dorsal sepal and the shorter petals accounting for three inches of the length, and the longer lateral sepals for the other four. They are pale yellow-green, spotted at the base. The lip is pinched in at the middle and is white with dark green warts. The phalanx of eight to ten flowers is borne in a neat row on a horizontal stem. Occurs in Guatemala.

Brassia longissima. Deep orange-yellow with a pale yellow lip that bears purple spots at its base, the extreme length of this species makes it a curiosity. The dorsal sepal and petals are two to three inches long, whereas the lateral sepals reach seven or eight inches. It is a native of Costa Rica.

Gomesa and **Palumbina** are the remaining genera of the tribe as given by Bailey. Both are pale by comparison to those already described and are therefore seldom grown.

Cochlioda, which is closely related to Odontoglossum, is given below under inter-generic hybrids, along with its relative **Aspasia.**

Inter-generic Hybrids

Bi- and tri-generic hybrids are common within this tribe. Crosses between Miltonia, Oncidium, and Odontoglossum are not the only possibilities. The genus Cochlioda, which Bailey gives as belonging to the Aspasia tribe, hybridizes very easily with all three of these genera, and Aspasia has recently been introduced into hybridization. Because its chief importance is in relation to members of the Odontoglossum tribe, we shall include this tribe here.

Cochlioda is similar to Odontoglossum in appearance, habitat, and cultural requirements. Its long sprays of small flowers come in shades of rose, red, and red-orange. It is for the sake of the colors that its species are bred with those of other genera.

Cochlioda noezliana. This species has arching spikes of small, bright red-orange flowers

Fig. 117 *Aspasia principissa* has an appeal for the collector. (Courtesy Jones and Scully, Inc.)

with a yellow disc on the lip. It occurs in the Andes of Peru.

Cochlioda rosea. Flowers of rosy-carmine have a pronounced white column. The blossoms are a little less than an inch in diameter but are numerous on the spikes. The plant occurs in Peru.

Cochlioda sanguinea. This Peruvian species is similar to *C. rosea,* but its flowers are rosy-pink.

Cochlioda vulcanica. Larger, dark rose flowers grow on erect spikes. The species is native to Ecuador.

Aspasia is a genus of Central American species not as well known as Cochlioda. The flowers are fewer and are produced on short stems close within the leaf axils. *Aspasia principissa* has greenish sepals and petals marked with brown, and a near-white lip. *A. epidendroides* is whitish yellow streaked with brown and has a white lip dotted with purple. The species *A.*

lunata and *A. variegata* carry out similar coloring. *A. pusilla* is a charming dwarf species with green sepals and petals and a bluish lavender lip.

Combinations among the genera are so varied that naming them has been a challenge. A few are easily distinguished by combining forms of the names of the genera, but so complicated do the combinations become that certain of them have been given names coined from names of persons famous in the orchid world.

Adaglossum = Ada × Odontoglossum. Adioda = Ada × Cochlioda. Brassidium = Brassia × Oncidium. Milpasia = Miltonia × Aspasia. Miltonioda = Miltonia × Cochlioda. Miltonidium = Miltonia × Oncidium. Odontioda = Cochlioda × Odontoglossum. Odontocidium = Odontoglossum × Oncidium. Odontonia = Miltonia × Odontoglossum. Oncidioda = Cochlioda × Oncidium. Crosses

given names of persons are: Burrageara =
Cochlioda × Miltonia × Odontoglossum ×
Oncidium. Charleswortheara = Cochlioda ×
Miltonia × Oncidium. Colmanara = Miltonia
× Odontoglossum × Oncidium. Sanderara =
Brassia × Cochlioda × Odontoglossum. Vuyl-
stekeara = Cochlioda × Miltonia × Odonto-
glossum. Wilsonara = Cochlioda × Odonto-
glossum × Oncidium.

Some of the inter-generic hybrids are beautiful things; others are curiosities with their
own appeal. More and more of this work is
being done, and it is a field in which the imagination of the amateur may have free play. The
warm reddish tones of Cochlioda, the soft hues
and ample proportions of Miltonia, the airy
grace and generosity of flowers of Oncidium
and Odontoglossum, and the intriguing traits
of other genera—all may be combined and

re-combined to create new and fascinating
things.

A new bi-generic creation has just recently
been made by W. W. G. Moir, (1960) Milpilia,
a cross between Miltonia and Trichopilia,
which shows an unexpected relationship between the genus Trichopilia and members of
this Tribe. The cross is *Miltonia spectabilis* ×
Trichopilia suavis, and has been named Milpilia
Magic. This, and new bi- and tri-generic hybrids
in other tribes, suggests that many kinds may
be more closely related than we have known.
Trichopilia is described in the next chapter.
Back in the 1920's Ada was crossed with both
Odontoglossum and Cochlioda, but apparently
nothing further has been done along this line.
Ada is also described in the next chapter.

18 | *Collectors' Items*

SOME of the orchids given in the preceding chapters could just as well have been included here, and some of those in this chapter are perhaps as well known, if not better known, than some of those described earlier. However, because it is interesting to relate one kind to another, and to know that famous kinds have less well known relatives, we have arranged them by tribes. We shall try as far as possible to continue with the tribal arrangement. Do not be disturbed, however, if you find in the future that one or another of the kinds has been moved to another tribe, or that separate genera have been combined into one genus. Sometimes it is difficult even for the experts to decide exactly how the orchids are related. A species may have a characteristic that is similar to one kind, and another feature that resembles another kind, and often it is a matter of opinion as to which characteristic is the more important in deciding where to place it. To help in locating the genera included in this chapter, we give below an outline of the contents.

Ada Tribe
 Ada
 Mesospinidum
 Quekettia

Bulbophyllum Tribe
 Bulbophyllum
 Cirrhopetalum

Catasetum Tribe
 Catasetum
 Cycnoches
 Mormodes
Coelogyne Tribe
 Coelogyne
 Neogyne
 Pholidota
 Platyclinis
 Pleione
Gongora Tribe
 Acineta
 Aganisia
 Coryanthes
 Gongora
 Houlettia
 Lacaena
 Peristeria
 Stanhopea
Ionopsis Tribe
 Comparettia
 Ionopsis
 Rodriguezia
 Trichocentrum
Lycaste Tribe
 Anguloa
 Batemannia
 Bifrenaria
 Lycaste
 Paphinia

Maxillaria Tribe
 Maxillaria
 Scuticaria
Phaius Tribe
 Acanthophippium
 Aplectrum
 Arundina
 Bletia
 Bletilla
 Calanthe
 Chysis
 Phaius
 Spathoglottis
Pleurothallis Tribe
 Pleurothallis
 Masdevallia
 Restrepia
 Scaphosepalum
Sobralia Tribe
 Calopogon
 Sobralia

Zygopetalum Tribe
 Chondrorhyncha
 Colax
 Huntleya
 Warscewiczella
 Zygopetalum

Miscellaneous Genera of Special Interest
 Coelia
 Cyrtopodium
 Hexisea

Lockhartia
Ornithocephalus
Sigmatostalyx
Stelis
Trichopilia
Vanilla

ADA TRIBE

The tribe contains few orchids that are generally grown, but since they are cool growing orchids, they add variety to an Odontoglossum house. There are three genera, consisting of very few species.

Ada has only two species, of which one seems to have been lost. The known species, *Ada aurantiaca*, bears sprays of orange flowers, which add a bright spot of color to the greenhouse. The petals and sepals are pointed and are held almost closed, barely showing the small, pointed lip. The plant occurs in Colombia at elevations of 8500 feet. It has been crossed with Odontoglossum and Cochlioda.

The genus **Mesospinidium** has five species, of which the species *Mesospinidium sanguineum* is cultivated for its sprays of bright rose-colored flowers. It is native to the Peruvian Andes.

The third genus of this tribe, **Quekettia**, is similar to Ada but little known horticulturally.

BULBOPHYLLUM TRIBE

Two genera make up this tribe, Bulbophyllum and Cirrhopetalum. They include some of the smallest orchids known, and some whose very odd shapes add variety to a collection. They are epiphytes, found in tropical Asia and Africa, and may be grown on osmunda or in a bark and tree fern mix. They require a warm, moist atmosphere, with ample water and frequent syringing during their growing period. During the winter they may be kept a little cooler at night, but should not be allowed to dry out.

Bulbophyllum

Single leaves are produced from pseudobulbs along a creeping rhizome. The flower stems grow from the base of the pseudobulbs and produce either several small flowers or a single large flower. The flowers are characterized by having the lateral sepals joined to the column at their broadened base, and by the small lip which is attached to the foot of the column. There are about 125 species.

Bulbophyllum grandiflorum. These plants bear a single eight-inch flower to the stem. The long, slender sepals are pale brown and yellow, the dorsal sepal bending forward, and lateral ones bending backward. The petals and lip are very tiny.

Bulbophyllum careyanum. One of the smallest of orchids. The flowers are only one-half inch in diameter, borne in a dense cluster. They are orange-yellow or greenish, spotted with red-brown or purple.

Cirrhopetalum

These rambling plants receive their name from their long, often tendril-like, lateral sepals, which grow like long, twisted tails away from the minute petals and lip. The little lip is often oscillating. Among the ninety species are found some weird and fascinating forms.

Cirrhopetalum medusae. Also called *Bulbophyllum medusae*, the plants are about six inches tall, and have odd little flowers, cream-colored and spotted with yellow or purple. The lateral sepals are hair-like, four or five inches long, and give the tight clusters of flowers the appearance of tiny Medusa heads. The lip and petals are extremely small. It occurs in Singapore.

Cirrhopetalum picturatum. A small plant with astonishing flowers that give the impression of a circus figure wrapped in a tight cloak. The greenish lateral sepals are extended together and their edges curve over so that they touch in the center. Above the "shoulders" of these sepals is a "masked face" formed by the tiny red lip in the center, tiny red petals to each side, and topped by the rounded dorsal sepal that is set off by a purple-knobbed thread at its peak. The little lip oscillates at the slightest breath of air. The plant, which comes from India, grows well with Cattleyas.

Fig. 118 *Cirrhopetalum picturatum*. Viewers will see different likenesses in these little cloaked and hooded figures. The tiny red lip bobbles with the slightest breeze.

CATASETUM TRIBE

The Catasetum tribe is made up of three genera, each with striking peculiarities. Catasetum and Cycnoches produce flowers of separate sexes, and Mormodes has flowers with the lip and the column twisted in opposite directions. All are native to the American tropics and are mostly epiphytic. They may be grown with Cattleyas. Catasetum and Cycnoches need a little warmer temperature and more water during the growing period than does Mormodes.

Catasetum

Catasetum is a genus that has puzzled orchidists for generations, and the species are not completely designated even yet. A few species produce perfect (bi-sexual) flowers. Most species have separate male and female flowers, but these occasionally produce perfect ones. Confusion among the species arose from the fact that female flowers were rarely seen. A plant may produce both male and female flowers at the same time or in successive years. But unless plants are found bearing both kinds of flowers, it is difficult to know which male form goes with which female form. Plants in cultivation have been known to give rise only to male flowers for periods of from twenty to forty years. At present, species are classified according to the male form, and a description of the female is given if it is known.

Male flowers are produced on a somewhat arching raceme bearing several blooms. They may be identified as such by the slender beak-shaped column, bearing at its base two curving antennae. These antennae (in some species only one is functional) serve as triggers which, when touched, cause the pollinia to fly out with some force. In nature the pollinia strike the body of a visiting bee and adhere to it by means of a sticky disc at the end of the caudicle. If you substitute a pencil to touch the antennae, the pollinia will strike and stick to it, or may shoot past it to a distance of two or three feet. Should you be holding the flower when you make it perform, the recoil will give you quite a start.

The males of some species (such as *Catasetum oerstedii* and *C. viridiflavum*) have a helmet-shaped lip, with the antennae curling around within it. The petals and sepals curve down in a semicircle. In other species (such as *C. fimbriatum*), the male form is slender and delicate, with a fimbriated lip. The petals and dorsal sepal overlap behind the upstanding column, whose antennae are completely exposed.

Female flowers occur only two or three to

Fig. 119 *Catasetum scurra,* a miniature catasetum with fragrant little green flowers.

an erect raceme. They are similar for all species, all having a helmet-shaped lip and a fat, blunt column.

In some species the female flowers have the lip uppermost (nonresupinate), while the male flower holds itself with the lip hanging down (resupinate). In other species the condition is exactly reversed, and in still others both male and female flowers are nonresupinate.

Colors tend to green, white, and yellow, often spotted with brown or purple, and the flowers last only a short time. The rather broad, pleated leaves are deciduous. The bases that are left attached to the pseudobulb are armed with sharp spines.

Catasetum fimbriatum. Purple-spotted green sepals and petals are bordered in white. The fringed lip is bright green, white inside. The pointed male column stands in front of the overlapping petals and dorsal sepal.

Catasetum oerstedii. A heavy, bold flower, dark because of the heavy spotting of purple in the lip, although the ground color of the lip is green and the petals and sepals are green. See illustration page 16.

Catasetum scurra. Pale greenish-white, delicate flowers have a daintily fringed lip and are very fragrant. The flowers are perfect.

Catasetum suave. Small, waxy, perfect flowers, bird-like in shape, very fragrant and long lasting. The stigma is entirely covered by the viscid disc of the pollinia, and is exposed only when the pollinia are removed.

Catasetum viridiflavum. Not as large as *C. oerstedii.* Yellow-green with few if any spots.

There are many more species, occurring through Central America and into Brazil.

Cycnoches

These are very lovely orchids, worth cultivating for their beauty as well as for their interesting habit. The name means swan's neck, referring to the arching column. The lip in some species is shaped like the body of a swan, adding to the illusion that gives them their name "swan orchid." Plants can produce either male or female flowers, or both at the same time, and occasionally may produce a spray of bi-sexual flowers. The pseudobulbs are columnar, bearing five to eight broad graceful leaves. The leaves are notoriously attractive to red spider, and should be sprayed regularly for this pest. They prefer a hanging position in an airy spot, and a daily misting with water. The flower spikes make their appearance from the axils of the leaves. During the development of the flowers the leaves will start to fall. After the leaves have fallen, the plants should be kept quite dry through the winter, with just an occasional syringing. When new growth starts in the spring, increase the watering as they develop. We feel that osmunda fiber makes a better medium than anything else for these heavy plants as it gives them a more solid footing, although a bark-hapuu mix is also good. Give them an occasional application of fertilizer in osmunda and more frequent applications in bark-hapuu. The species occur in Central America and northern South America.

Cycnoches aureum. Shown in the accompanying illustration. The male flowers are borne in a long slender inflorescence, while the female flowers are borne on a short erect stem. In the male flowers the long column arches over a delicate green and white lip which has small finger-like processes around its edge. Each little process is forked at its tip. The lip narrows to a fleshy stalk at its base called a "claw." The slender dorsal sepal bends backward, the broader lateral sepals are spreading. The petals curl under between the sepals. The male flower is yellow-green, somewhat toned with tan, becoming more and more yellow with age, and the parts are veined with darker green. The female flowers are broad and fleshy, more like those of *C. chlorochilon*, with a short, stocky column above a wide, plain white lip, which is extremely waxy and about one-third of an inch thick. The species occurs in Panama and flowers in the late summer and early fall.

Cycnoches chlorochilon. This is the best known species, the one most people know as the "swan orchid." The green or chartreuse flowers are marvelously fragrant and last a long time. The white, fleshy lip has a raised dark green callus in the center. The margin of the lip turns down and then flares out at the bottom. The spike holds from four to ten flowers that are four to five inches across. In this and similar species the female flowers are very much like the male, distinguished by having no pollinia at the tip of the shorter, more blunt column. This native of Panama flowers in fall or early winter.

Cycnoches egertonianum. This species is quite like *Cycnoches aureum*, except that the color is pale green, veined with darker green and lightly spotted. The color can run to purple. The male flowers are about three and one-half inches long, and narrow because the petals curve backward and the lateral sepals are held forward and together. Around the edge of the lip is a ring of finger-like processes, each slightly knobbed at the tip. In spite of their thin substance, the flowers last a long time. The female flower is large and fleshy. The species occurs in Costa Rica and other Central American countries.

Cycnoches ventricosum. Very similar to *Cycnoches chlorochilon* in shape, this species has a green-white color, and lasts only a short time. The sides of the lip turn more directly down and the lip has a long point. The lateral sepals are held close together. The flowers are three to four inches across. The plant grows throughout Central America. The female flowers are similar to the male.

Cycnoches warscewiczii. Even more like *C. chlorochilon* in shape, but perhaps more fleshy, and with the dorsal sepal longer and narrower than the lateral sepals. The flowers are yellow-green with a white lip whose edges roll upward at the bottom.

By some botanists, *C. chlorochilon* and *C. warscewiczii* are held to be varieties of *C. ventricosum*.

MORMODES

Mormodes is the third member of the Catasetum tribe. The name means grotesque creature, descriptive of the distortion of the lip and column. The flowers, contrary to those of the other two genera, are not separately male and female. The leaves are deciduous.

Fig. 120 Two species of Cycnoches. Left, the familiar green "swan," *Cycnoches chlorochilon,* whose color sometimes verges on chartreuse. (Courtesy H. A. Dunn and H. Griffin) Right, *Cycnoches aureum,* with a long chain of delicate male flowers and a short cluster of plump female flowers. (Courtesy of Montreal Botanical Garden)

Mormodes colossus. Largest flowered of this genus, the color varying, but more or less yellow and rose. The pseudobulbs are six to twelve inches high, topped by large leaves. The flower spike holds several blossoms. The plant occurs in Costa Rica and Panama.

Mormodes luxata. The fragrant, rather fleshy, globular flowers are lemon-yellow with a streak of brown down the center of the lip. The twisting of the lip and column is quite marked. The species, which is a native of Mexico, flowers in July.

It is interesting to note that in this genus there is quite a bit of variation from flower to flower on the same stem. Especially the lip varies in shape and size.

COELOGYNE TRIBE

The Coelogyne tribe contains several genera, of which the most popular is Coelogyne. The members of the tribe grow natively from Australia north to China. All are characterized by short, rounded or oval pseudobulbs, topped by two bright green, attractively ribbed leaves. Their small flowers are produced in dainty sprays.

Coelogyne

The genus Coelogyne is native to North India and Ceylon. There are over a hundred species, and though the species *Coelogyne cristata* is the best known, many are attractive and popular. They are easy to grow, and reward the amateur with a profusion of blooms for very little effort. Osmunda is a good potting medium, and pots, shallow pans, or baskets may be used. They have rather a rambling habit, and should be given plenty of room in the pot. Divisions are made after flowering, when necessary, by cutting the plant into groups of three pseudobulbs behind each new growth. They like firm potting and good drainage.

The species vary in exact temperature requirements. Many of them can be grown in the Cattleya house, however. They need copious water during their growing period, but are kept on the dry side, with only occasional waterings, during their period of lessened activity. They require some shade, adjusted to their needs. In some regions they may be placed out-of-doors in protected, shady places during the hottest months.

Coelogyne cristata. Considered by some to be the most beautiful of East Indian orchids. The combination of sprays of snow-white flowers, apple-green pseudobulbs, and dark green leaves is most attractive. The blooms measure three to five inches, and occur many to the spray which arises from the base of the pseudobulb. The petals and sepals are wavy, and project forward. The lip is three-lobed, the middle lobe decorated inside by five yellow, fringed keels. They keep beautifully and are highly decorative as sprays or for corsages. *Coelogyne cristata* likes fairly cool treatment and does not thrive in great heat. It occurs in the Himalayas and flowers in the winter.

Coelogyne pandurata. Sometimes called the "black orchid," although there are others that fit the name as well. The sepals and petals are emerald-green, and the fiddle-shaped lip is heavily veined and stained with black on a greenish ground. The middle lobe of the lip is ruffled and fringed and carries black warts and ridges. This species does well in the semitropical states. It is a native of Borneo. The blossoms appear in the summer.

Coelogyne tomentosa. Pendulous sprays of fifteen to twenty pale orange-red flowers are

Fig. 121 *Coelogyne cristata.* Ruffly white flowers decorated with yellow fringe within the lip. (Courtesy of Montreal Botanical Garden)

quite striking in appearance. Occurs in Borneo and Sumatra. Flowers in the summer.

Coelogyne dayana. A large plant, with pseudobulbs five to ten inches long and leaves measuring two and one-half feet. The long sprays bear many flowers which are pale yellow except that the lip is decorated with brown fringed ridges and has brown lateral lobes. This spring and summer blooming plant comes from Borneo.

Other Members of the Coelogyne Tribe

The four other members of the Coelogyne tribe are of lesser importance.

Neogyne is a genus of one species, *Neogyne gardneriana,* which produces small white flowers that quickly wither. It occurs in the Himalayas.

Pholidota has acquired the name "rattlesnake orchid" because the scales of the unopened flower raceme are reminiscent of the rattles of that snake. The flower stem grows from the top of the pseudobulb along with the developing leaf. Although the flowers are not colorful, being a yellowish white, a plant with many slender, trailing stems, each with over a hundred tiny flowers, is most attractive. Each flower peeks out from under a brownish bract. The best known species is *Pholidota imbricata,* which is easy to grow along with Cattleyas. See drawing in Chapter 1. *Pholidota chinensis* is seen in old Chinese paintings, and is native to India and China.

Platyclinis produces very delicate fragrant sprays of tiny white or yellow flowers, set close together on a thread-like stem. The pseudobulbs are crowded, each producing a single tall broad leaf. The plants are found in India, China, and the Malay Islands. Also known as Dendrochilum.

Pleione, "mother of the Pleiades," has rather large, attractive flowers and unusual plant characters, but seldom seems to be grown in this country. The pseudobulbs, which last only a year, are persimmon-shaped, sometimes warty, topped by a single leaf that is large in proportion. The leaf falls as the bulb matures. The flowers arise singly or in pairs on short stems that grow from the base of the bulbs.

Pleione praecox. The slender sepals and petals are pink, and the trumpet-shaped lip is fringed at the edges and striped yellow and white. The plant requires cool treatment as the species comes from high altitudes of India. It flowers from October to November.

GONGORA TRIBE

The eight genera of the Gongora tribe spread from Mexico to South America. They are distinguished for the curious formation of the lip, which is different in each genus, and which in some cases gives a reason for the cultivation of the flower. The plants have conical to globular pseudobulbs from which arise broad, pleated leaves. All are epiphytic. Those with pendulous flower stems should be grown in baskets, or at least in suspended pots, and those whose flower stems bore down through the potting medium must be assured of an open bottom in the container so that the stems can come through. We have grown them in pots with the bottom knocked completely out—potting them first in osmunda and then breaking off the bottom half of the pot. They like to have plenty of water through their growing season and to be somewhat dry while at rest. Hanging plants should be soaked in a bucket occasionally. Cattleya conditions suit them,

that is, a night temperature of fifty-five to sixty degrees.

Coryanthes

A fascinating genus, in which nature has certainly gone to extremes in the way of modifying the flower to insure pollination. Instead of merely offering nectar to a visiting insect, this genus employs incredibly devious means, as observed and charmingly described by Paul H. Allen. In the first place, it requires the services of one particular species of bee, so that it goes to great pains to make itself attractive to this bee and no other. In the second place, it causes the bee some pain and trouble, so it must make sure that its attraction is strong enough to "keep the bees coming" in spite of their difficulties. The flowers hang down from their stems. The lip is divided into three sections—the basal section (hypochile), the central section (mesochile), and the free outer part (epichile). This lip is marvelously molded into a scuttle-shaped bucket. The outer lobes (epichile) curve in to form the bucket with its spout, the meso- and hypo-chile form a long handle from which it hangs. The column swings down into the spout, with its end recurved to form a small tunnel together with the spout. The sepals curve together to form a hood over the spout. At the base of the column just above the bucket are two protuberances that have at their tip glands that secrete a fluid, which drips constantly into the bucket and keeps it about half full. (Whether the fluid is an intoxicant or simply a good wetting agent is not known.) The flowers emit a fragrance that attracts the bees very forcefully, for they come from some distance the minute the flowers open. In trying to make their way up the smooth mesochile of the lip to get to the source of the fragrance, they come in contact with a drop of the liquid secreted by the glands at the base of the column. This liquid fells the bee instantly, and it falls into the bucket. The bee flounders around, trying to find an exit, and finally makes its way to the spout. The opening is small and it has to struggle for some time to force its way out. In doing so, it removes the pollinia, and makes its exit with the pollinia stuck to its back. It is said that the flowers lose their fragrance within a few hours, so that no more bees visit them that day, but the next morning the fragrance is renewed and the visits again commence. This time, bees bearing pollinia will effect pollination in their route through the flower.

There are a number of species, all from Central and South America. They are variously colored and speckled, being mostly in shades of yellowish greens and browns with dots of red, purple, and green. The drooping flower stem emerges at the base of the pseudobulb and bears two to five flowers. The popular species are *Coryanthes macrantha*, *C. maculata*, and *C. speciosa*. They do well hung in the Cattleya house, and flower in the summer.

Gongora

The flowers in this genus are somewhat similar to Stanhopea, on a smaller and not so lurid scale. The petals are fused to the column for part of their length, standing up behind it like wings. The dorsal sepal stands close behind the petals. The lateral sepals are broad and swing sharply down (actually up because the flower is held upside down). The column is decorated with a pair of horns. The lip is fleshy and its parts curve into humps and horns, much like the Stanhopea lip. The species occur from Mexico to Brazil.

Gongora atropurpurea has two-inch chocolate colored, spotted flowers, borne about twenty on a long drooping stem. Occurs in Trinidad and British Guiana.

Gongora maculata has brownish red flowers, sometimes marked with yellow or white. Occurs from Mexico to Panama.

Other species are *G. armeniaca*, *G. galeata*, and *G. portentosa*.

Peristeria

A genus of stately plants, which produce their flowers on tall and erect stems from the base of the pseudobulb. Of the five species, one is very popular.

Peristeria elata. The waxy creamy-white

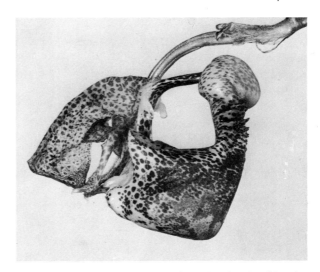

Fig. 122 *Coryanthes macrantha*. The bucket-like lip hangs under the tip of the column. Note the drops of fluid formed by glands on each side of the base of the column. (Courtesy of Montreal Botanical Garden)

flowers are often nicknamed the "dove orchid" or the "Holy Ghost flower." The flower spike starts along with the new growth in the spring. The purple-spotted lip is cup-shaped, with two wing-like appendages that stand up beside the column. The effect is that of a pulpit, in which stands the dove-shaped column. The sepals are round and, together with the smaller petals, form a solid background. The flowers are fragrant, about two inches in diameter, and are produced on a tall, straight spike. They open slowly, and each lasts a long time, so that the whole spike may be enjoyed for two or three months. Water is reduced while at rest. Repot in the spring, in large pots, using osmunda or bark mixed with shredded fiber or leaf mold. This is the national flower of Panama.

Stanhopea

The flowers of this genus possess a fleshy, horned lip which curves down under the long, arching column. The column is sometimes so long that it sweeps in a good half-circle and reaches out almost to touch the tip of the lip. The sepals and petals are thin, and the flower lasts only a few days. However, for its fragrance and curious shape it is worth having even for that short time. The flower stems bore

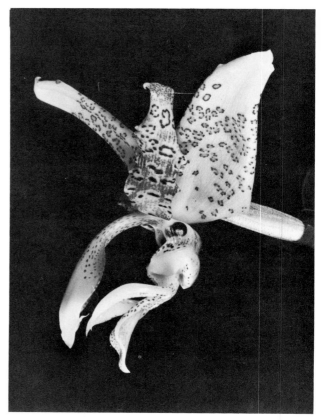

Fig. 123 Possibly no other pair of orchids could better show the intriguing diversity of form in this great family of plants; yet these two are not distantly related, but belong to the same tribe. Left, *Peristeria elata,* the "Holy Ghost" or "dove" orchid, personifica- tion of purity and serenity. Right, *Stanhopea wardii,* lurid with its tawny color, purple spotting and large purple eye, and threatening in its attitude of bird of prey. (*Peristeria elata* courtesy of H. A. Dunn and H. Griffin)

their way down through the potting medium and emerge at the bottom of the basket, for which reason the plants must be grown in an open container.

Stanhopea oculata is very much like S. *wardii,* except the basal portion (hypochile) of the lip is not so large. It is variously dotted with purple, perhaps not so heavily as is S. *wardii.*

Stanhopea wardii. These huge, lurid flowers almost defy description. They look something like a cross between an eagle and a squid, and if that is too fantastic a creation, they do surely resemble a bird of prey swooping down out of the sky. The flower stem emerges from the bottom of the basket, bearing two to six buds, which grow rapidly larger until they burst open quite suddenly. You can tell when you open the greenhouse door that the Stanhopeas are open by the strong fragrance, in the case of S. *wardii* something akin to menthol. The flowers are a rich gold in color, with a greenish column and a whitish, very fleshy lip. The column is dotted with small spots of purple, the petals with larger dots, and the sepals with somewhat circular tiger spots. The sepals flare up like wings, the petals, which are much smaller, curl up between them, and the lip and column swing down together. The column is broadened by wings along its sides, and has two horns at the tip. The lip has two long horns that curve toward the triangular tip from the mesochile. The hypochile is boat shaped, hollow on the inside, with two large dark purple eyes on either side. The plants occur from Mexico to Panama.

Other species that are popular are S. *bucephalus*, S. *eburnea*, S. *insignis*, S. *lowii*, all from South America, and S. *devoniensis*, S. *ecornuta*, S. *graveolens*, S. *martiana*, and S. *tigrina*, all from Central America.

Other Members of the Gongora Tribe

Acineta is a genus not very well known, but which is well worth growing. It needs a warm spot in the Cattleya house. The flower stem bores down through the potting medium, to a length of a foot or so, and holds many small flowers.

Acineta barkeri has bright yellow flowers striped with red. The flowers are globe-shaped, the petals and sepals holding the lip hidden within them. The lip is marked with a spot of bright red. This plant is a native of Mexico.

Acineta superba (also called *A. humboldtii*) has chocolate colored flowers spotted with crimson and grows in Colombia.

Aganisia is a genus rather rare in cultivation. Its two species need quite warm conditions. The flowers are small on an erect stem. *Aganisia cyanea* has bluish lavender flowers, and *Aganisia pulchella* white blossoms with red spots.

Houlletia has a number of attractive species. The flowers are somewhat reminiscent of Peristeria, except that they are more open, and are richly colored. The column gives the appearance of a little figure standing on the platform of the short, out-curved lip. *Houlletia brocklehurstiana*, from Brazil, has seven to ten red-brown flowers spotted with a darker shade and striped with yellow. The pseudobulbs bear a single very tall leaf. *Houlletia landsbergi*, possibly from Guatemala, has large reddish orange flowers spotted with red-brown.

Lacaena is a rather rare genus, with rather globose flowers which are very fragrant and are white spotted with purple.

IONOPSIS TRIBE

The four genera that make up this tribe range natively from Mexico to Brazil. All are small, even dwarf, epiphytes and produce sprays of dainty flowers. Some are quite striking, whereas others are interesting purely as botanicals.

Rodriguezia

The most popular genus, and the most showy, is Rodriguezia. The plants are small, with delicate sprays of dainty flowers. The lateral sepals are united, and the lip is more or less spurred. Their culture is similar to that of Laelia and Cattleya.

Rodriguezia secunda. The whole plant is dwarf in habit, and the six-inch long spray carries twenty to thirty rose-colored flowers, all on one side of the stem. The plants, which occur in Trinidad and Guiana, flower in August.

Rodriguezia venusta. The flowers are a little larger than they are in *secunda*, and the sprays more open. They are white, tinged with pink, and the lip is marked with yellow. Occurs in Brazil. Flowering time variable.

Comparettia

These are graceful little plants, whose small flowers are brightly colored and curiously constructed. The lateral sepals are united and form a horn at their base. The petals and upper sepal form a sort of hood over the column. The lip has a double spur at its base which fits into the horn made by the sepals. The front lobe of the lip is broad and somewhat heart-shaped. They will grow well in a Cattleya house and must never be allowed to become dry. The flowers last well.

Comparettia coccinea has pretty little flowers, one inch in diameter, light yellow margined with orange, with a crimson lip.

Comparettia falcata is similar to *coccinea*, but with flowers entirely deep crimson or purple.

Ionopsis

The third genus of the tribe is Ionopsis. It is interesting because of its many-branched flower stem, which rises to two or three times the height of the small plant, and carries almost innumerable delicate flowers.

Ionopsis paniculata. The tiny petals and sepals are pointed, and overlap one another.

The lip is large and spreading and curves downward. It is downy, usually white, sometimes with a patch of purple or yellow.

Trichocentrum

This genus is characterized by its odd trowel-shaped lip which is prolonged at its base into a prominent spur. The sepals and petals are free, sometimes longer than the lip and spreading, sometimes smaller and overlapping. The flowers are brightly colored.

Trichocentrum albo-purpureum. This species has stunning little flowers greenish on the outside, maroon-brown within, and a white lip decorated with two purple spots.

Trichocentrum panduratum. The sepals and petals of this species are extremely short and overlapping, and the lip is long and narrow with a long tail-like spur. The general appearance of the flower is that of an old-fashioned salt shovel.

LYCASTE TRIBE

Most orchid collections contain a few members of the Lycaste tribe, particularly of the genus Lycaste itself. They are grown not only for their ease of culture, but for their distinct individuality and charm. All members of the tribe are natives of Central or South America or the West Indies. They are mostly high altitude plants and therefore grow best under fairly cool conditions. The coolest spot in the Cattleya house may suit them, with night temperatures in the winter of fifty to fifty-five degrees. They like to be cool in the summer, too, and shaded from direct sunlight both winter and summer.

Finely chopped osmunda fibre or a mix such as used for Cymbidiums will make good potting media. Watering must be handled judiciously so as not to let the medium become soggy. Propagation is by division, cutting through the rhizomes to separate the bulbs in groups of two. Repotting and division should be done just as new growth starts.

Bigeneric hybrids have been made between Lycaste and Anguloa (Angulocaste) and Lycaste and Bifrenaria (Lycasteria).

Lycaste

The oval, somewhat corrugated pseudobulbs bear broad, pleated leaves which last but a year or two. When the bulbs are newly growing they are sheathed with smaller leaves which soon fall. The quaint flowers are borne singly on stems that arise from the base of the pseudobulbs starting as the new leaves form. The broad sepals stand out gracefully, while the petals and lip give the impression of a sunbonnet in the center. The petals stand forward, each with its tip gracefully turned out, and surround the small lip which just protrudes from within. The lateral sepals are united at the base to form a short spur or chin. The blooms last a long time, and a plant may flower for months. The plants are kept fairly dry through the winter, and are watered generously during growth and flowering.

Lycaste aromatica. This is an attractive species with flowers about three inches across, yellow, tinged with green. The lip is spotted with orange. It has a strong, pleasant fragrance. During its resting period it should have considerably less water but should not be allowed to remain dry for long periods. The plants occur in Mexico and flower in winter and spring.

Lycaste deppei. This interesting species has curiously colored flowers. The sepals are dull green, spotted with chocolate-purple. In striking contrast, the petals are white, and the little lip, with its middle lobe waved, is yellow. It occurs in Guatemala and flowers nearly all year round.

Lycaste dowiana. Prim, quietly colored flowers are produced in profusion. The sepals are olive green on the back, brown in front, and the petals and little fringed lip are pale yellow. The species is native to Panama.

Lycaste skinneri. Also called *L. virginalis.* This most often grown species has flowers that reach six inches in diameter. They are waxy, white, tinged with rose. The middle lobe of the lip is tongue shaped, marked with a purple callus, or variously dotted with purple. *Lycaste skinneri* is one of the easiest of all orchids to grow. Its flowers last well and can be enjoyed for a long time. There are many named varieties, which range from pure white to dark purple. This species requires a much less intense rest period than the more deciduous ones. It is the national flower of Guatemala and flowers in the spring.

Anguloa

The genus Auguloa is native to the Andes. It has only three species, but each is attractive and easy to grow. They are noted for their fragrance, and for their peculiar globular shape which has given them a number of nicknames, such as "tulip orchid" or "boat orchid." Their hinged lip oscillates gently with the least movement. The plants themselves are rather striking, with their long, broad, pleated leaves, and the tall, sheathed flower stem rising from the base of the conical pseudobulbs, bearing a single flower. Although they are more or less terrestrial in habit, they will grow in osmunda fibre, to which may be added a third part soil, or possibly some well-dried cow manure. A night temperature of fifty degrees is desirable in the winter, and a cool, shaded environment in the summer. They require ample moisture and water all year round.

Anguloa clowesii. These lemon yellow flowers are green inside with a white downy lip.

Anguloa uniflora. Creamy white blossoms are flushed or dotted inside with pink.

Anguloa ruckeri. These flowers are greenish-yellow, flushed with brown on the outside, spotted inside with red.

Batemannia

This genus has a number of species, the best known of which is *Batemannia colleyi.* Its flowers are strikingly colored and make it worthy of attention. The sepals and petals are red, backed and tipped with green. The dorsal sepal and the petals are about equal in size and form a solid background for the cup-shaped lip which is white sprinkled with red dots. The lateral sepals are longer and trail down under the lip. It occurs in Guiana, Peru, Trinidad, Colombia and Brazil.

Fig. 124 *Lycaste dowiana,* softly colored appealing little flowers each produced on a single stem. (Courtesy of H. A. Dunn)

Bifrenaria

A genus that is rarely grown, Bifrenaria is of interest to botanical collectors. The pseudobulbs are shorter and thicker than in Lycaste, and the leaves are broader. The flowers have a definite spur where the lateral sepals enclose a foot-like projection at the base of the column.

Bifrenaria aurantiaca. Clusters of little yellow flowers are spotted with bronze-purple.

Bifrenaria indora. Small apple green flowers have a white, yellow, or rose lip and a long spur.

Paphinia

A genus native to South America, Paphinia is similar to Lycaste in requirements. The flowers have the lip uppermost, which gives them a curious appearance.

Paphinia cristata. These rather large, star-shaped flowers have white sepals and petals which are streaked and striped with chocolate-purple. The small spade-shaped lip is chocolate-purple fringed with white. The plant occurs in Trinidad.

Fig. 125 *Maxillaria sanderiana*. The flowers hold themselves upward with the prominent chin nestled down into the sheathing leaves of the short stem. (Courtesy of Montreal Botanical Garden)

Paphinia grandiflora. The flowers of this species are chocolate brown. The sepals and petals are bordered with greenish yellow, and banded on their lower halves with this same color. The lip is purple with a white middle lobe.

Paphinia rugosa. These flowers are creamy white, spotted with red.

MAXILLARIA TRIBE

The two members of this tribe, Maxillaria and Scuticaria, are appealing to those who enjoy a wide variety in their collections. They grow natively from Central America to Brazil. They can be grown in osmunda fibre, prefer shallow pots with good drainage or baskets, and are kept moist all year round. They may be grown with Cattleyas and should be well shaded.

Maxillaria

There are two sections of this genus of over a hundred species—those which have more or less climbing stems and those which grow with clustered pseudobulbs.

Maxillaria houtteana. This is an example of the climbing type. The pseudobulbs rise out of a sheathed stem. The flowers are oddly colored. The spreading sepals are dull yellow on the outside, marked with a purple patch on the upper inside half, and purple spots toward the

base. The smaller petals are similarly marked and curve toward each other. The tongue-like lip is yellow with red-brown spots. It occurs in Guatemala. The flowers, which appear in April, last a month if kept cool.

Maxillaria sanderiana. This is the finest of the nonclimbing type. The pseudobulbs are small, and the leaves are about six inches tall. The large flower is borne on a short stem, so that it appears to be nestled at the base of the plant. The large, wide sepals and the smaller petals are white, spotted with purple near the base. The lip curves upward, almost forming a cup, and exposing the chin formed by the base of the sepals joined to the column foot. This species is a native of Ecuador.

Maxillaria longissima. This is an example of a type whose sepals are extended into long tails. The petals are also extended, though not

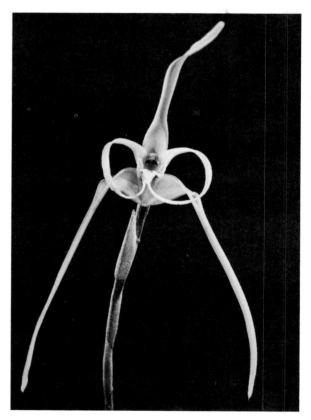

Fig. 126 An unusual species, *Maxillaria longissima*. In contrast to the other members of this genus, this one has its sepals and petals prolonged into tails. (Courtesy of Montreal Botanical Garden)

as much as the sepals, and curve in a graceful circle. The brownish flowers are produced singly on upright stems. The plant occurs in Ecuador.

There are many other species and there is quite an array of dwarf types.

Scuticaria

The two species of this genus are characterized by their whip-like leaves, which are about as thick as a goose quill, and by their lack of pseudobulbs. *Scuticaria steelii* has leaves one and one-half feet long, whereas in *Scuticaria hadwenii* they are four feet long. The flowers of both are similar to those of Maxillaria, and their culture is the same.

PHAIUS TRIBE

This tribe of mostly terrestrial orchids covers a large part of the world with its various genera. Many are deciduous and flower after the leaves have fallen. Two of the genera, Phaius and Calanthe, are rather widely grown.

Phaius

A genus of large, handsome plants, Phaius is composed of some twenty species that produce tall spikes of showy flowers. There are among the species some that are epiphytic as well as the better known terrestrial ones. The former are seldom grown.

The terrestrial species are native to tropical Asia, Africa, Australia, Madagascar, China, and Japan. They have been cultivated since 1778, when *Phaius tankervilliae* (*grandifolius*) was imported from China. This is commonly known as the "nun's orchid" or the "veiled nun."

This genus likes an intermediate greenhouse with adequate shade, and night temperatures that do not fall below fifty-five degrees. The potting compost is a mixture of sandy loam, well-rotted cow manure, and shredded peat moss or osmunda, in equal parts. The pots must have plenty of drainage crock in the bottom. To insure adequate nutrition, the top surface of the soil is covered with a mulch of cow manure. A fertilizer solution may be added after the flower spikes have started. The plants grow vigorously, and require plenty of water all year round.

Plants of Phaius may be divided every two or three years, when the blooming season is over. Young plants may be grown from dormant buds on the flower scapes, in the manner described for Dendrobium canes. After the flowers have withered, cut the stem, lay it on moist sand in a flat. Cover with glass or muslin to keep in the moisture and provide shade. The little plants that grow from the dormant buds will be large enough in a few months to be potted up.

Dwellers in the southern states may grow members of this genus out-of-doors under the trees. In some regions they may be kept (in their pots) in the garden at least for the summer, being brought into the greenhouse before the nights turn cool.

Phaius maculatus. Attractive yellow flowers, two to three inches in diameter, are borne in clusters of ten to fifteen on spikes two feet tall. The lip is erect with the front lobe recurved and streaked with orange. The base of the lip forms a prominent spur. The foliage of this plant is attractively variegated with yellow. It occurs in North India and Japan and flowers in the spring.

Phaius tankervilliae (*grandifolius*). These are majestic plants, familiarly known as the "nun's orchid." The tall flower spikes carry ten to fifteen flowers whose petals and sepals are white on the back, reddish brown inside. The lip is tubular, with a short spur, a yellow throat, and crimson sides. The species occurs in China and Australia. The flowers appear in winter and spring.

A number of bigeneric hybrids have been made between Phaius and Calanthe, which are named after both genera, Phaiocalanthe.

Calanthe

The name Calanthe means "beautiful flower," and each of the species known in cultivation lives up to this name. The genus contains some forty or fifty species, some of which are deciduous and some evergreen, but all are terrestrial. The deciduous species have

Fig. 127 *Calanthe vestita*, a lovely and distinctive species. (Courtesy of Montreal Botanical Garden)

tall, conical pseudobulbs that reach eight or nine inches in height, from which rise the handsome, heavily ribbed leaves. The leaves fall before or at the time of flowering. In the evergreen species the pseudobulbs are lacking and the leaves grow directly from the creeping rhizome.

Mr. Dominy, the original orchid hybridist, made his first cross with Calanthes. In 1856 Calanthe Dominii (*Calanthe masuca* × *Calanthe furcata*), the first hybrid orchid, flowered.

Calanthe is potted in the same manner as Phaius. The bulbs may be separated once a year, when growth is just starting in the spring, or the plant may be repotted without being divided. New growths come from the base of the old bulbs. A method often used is to separate the bulbs and put several in one large pot, to be assured of a good display of flowers. Water sparingly until growth starts, and give the new leaves extra shade for a while. After

the leaves are well along, the plants need more light, but, as for Cattleyas, the light must be properly moderated. Calanthe thrives in warm places in the greenhouse, with a temperature of fifty-five to sixty degrees at night and with generous daytime humidity.

During their growing season, water the deciduous species generously. The frequency of watering is reduced when the foliage begins to turn yellow in the fall. When the flower spikes show, increase the watering and continue until the blooms are finished. After their winter flowering, the plants must have a decided rest. The pots may be laid on their sides in a cool place and given no water until the following spring. Some growers separate the bulbs, dust them with a fungicide such as Tersan or Arasan (or dip them in a solution), and store them in a dry place at 60°. As soon as root growth begins, the plants must be repotted. The evergreen species are watered all year round.

Calanthe vestita. Once one of the most widely grown of all orchids, this species is still very popular. The lovely sprays of white flowers appear in winter, keep well, and lend themselves to decorations for holiday social affairs or to dainty corsages. The sepals and petals are more or less overlapping, and hold themselves up and back from the long, beautiful lip. The front lobe of the lip is scalloped, and flaring, with a touch of yellow or crimson in the throat. The pseudobulbs are silvery green and the deciduous leaves are nearly two feet long. The flower spike rises to a height of two or three feet. The plants occur in Malaya.

The hybrid Calanthe Veitchii (*Calanthe rosea* × *Calanthe vestita*) is one of the most popular and is as widely grown as *Calanthe vestita* itself. The flowers are rose colored, and the lip is decorated with a white spot near the base.

The parents of the first hybrid orchid were evergreen Calanthes. *Calanthe furcata* bears creamy white flowers generously distributed on a long spike. The plant has large fan-like leaves. *Calanthe masuca* has deep violet flowers on spikes somewhat shorter than those of *C. furcata.* Both require warm, humid growing conditions.

Other Members of the Phaius Tribe

Acanthophippium comes from the hottest moist jungles of Java, where it grows in heavy shade. The odd flowers are borne on stems that grow from the base of the pseudobulbs. The broad, fleshy sepals enclose the petals and lip, giving the flower the shape of an urn. The species *A. javanicum* has yellow flowers flushed and striped with red.

Aplectrum is a genus that grows wild in our own northern woods. The single species, *A. hyemale,* produces a single evergreen leaf and in the spring a spike of brownish flowers. It is commonly called "Adam and Eve."

Arundina is a genus whose plants resemble Sobralias and whose flowers are similar to Cattleyas. A very tall plant, up to four feet, it needs plenty of room and can be grown out-of-doors in warm climates. The flower scape has few flowers, but the rosy-lilac blossoms are attractive. The popularly known "bamboo orchid," *Arundina bambusaefolia,* should correctly be called *Arundina graminifolia.* It occurs in Indo-Malaysia.

Bletia is a genus of twenty species native to tropical America. The plants have spherical pseudobulbs, from the apex of which the tall flower spikes are produced.

Bletia verecunda produces rose-colored flowers, the blooms of *Bletia shepherdii* are deep purple, and those of *Bletia sherrattiana* are bright rose. These plants all have leaves from three to four feet long.

Bletilla, a genus from China, includes the species *Bletilla striata,* popularly known as *Bletilla hyacinthina* or *Bletia hyacinthina,* often sold in grocery stores and by garden supply companies. It is terrestrial, with small corms underground, and can be grown out-of-doors in most parts of this country. The stem is a foot tall, with several pleated leaves, and bears a spike of small Cattleya-like flowers that are amethyst-purple.

Chysis is a genus of attractive epiphytes native to tropical America. They are deciduous, and require warm growing conditions (sixty degrees at night) and plenty of water. After flowering, they should be given little or no water and kept cool. The flowers are brightly colored, of heavy, waxy texture, and are produced in clusters from the axils of the leaves.

The species, *Chysis aurea, laevis,* and *chelsonii* have yellow flowers marked with red.

The species, *Chysis bractescens, limminghei,* and *sedenii* have white flowers marked with red, purple, or yellow.

Spathoglottis is a genus of terrestrial orchids native to India and China. They have small corm-like pseudobulbs and grassy foliage. The small, bright flowers are usually produced in small numbers on rather tall spikes. Where they may be grown out-of-doors, for instance in our warm states where the climate is humid, they might be worth a try, for their foliage is quite attractive.

PLEUROTHALLIS TRIBE

This tribe is interesting because of one member in particular, the genus Masdevallia. They are native to high altitudes in tropical

Fig. 128 *Chysis bractescens,* waxy flowers of ivory white, the lip toned with yellow and striped with red. (Courtesy of Jones and Scully, Inc.)

Central and South America and are all cool-growing.

Masdevallia

The over one hundred and fifty species of this genus are distinguished by their weird and grotesque shapes, to which some of them add brilliant coloring and fragrance to make them spectacular and amusing additions to collections. The plants have no pseudobulbs. The stems grow from the rhizome in a bushy or tufted manner and bear ribbed leaves. A first glance at a flower reveals little of the familiar orchid shape, for the petals, and often the lip, are so tiny that they are hardly visible. The conspicuous parts of the flower are the sepals, which are transformed in a most unusual manner. They are united at the base to form a calyx tube, and the spreading parts are often prolonged into horns or tails. The petals and lip are usually hidden within the calyx tube, and the lip is sometimes sensitive.

The plants may be grown in pots or baskets in osmunda fiber to which is added one-third chopped sod. Winter temperatures should be fifty degrees at night and sixty to sixty-five degrees in the daytime. In the summer the temperatures should be kept as cool as possible in the manner of Odontoglossum culture. They need a generous supply of water all year round, with good air circulation and atmospheric moisture.

Masdevallia coccinea. The small flowers are crimson-magenta. The dorsal sepal is slender and tail-like, bent backward from a triangular base. The lateral sepals are broad and ribbed, tapering to a point, the tips curving somewhat toward each other.

Masdevallia chimaera. This grotesque species has the sepals prolonged into tails sometimes nearly a foot long. The yellow tails taper away from a continuous, out-turned base that is heavily spotted with purple. These must be grown in baskets as the flower stems sometimes grow down through the potting medium.

Masdevallia elephanticeps. The formation of the flower suggests an elephant head with the trunk raised. The dorsal sepal is yellow, the other two crimson.

Masdevallia muscosa. The sensitive lip has a raised yellow disc. When the disc is touched the lip moves upward with a jerk. The sepals are alike, triangular, with the tips prolonged into tails and curving backward. The leaves are covered with round papillae, and the flower stem is hairy.

Masdevallia roezlii. The flowers are similar in character to *M. chimaera*, but are the darkest in coloring of the genus. The yellow ground color is almost obscured by the brown crossbars. The long tails are solid brown, and the small lip is pink.

Other Genera of the Pleurothallis Tribe

The genus **Pleurothallis** has 400 species, but most of them have inconspicuous flowers and for this reason are seldom cultivated. One species, *Pleurothallis ornata*, is interesting for its dwarf habit. The tufted leaves are barely an inch tall, and the tiny flowers are produced in a little feathery spray. They are yellow, spotted with brown, and the sepals are fringed with silvery hairs.

Restrepia is a genus whose members look like little Masdevallias. They are dwarf plants, with interesting flowers that are less spectacular than the latter.

Scaphosepalum is distinguished from Masdevallia by having the dorsal sepal nearly free, and the lateral sepals united into a boat-shaped body. The plants are less compact, and the flowers are borne on a long spray on which they open in succession over a period of several months.

SOBRALIA TRIBE

The Sobralia tribe is a group of terrestrial orchids which includes two genera, Sobralia, native to Mexico and tropical America, and Calopogon, native to North America.

Sobralia is a genus of reed-like plants, whose stems grow close together in thick, bushy clumps. They take up quite a bit of room in a greenhouse, but if space can be afforded they are worth growing for their hand-

Cypripedium Christine 'Golden Beauty'. (Courtesy of Dos Pueblos Orchid Company)

Vanda Sanderiana. (Courtesy of L. Sherman Adams Company)

some foliage and large, Cattleya-like flowers. They vary in height from one to ten feet, and the flowers are from one and one-half to nine inches in diameter. The individual flowers do not last long, but the plants produce a succession of blooms that give a continuous show.

The Sobralias lack pseudobulbs. They require a rich, porous compost, a mixture of loam, leaf mold, osmunda shreds, and cow manure. The pots should be large, with ample drainage to allow for the copious water supply they need during their growing period. During the winter they require somewhat less water, but should never be allowed to become dry at the roots. They may be grown out-of-doors in our subtropical states, but require cool greenhouse treatment farther north.

Sobralia fragrans. One of the smallest of the genus, this species has flowers of sulfur yellow, one and one-half to two inches in diameter and borne two to a stem. One of their charms is the fringed lip, which is decorated with many fringed crests. It occurs in Costa Rica, Panama, and neighboring countries.

Sobralia leucoxantha. Plants three feet tall have a profusion of flowers. The sepals and petals are pure white. The gracefully waved lip is white, with its golden throat striped with brown. The species is native to Costa Rica and Panama; it flowers in August.

Sobralia macrantha. Tall, handsome plants reach a height of from four to seven feet, with rose-purple flowers often nine inches in diameter. The sepals are slender and twisted, the petals broader and wavy. The front lobe of the lip is almost round, deep purple, and beautifully ruffled. The throat is whitish with several yellow ridges. This native of Mexico and Guatemala flowers from May to July.

Calopogon

Of the several species in this genus, the well known *Calopogon pulchellus* grows from Newfoundland to Florida in bogs and moist meadows. It will do well in a shaded place in your garden in a porous soil, with ample water. The plants should not be disturbed very often, but offsets may be separated from the large clumps occasionally. The small offsets take several years to reach blooming size, whereas large clumps bought from collectors will flower immediately. *Calopogon pulchellus* grows in clusters of solid bulbs or corms, each producing a single, grassy leaf. The flower stem carries two to twelve attractive flowers that vary in color from magenta-crimson to white. The lip is uppermost in the flower, and is bearded with white, yellow, or purple hairs.

ZYGOPETALUM TRIBE

A number of genera have been moved into and out of this tribe, so it is not certain how long those which we will give here will remain. They all come from Central and South America, some being limited to one country.

Zygopetalum

This is a genus of stunning flowers, the best known of the tribe. The flowers are large, with greenish petals and sepals marked and blotched with brownish tones, and a lip that is usually colored quite differently, making a striking contrast. The short, rounded pseudobulb is revealed after the luxurious pleated leaves mature. The name Zygopetalum comes from the fact that the nearly equal sepals and petals are somewhat united at the base. The rather tall flower stem comes from the base of the pseudobulb and carries several flowers. The plants like Cattleya conditions and prefer to be fairly cool in the summer. They are grown in osmunda fiber or in a mix consisting of chopped fiber, chopped bark, leaf mold, and some sand. They should be kept damp all year round.

Zygopetalum crinitum. The sepals and petals are green, barred with brown. The wide downy lip is white, with purple veins radiating from the thick crest at its base. The species occurs in Brazil; its flowering time is variable.

Zygopetalum intermedium. The green sepals and petals are marked with confluent patches of brown. The rounded lip is two lobed in front, downy, with bluish white radiating broken lines of purplish-blue. A native of Brazil, this species flowers in the winter.

Fig. 129 Upper, *Zygopetalum mackayi*, a stunning species that combines yellow-green, purple, and blue in its coloring. A fine plant for cool conditions. (Courtesy of Jack Sweet). Lower, *Warscewiczella discolor*, a delightful plant in every way, from its light green foliage to its charming flowers with their pale greenish sepals and petals, and lip tinged with deep blue.

Zygopetalum mackayi. The sepals and petals of this Brazilian species are greenish yellow, marked with blotches of purple. The large round lip is smooth, white, veined with broken lines of deep blue. The flower spike starts within the newly developing growth. The flowers open in the winter, often in December, and last eight or nine weeks.

Other species less well known are *Z. maxillara, Z. burkei, Z. grandiflorum,* and *Z. rostratum.*

Warscewiczella

The beautiful example of this genus, *Warscewiczella discolor,* has been called Warrea, Zygopetalum, and Chondrorhyncha, and seems now destined to go back to the latter genus. However, it is well known by the name Warscewiczella. It is a delightful plant, pretty in its own right, with no pseudobulbs and the growths consisting of several light green pleated leaves about ten inches tall. The flowers arise singly on stems from the base of the growths, one after another, so that the plant is in flower for several months through winter and spring. The plant is vigorous and spreads rapidly, so that within a short time there are many growths completely encircled by flowers. The flowers have pale green slender sepals that bend backward and petals of the same color that form a hood over the lip. The lip is purplish blue, a generously open tube, within which can be seen a toothed yellow crest.

Other Members of the Zygopetalum Tribe

Huntleya. *Huntleya meleagris,* also called *H. burtii,* although they seem to be separate species, is a member of a small genus that occurs from Costa Rica to Panama, Colombia, and Brazil. There is no pseudobulb; the leaves are like those of Warscewiczella but arranged somewhat like a fan. The heavy star-shaped flowers are about three inches across, with sepals and petals yellow at the base and marked with brown on the outer portions. The lip is triangular, white marked with greenish brown, with a fringed white crest. The cool end of the Cattleya house suit them.

The genus **Colax** has only two known species, of which *Colax jugosus* has striking red, white, and blue flowers. The sepals are pure white, the petals white spotted with red or red-violet, and the fiddle-shaped lip striped and spotted with blue-violet. It occurs in Brazil. It has been crossed with several species of Zygopetalum.

Chondrohyncha is a genus of several species, some of which have flowers similar to Zygopetalum. The plants have no pseudobulbs, and the leaves are broad and pleated. The flowers arise singly from the axils of the leaves. *Chondrorhyncha chestertonii* has flowers three inches across, of a pale yellow-green. The sepals and petals are similar, but the lip is broad, yellow spotted with red, and decorated with fringe. The plant should be kept damp throughout the year, and likes a slightly shaded spot in the Cattleya house.

Miscellaneous Genera

Coelia. The best known of this genus is *Coelia triptera*, which produces a brush-like cluster of small white, very fragrant flowers. The plants have a rounded pseudobulb which bears two or three tall, veined leaves. They like a cool spot in the Cattleya house.

Cyrtopodium. This genus includes the famous "cigar orchid" of Florida, *Cyrtopodium punctatum*, which also has the nicknames "bee swarm orchid" and "cowhorn orchid." The curved, pointed pseudobulbs grow up to three feet tall, with leaves up to two feet long. In nature they develop into heavy masses of pseudobulbs. The flower spike is up to five feet tall, and bears a showy display of bright yellow flowers spotted with crimson. This species occurs from Florida to South America. The species *C. andersonii* has been known to produce over a hundred flowers to the spike.

Hexisea. A burst of tiny bright red flowers comes from the rather tall, slender stems of *Hexisea bidentata*. The plants are rather awkward, with tall jointed stems bearing leaves at each node. Smaller species, that are more attractive as plants but with less bright flowers, are sometimes available from collectors.

Lockhartia. These beautiful little plants would be worth growing whether they flowered or not. The stem is clothed with little fleshy alternate leaves that give a braided effect. From the axils of the top leaves come stems of tiny flowers that are very charming. The species *Lockhartia hercondonta* has white to pale green flowers, while in *Lockhartia oerstedii* they are bright yellow. All are from Central America. They prefer a warm spot in the Cattleya house, with moisture all year around.

Ornithocephalus. The leaves of these dwarf plants are arranged in a round flat fan. The little flower spikes come from between the leaves, and a plant may have a dozen or so at one time, each with twenty or more tiny greenish white flowers. The flowers are so small, and their parts so complicated that a hand lens is required to find the parts. The reason for the name is that the rostellum of the column is projected into a long beak-like structure. The best known species is *Ornithocephalus bicornis* which comes from Central America. See illustration page 247.

Stelis. These dwarf plants have paddle shaped leaves and stems of tiny rounded flowers like a string of beads. There are more than 200 species, all from Central America and South America. The flowers are round, three pointed because the sepals are rounded and flat, holding within them the tiny petals and lip. A well known species is *Stelis bidentata*, whose little flowers are bright red, with at least a hundred on a stem four inches tall. It occurs in Panama.

Sigmatostalyx. Another dwarf plant of great charm, this one has tiny pseudobulbs each bearing two or more leaves. The whole plant is about four inches tall. The delicate flower spikes come from the base of the pseudobulbs, and hold a dozen or so jaunty flowers less than one-quarter inch long. The most outstanding

Fig. 130 *Lockhartia micrantha.* Dainty little flowers come from the axils of the "braided" leaves. (Courtesy of Montreal Botanical Garden)

feature of the flower is the long column which is conspicuous in a flower so small. *Sigmatostalyx guatemalensis* has yellow flowers marked with red. Others are yellow, white, or greenish-white. They occur from Mexico to Panama.

Trichopilia. These are strong dark green plants with a round flattened pseudobulb bearing a single leathery leaf. The flowers are fragrant, large, with slender sepals and petals and a large wavy lip curled around the column and spreading at its outer edge. The flower stem arises from the base of the pseudobulb and

with a green border, and are conspicuously twisted. The lip is white to cream color, spotted with brown or red. This species is native to Central America.

Vanilla. These tremendously tall, climbing plants can find room only in large greenhouses, where they are very ornamental with their heavy velvety leaves. *Vanilla planifolia* is the source of the vanilla used for flavoring, extracted from the long seed pods. The leaves are produced all along the stem and in their axils occur the sprays of small, yellow Cattleya-

Fig. 131 A miniature among miniatures, Sigmatostalix is a tiny plant that gives flowers barely one-fourth inch long. A hand lens reveals their charming details. Left, a plant still perched on the little tree branch on which it lived in the tropics. Right, a single flower enlarged.

curves outward or trails across the potting medium to hang down over the edge. Three, four, or more flowers are borne on each stem. *Trichopilia suavis* is one of the best known species, loved for its crystalline texture and the dainty rosy spotting of its large white lip. The sepals and petals are cream colored. It occurs in Central America. *Trichopilia fragrans* is another popular species, occurring in Colombia. Its sepals and petals are long and twisted, greenish-white; the large lip is white with a spot of yellow. *Trichopilia tortillis* bears its flowers singly. The long slender sepals and petals are brownish purple to light lavender

like flowers. The vine is grown from cuttings which are tied a little above the soil to some sort of support. In greenhouses the plants will grow in a compost of leaf mold and chopped osmunda. The aerial roots sent out from the cutting grow down into the compost. As the vine grows, it is trained around a post. The plant begins to produce about three years after becoming established, and continues to flower for thirty or forty years.

Vanilla planifolia. This is the only species cultivated commercially from the twenty or so species that represent the genus. It is native to Mexico and is cultivated in many of the

Fig. 132 *Trichopilia suavis* produces its showy, daintily colored flowers in clusters at the base of the plant.

(Courtesy of H. A. Dunn and H. Griffin)

tropical islands. It may be grown in greenhouses and does best with warm humid conditions. Pollination baffled growers who cultivated Vanilla away from its native habitat, for the insects required for the function were not transported with the plants. Hand pollination was a mystery. Placing the pollen on what appeared to be the stigma produced no results.

Finally, a Creole worker discovered that the stigma was covered by a shield, which had to be lifted in order to place the pollen on the stigma. After pollination, the shield snaps back into place. Now native workers go down the rows of plants, pollinating thousands of flowers in a day.

19 | *Jungle Orchids*

Next to seeing orchid plants growing in their native haunts, the most thrilling experience is to receive them fresh from the jungle. You can buy them from people who make a business or a hobby of collecting plants in the wilds, and have them shipped directly to you just as they come from the trees. When you open the box and take out the plants you will be intrigued by their myriad shapes, and as you turn them over in your hands you will find yourself transported in imagination to the places from which they came. Clinging to the stubs of their roots may be pieces of the bark and debris in which they were growing. A small plant may still be perched on a piece of the branch from which it was collected. Their rhizomes assume odd shapes where they wound around a branch, or traveled over a hump or up and down in a crotch. A large plant may have a seedling or some smaller variety nestled among its roots. It will tax your ingenuity to fit them into pots. Some which were growing upward on a tree trunk will naturally lend themselves to being placed upon a slab of tree fern or a slab of wood to which is attached a piece of osmunda fiber. Potting them, caring for them, watching them take hold and grow for you as if they had never left their jungle home, is a rewarding experience.

The range of choice among the wild species is almost limitless. Each collector will furnish a list of things within his area, or you can learn through correspondence what he can get for you. One may have certain species of a genus, another may have different species of that genus. There are many more genera than could be described in the preceding chapters. You may locate these through dealers and collectors.

All plants entering this country must be inspected and fumigated, and this is done without charge by the United States Department of Agriculture, Plant Quarantine Division at various ports of entry. This is done for your protection as well as that of the whole country. Every day the inspectors of imported plants find pests which, if allowed to reproduce in this country, could become dangerous plant enemies. It is far better to exclude possible enemies than to try to fight them once they have gained a foothold. Orchid growers used to battle pests that we hardly see nowadays, thanks to the service of the U. S. Department of Agriculture.

Importing orchids includes buying them

Fig. 133 Nothing can really describe the fun of opening a box of newly arrived jungle orchids. This box contains over a dozen species, many of them miniatures.

from collectors who ship them to you, as well as finding them yourself on trips to foreign countries. If you should take such a trip, for your own good have the plants you acquire shipped back to you by way of one of the ports of entry. They will then arrive in your greenhouse free from pests. It is not always easy to detect these yourself. Some bore holes in the rhizomes or pseudobulbs and lay eggs therein, so that even if you can see no insects they may later emerge. Small insects can conceal themselves under the covering scales of rhizomes and leaves. If you should succeed in bringing in plants without inspection, you may regret it later on. If plants are found in your luggage, they may be confiscated. The procedure for importing plants properly is so simple and so worthwhile that everyone should take advantage of it.

First, you must obtain a permit. Even though you do not expect to import any right away, you can obtain the permit so that this matter will be all taken care of if you should later desire to do so. A letter to Permit Unit, Plant Quarantine Division, 209 River St., Hoboken, New Jersey, is all that is necessary. State that you wish a permit to import orchid plants. You will be issued a permit number that is good for three years, and which must be renewed every three years in order to be kept active. The permit number goes in their files

and in the files at each port of entry. You may import one or a hundred plants, as seldom or as often you wish.

Second, you must obtain shipping labels from the same office, which must accompany each package of plants. The labels bear your permit number and are your tag of identification for the plants as well as your ticket for the services of the laboratory that will inspect and fumigate the plants. Labels are issued for specific ports of entry, so you must know before you order them to which one your shipment will come. From Central and much of South America they will go through Miami, Florida; from western South America and the Pacific area, they will arrive at San Francisco; from Mexico, at Brownsville, Texas; and from Europe, at Hoboken, N.J. The collector from whom you buy the plants will tell you, if you ask him, to which port he will ship, and you can then ask for labels for that port. You send the labels to him, and he will put one on the inside of the package, and one on the outside.

Third, the matter of how the plants will be shipped should be decided upon between you and the shipper. Those who make a regular business of shipping plants will know how best to send them. It has been our experience that Air Parcel Post is most satisfactory. Not only is it speedy, but the Postal Service will

Fig. 134 A whole flowering plant smaller than one Cattleya flower. Here is a species of Ornithocephalus, whose little "bird beak" flowers are individually the size of a single pollinium of the Cattleya.

collect the duty on the plants at your door, obviating the necessity of employing the services of a broker to handle this for you at the port of entry. If the plants come by air, they can travel in a closed box, but if they are to be shipped by a slower method, the box should have some holes cut in it for ventilation.

That is all there is to it. You obtain a permit and shipping labels, you send the labels to the dealer from whom you are buying the plants,

Fig. 135 New growth is fairly well along on some jungle plants when they arrive. The growth on this Cycnoches appears to be in good condition, but minute bruises on the tender leaves can become infected with fungi or bacteria if care is not taken. It is well to dip new growths in a fungicide solution on arrival.

and you receive the plants clean and pest free. Usually it is only a matter of a few days from the time the plants are shipped until they arrive at your door.

If you wish to send home plants that you acquire in your travels, take the shipping labels with you on your trip. When you are ready to leave for home, pack the plants yourself in a cardboard carton with excelsior as stuffing material. They will travel better in excelsior, as it is strong and allows some circulation of air in the box. Put one of the shipping labels in the box and wrap and tie it securely. Address it to yourself, or in care of someone at home with whom you have arranged to receive it and look after the plants until you get there. Affix the other shipping label to the outside. Pay the postage all the way to your home. The box will go to the port of entry, be opened and inspected and the plants fumigated, and the original wrapping will be put back on for mailing on to your home. One precaution you should take when sending plants out of a foreign country is to check with the proper local government office to see if it is necessary to obtain a release for the plants. Some countries have restrictions on shipping out native plants, and you may save yourself many days of waiting if you do this early.

Many growers in this country deal in "collectors' items" as a specialty, importing plants from many different countries. You can obtain jungle plants from them if you wish. Write for their lists when you see them advertised, but be sure they are known to be reliable growers. This, of course, holds for dealers in foreign countries as well. Often you can pick up a plant or two this way, when it would not be worth a special order to a collector in a foreign country. No permit is needed on your part when you obtain plants from a dealer in this country.

■ CARE OF JUNGLE PLANTS

As soon as the box arrives, open it and remove the plants. Examine them for any soft areas that show breakdown of plant tissues. It is always wise to dip the plants in a fungicide to prevent infection of any part that may have been damaged in handling or shipping. It is not likely that thick, hard leaves will show any injury, but the thin leaves of some kinds may be broken or bruised. Cut off any badly damaged leaves, and keep a watch over any that have slight damage. (If these later show evidence of infection, treat them again with fungicide.) Lay the plants on a shaded bench where they can have free air circulation.

Some plants will arrive with new growth started; others may be quite dormant. Some may be plump, others shrivelled. For the most part, plants come through the shipping very well. But collecting is not a thing that can be done in a moment; rainy seasons interfere and distances are great. Some plants may have to wait some time before shipment. Those that have growth started should be potted right away. The others can wait for a few days. Syringe those lying on the bench once or twice a day to keep them from shrivelling, or to help plump them up, but don't wait too long before you pot them.

We have found the magic polyethylene bag of great help in handling jungle plants. It furnishes a wonderfully damp atmosphere that

Fig. 136 *Oncidium ampliatum* lends itself well to growing on a slab. Wire a piece of osmunda fiber to a slab, as shown in A & B, and then wire the plant in place, C. Plastic coated wire is a good type to use. Note the turtle-like pseudobulbs of this species.

encourages new roots to form and eyes to start growing. The jungle plants can be handled just like backbulbs. Put a little wet bark in the bag, set the plant upon it, close the bag with a rubber band, and stand it upright on the bench so that the new growth will start in the proper direction. When the new roots can be seen starting, remove the plant and pot it just as you would any other plant. Stake it carefully so that it will not wobble in the pot. Keep newly potted plants a bit shaded, and mist the foliage once or twice a day and just the surface of the potting medium, until new roots are growing vigorously. Those which are potted right away are also kept shaded and are given mist sprays until growth is advancing nicely.

It is fun to have some hanging plants, and some lend themselves very well to growing on a slab. Since plants on slabs dry out faster than those in pots, we choose kinds that do not need a particularly damp condition. Little plants with fine roots and the miniatures should probably be grown in pots unless you can give them utmost care. The accompanying illustration shows how to prepare a slab from the trunk of a tree (in this case pine, but any other kind will do as well) and affix a plant of *Oncidium ampliatum* to it. A flat piece of osmunda fiber is wired to the slab, and the plant is then fastened on with a wire that encircles both plant and slab. The roots will go through the fiber and cling to the bark, just as they do in nature. After a year or two it is impossible to remove the plant without cutting the roots, so tightly do they cling. However, plants grown in this way do not have to be changed often, and when it becomes necessary it is not difficult to re-establish divisions on slabs again. A piece of tree fern trunk will serve just as well as the slab with osmunda fiber. Because of the free aeration of a slab or a piece of tree fern, the

organic material does not break down as rapidly as it does in a pot, and plants can stay on them for many years. They should be watered quite frequently, and should have a thorough soaking in a bucket every now and then. They appreciate fertilizer every other watering. We have been especially successful with *Epidendrum atropurpureum* and many oncidiums on slabs.

A hanging basket can be made from a dime-store egg basket, the kind that has the wire covered with plastic. Redwood baskets made of slats of wood wired together are perhaps more elegant looking. Lay a tough piece of osmunda fiber, cut to the right size, on the bottom, and then fill in around the plant with other pieces, packing it tightly enough to hold the plant firmly. If necessary, the plant can be held down by a hoop of wire until it forms a good root system. Such baskets are especially good for Stanhopeas and other kinds whose flower stems extend down through the potting medium, but they can be used for other kinds as well.

For plants which are to be grown in pots, the materials you use for your other orchids can be used—osmunda fiber, bark, tree fern fiber. For terrestrials a mix such as recommended for Cymbidiums is good. If you use bark for the small plants with short, fine roots, however, we suggest mixing some shreds of osmunda or tree fern fiber with the seedling grade of bark. Chopped peat moss or dried sphagnum moss may also be added, but if you let it get dry it is difficult to wet up again. If the little plants need help in getting a start, put them pot and all, in a polyethylene bag until they become well rooted. Some seem to do better with straight osmunda fiber as it holds water better from the start and offers the tiny roots a damp surface on which to grow.

20 | *Mineral Nutrition*

MAN cannot live by love alone. Nor can a plant live by air and water. Every living thing, both animal and plant, depends on certain minerals for the development of its body structure and the maintenance of the living substance within it, protoplasm. Even plants that hang on such a sterile perch as a telephone wire (Tillandsia) have a source of minerals to nourish them, dust settling on the wire and minerals dissolved in rain water—small amounts, to be sure, but enough for these particular plants.

It used to be thought that orchids lived entirely on materials taken from the air. Observers overlooked the accumulation of humus material present in breaks in the bark of trees or crevices in weathered rock, the fertilizing minerals dissolved out of bird droppings and washed down to the plants by rain, and the yearly collection of dead leaves among the bulbs of the plants themselves. Even rain water is not pure, since rain droplets form on dust particles and take up more dust on their way earthward.

A ten-ounce plant consists of nine ounces of water and one ounce of sugars, starches, proteins, fats, waxes, and numerous other substances. This single ounce represents the other chemical substances accumulated by the plant during its lifetime plus the amount of food it has on hand at the moment of weighing. To find out what part of the dry weight of the plant is mineral, the dried plant is ignited and burned to remove carbon, hydrogen, nitrogen, and oxygen. The ash remaining is the total mineral content of the plant, and amounts to approximately 0.076 of an ounce for a ten-ounce plant. A fraction of a cent would buy the chemicals that make up the plant. The value of the living plant is based on the marvelous things its protoplasm, governed by its genes, can do with that minute quantity of nonliving substances.

The minerals, in the form of mineral salts, are absorbed by the roots from the medium in which they grow. The salts are released from the organic matter by slow decay and are put in solution by moisture in the soil. The salts in solution are then taken up by the roots, and transported to every part of the plant, where they enter into various vital activities.

In addition to the minerals, the plant needs water and two things absorbed from the air, oxygen and carbon dioxide. Oxygen, necessary for respiration, is absorbed by the leaves and stems from the atmosphere and by the roots from air in the soil. Carbon dioxide is absorbed by the leaves (and other green parts of the plant) and combined with water taken up by the roots to form sugar, the food of the plant. This process is called photosynthesis because it is carried on only in the presence of light. The simple sugars are turned into complex sugars, starches, and cellulose; and various products formed from carbohydrates are combined with nitrogen, sulfur, and phosphorus to form proteins.

The major mineral elements, necessary in relatively large amounts, and their activities, follow:

Calcium is necessary for cell wall formation and for regulation of cell activities. If calcium is deficient the new growths are stunted and distorted.

Nitrogen, an essential ingredient of proteins and of chlorophyll, is necessary for good vegetative growth. When nitrogen is deficient the plants are stunted and mature too early. Older leaves turn yellow and drop off. Too much nitrogen produces excessive vegetative growth and delayed flowering.

Sulfur is also an ingredient of proteins. Sulfur deficiency may stunt root growth.

Phosphorus, the third important mineral in protein formation, is a catalyst and regulator of vital activity. Sometimes called the "dynamite of living cells." Phosphorus deficiency leads to stunting, but the leaves, instead of turning yellow, become dark green.

Potassium, another important catalyst, regulates many activities. Deficiency results in dwarfness with the edges of the leaves frequently scorched and dead.

Magnesium is part of the chlorophyll molecule, and therefore necessary to the manufacture of food. With lack of magnesium the older leaves become yellow between the veins and the plant does not thrive.

Iron is a catalyst in many reactions, including the formation of chlorophyll. Iron is seldom deficient but is insoluble unless the soil is sufficiently acid. Deficiency of iron causes the younger leaves to become yellow.

Certain other minerals are also necessary, but in extremely minute amounts. Very little is known about their specific activities, and it is thought that they act as catalysts in vital chemical reactions. These minor elements are *boron, molybdenum, manganese, copper,* and *zinc.* They are seldom deficient, for the faint traces found in most soils and as impurities in most chemicals, are enough to supply the needs of the plants. Manganese is the only one of the minor elements that at times needs to be added to nutrient solutions. In fact, in order to do research on the role of the trace elements, workers must first remove the minute amounts of boron, copper, manganese, molybdenum, and zinc contained in the chemicals they will use. They must also redistill water many times before it can be considered pure. They can then study the effects of the minor elements by using them one at a time in measured amounts. It is known that their complete absence causes poor growth, and it is also known that amounts over the smallest trace are toxic to plants.

We have been talking about the various elements necessary to plant nutrition, but plants can use these elements only in the form of inorganic salts. In nature some inorganic materials are dissolved out of the rock particles in the soil. Additional inorganic salts are released from the humus material in the soil by bacteria and fungi that feed upon it. The same events take place in the potting materials used for orchids. The "breakdown" of organic materials such as osmunda, tree fern fiber, bark, leaf mold, etc., requires the activities of soil bacteria and fungi. We augment the store of chemical salts available to the plant when we apply additional amounts in the form of fertilizers and nutrient solutions. Inorganic salts occur as a variety of compounds, and choices may be made among them. We cannot list all the possibilities, but will give some of the more generally used compounds. Nitrogen may be furnished as nitrate salts or as ammonium salts, for example as ammonium nitrate, ammonium sulfate, potassium nitrate or calcium nitrate. It is generally agreed that plants need nitrogen in both the ammonium form (NH_4) and nitrate form (NO_3), but there is no agreement as to which form should be in greater quantity. Potassium may be furnished as potassium sulfate, potassium nitrate, or potassium chloride; calcium as monocalcium phosphate, calcium nitrate, calcium chloride; phosphorus is furnished in phosphate salts such as calcium phosphate or monopotassium phosphate; iron as ferrous sulfate; magnesium as magnesium sulfate; manganese as manganese sulfate; and sulfur as the sulfate salts just mentioned.

In order for a plant to thrive, it must have a balanced "diet" of the essential minerals. It needs larger quantities of some than of others. And in order to make use of the nutrients, it must have the proper conditions of light, water, and temperature. Curiously, a plant can starve in the midst of plenty if for some reason it is unable to take up the minerals it needs. Overwatering with the resultant inhibition of root function can produce a mineral lack for the plants. Under-watering, not as dangerous as over-watering, can deprive the plant of sufficient materials for growth. Excessive accumulation of salts in the potting medium can prevent the roots from absorbing both water and minerals. Insufficient light can prevent the plant's using the available minerals, through failure to make the necessary amounts of sugars, the building blocks for more complicated carbohydrates which, in turn, are combined with minerals from the soil to form proteins, enzymes, etc. The pH of the growing medium is important to root health, for roots function best somewhere between pH 5.2 and pH 6.5. Under proper growing conditions and where an organic medium such as osmunda, tree fern, bark etc. is used, pH seldom becomes a problem. Such media, as well as mixes containing a large proportion of organic matter, are more or less self-conditioning, that is, they maintain a pH suitable for plant growth through bacterial

Fig. 137 Mineral deficiency shows in the stunted growth of the seedling on the left. This can be caused by too loose potting in osmunda, by overwatering, or by any condition that prevents the roots from functioning normally. Contrast the growth of this plant with the vigorous plant on the right.

action as well as chemical action. The problem of pH in relation to water that is excessively alkaline or acid was discussed earlier, page 35. The control of pH in nutrient solutions used for orchids on an inert medium is a matter for constant attention.

An important contribution to plant nutrition has been made by the introduction of chelates. In a culture solution, or (less likely) in a potting medium, the iron may combine with other ions such as the phosphate ion (PO_4) to form an insoluble compound. This removes the iron from solution and makes it unavailable to the plant. Chlorosis (yellowing) of the leaves will follow, with resultant poor growth. Other metals such as copper, zinc, etc. may be similarly precipitated from solution, although probably iron is the most important to be considered. A chelate is an organic substance which has a chemical attraction for certain elements and which holds them loosely in solution, making them continually available for plant use. The chelate thus prevents precipitation of the particular element. Called the versene compounds, they have quite a complicated structure exemplified by one, called for short EDTA, which is ethylenediaminetetraacetic acid. It is possible to add this to a culture solution or to a fertilizer solution, but it is probably easier and better to obtain one that has already been combined with iron, such as the product called "Sequestrene." Some manufacturers of orchid fertilizers are including chelates in their prepared products. When used thus, the chelated iron may be substituted for iron sulfate or whatever other iron compound would have been included, or it may be used in addition to it.

Basic nutrient solutions have been worked out for orchids on inert media—seedlings on agar and plants in gravel. As we saw in the chapter on germinating seed, various workers have proposed slightly different formulas for germination, and the same is true for solutions to be used with gravel. Sometimes substitution of one salt for another gives better results for a certain species. The formulation of fertilizers has been an equally experimental endeavor, and here the matter is complicated by the fact that the materials on which the fertilizers will be used vary so much from each other. The barks of different species of trees contain different amounts of nitrogen, phosphorus, potassium etc.; osmunda fiber collected in different regions varies quite strikingly in content. Any one of these materials may vary in the rapidity with which it releases its minerals under different conditions of watering, temperature, and atmospheric moisture. It is to be expected that fertilizers made up according to the experiences of one grower or another will also vary. There are also organic fertilizers, such as fish emulsion, favored by some. After trying several on your own plants, you yourself may come to have a preference for a certain one. This is good. It shows that all is *en rapport* between you and your plants. Such experiences among growers everywhere show that orchids can get along on quite varied diets, provided they are given the basic essentials.

■ GRAVEL CULTURE

Gravel culture quite took orchid growers by storm some ten or more years ago. The freedom from toil that it offered gave it the same appeal that bark culture has today.

We may now even have the answers to some of the problems that developed with gravel culture and caused many growers to give it up. Certain it is that this method still has some loyal adherents, and it is still a useful method for those who are interested in research on nutrition.

Essentially, gravel culture differs from bark culture only in that gravel is used instead of bark, and that the entire array of necessary minerals must be supplied rather than just a supplemental fertilizer. The chief disadvantage of gravel is that it is heavy.

Plants can be grown in gravel all the way from community pot size to flowering size. For the smallest plants a very fine size is used, between one-sixteenth and one-eighth inch diameter. The size of the gravel is gradually increased as the plants become larger, until for mature plants a size of one-half to three-quarters of an inch is used. The gravel should be from a type of rock that does not readily give materials into solution. For example, limestone is to be avoided. Weathered gravel is preferable to crushed gravel. The manufactured light-weight aggregates used for making concrete are excellent. Haydite was the first of these. They can be obtained from manufacturers directly or from construction companies.

Because gravel dries out very rapidly, growers used to like to put small seedlings in a mixture of fine gravel and chopped osmunda fiber. Not only did the osmunda fiber help to retain moisture, but it gave the small roots a more intimate contact with the growing medium. Plants were grown in this combination until ready for three- or four-inch pots. Moving them out of this mixture causes very little shock.

The pure gravel can be used over and over again. The mixture of gravel and fiber should not be reused, unless one wishes to go to the trouble of washing the fiber out of it.

From the time plants are in three-inch pots, unless they have a good root system to hold them in place, they should be supported with one of the rigid stakes used in bark culture; or should have the rhizomes fastened down by means of a wire extending from one side of the pot to the other.

Plants in small pots have to be watered more often than those in large pots, but all have to be watered more frequently than they do with other media. Each grower must devise his own schedule from observation of his own plants. During the winter, three- and four-inch pots may have to be watered every other day, and in the summer every day. Larger pots may need water every four to six days in the winter, and every three days or so in the summer.

Fertilizer should be a water-soluble, complete formula. Hyponex, Instant Vigoro, or a complete orchid fertilizer can be used. Or you can mix your own according to the formula given below. This formula is the one used in experimental work with orchids in gravel at Ohio State University. The frequency of fertilizing recommended by those who did the work at Ohio State was once a week, with plain water being given in between times when needed. Now that we can give the plants better light because we can keep down the greenhouse temperature by means of cooling apparatuses, I believe that the fertilizing schedule could be stepped up to twice a week or even to every watering during the growing season. They should be flushed with plain water after every few feedings. Once-a-week fertilizing is still probably best during the winter. A concentration of one-half teaspoon of fertilizer to a gallon of water would be best to start with, but you may wish to vary this experimentally.

The fertilizer can be applied by means of a Hozon attachment, or could be mixed in a tank and applied by a hose. It is best to mix it fresh each time, or at least not to let it stand in the tank for longer than two weeks. Chemical changes can take place in a mixture that is allowed to stand for a long time, and the pH can also change. The plants in gravel do not have a store of minerals from which to draw as they do in organic media, nor do they have the protection from changes in pH furnished by an organic medium.

One of the problems which arises in gravel culture is the accumulation of salts, particularly in the pots. This problem can probably be eliminated by the use of plastic pots. Plastic pots would also alleviate the rapid drying, making it easier to keep the plants well watered, especially in the smaller sizes. When clay pots are used, care must be taken to flush out the pots with plain water very thoroughly every week or two. If plastic pots are not available in the larger sizes, the inside of large clay pots may be coated with horticultural asphalt, or painted with an asphaltum base paint.

A second problem with gravel culture is that the iron may become precipitated from the solution, causing chlorosis and abnormal growth. The use of chelated iron should prevent this. It would be well to use a fertilizer containing an iron chelate, or to add a small amount to each batch of fertilizer as it is mixed —approximately 5 grams for each ten gallons of solution.

If you wish to mix your own nutrient solution, the following is a good one to use, with the addition of about .5 gram of iron chelate.

THE OHIO W. P. SOLUTION (to be used half strength)

Name	Symbol	Amount
Potassium nitrate	KNO_3	2.63 grams
Ammonium sulfate	$(NH_4)_2SO_4$	0.44 grams
Magnesium sulfate	$MgSO_4 \cdot 7H_2O$	2.04 grams
Monocalcium phosphate	$CaH_4(PO_4)_2 \cdot H_2O$	1.09 grams
Calcium sulfate	$CaSO_4 \cdot 2H_2O$	4.86 grams
Iron sulfate (Ferrous sulfate)	$FeSO_4 \cdot 7H_2O$	0.5 grams
Manganese sulfate	$MnSO_4$	Make a 1% solution and add 2.5 c.c. of this
Water	H_2O	1.0 gallons

In preparing this solution dissolve each salt completely in the gallon of water before adding the next salt. Manganese is added by first dissolving one gram of manganese sulfate in 99 cc of water, then 2.5 cc of this solution is used per gallon of nutrient solution. The pH ranges between 5.5 and 6.5, and should be checked before use.

■ SUBIRRIGATION

This method involves the use of specially constructed watertight benches, filled with gravel, into which the nutrient solution is pumped, and from which it drains back into the storage tank. It saves a great deal of time, for a whole bench of plants is automatically watered at one time.

When subirrigation is used for orchids, the plants that are irrigated together must all have the same growth and flowering habits. You cannot put plants together that have different blooming seasons and growth habits. For this reason subirrigation is more readily applicable to collections that include large blocks of species and hybrids whose seasonal behavior is similar. For instance, where there can be a bench for mid-winter blooming varieties, another for late winter and early spring flowering kinds, and so on. With some ingenuity, however, a small grower could divide one bench into sections that could be irrigated independently so that small groups of plants could be grown according to their needs. Since seedlings do not have rest periods, they can be grown together until they reach maturity when they can be sorted out.

A good strong wooden bench may be made over for subirrigation by coating it with horticultural asphalt. The horticultural asphalt is made especially for this purpose and is not toxic to plants. It comes as a solid, and when heated becomes fluid enough to be spread over the bottom and sides of the bench, filling all cracks. A hole is drilled in one end of the bench for connecting the pipe, and a row of half-round tile laid down the center of the bench for distributing the nutrient solution.

V-bottom concrete benches are fine for the purpose. Perhaps you can make the forms and pour them yourself, or have a contractor do the work. A steel bench made in sections to suit your purpose may be bought from Lord and Burnham. Both types must be coated inside with horticultural asphalt to prevent possible reaction with the mineral salts of the nutrient solution.

A set of V-bottom concrete benches with pipe lines connected to pump and storage tank is shown in Figure 138. A valve on the pipe leading into each bench allows separate control. The nutrient solution is distributed throughout the bench by a line of half-round tile. All pipes and fittings, and the pump itself, should be made of iron. The time switch shown in connection with the pump may not be needed for your purposes.

The cistern to hold the nutrient solution should have a capacity of at least one-fourth, preferably one-third, of the volume of the benches. The amount of fluid necessary to flood the benches will depend partly on the size of the gravel used, since small particles have less space between them than large particles. The cistern should be of concrete, coated with horticultural asphalt. It is well to cover the cistern to prevent the growth of algae by eliminating light. The pump is placed in a pit next to the cistern. It should be far enough

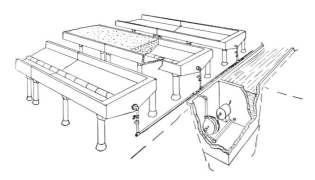

Fig. 138 V-bottom benches for subirrigation. Nutrient solution is pumped from the cistern to the benches, where it is distributed through the row of half-round tile in the bottom of each. After flooding, the solution drains back to the cistern. A valve on the pipe leading to each bench allows separate control. (Courtesy of Purdue University, Agricultural Experiment Station)

Miltonia Marietta Armacost. (Courtesy of Flower Grower Magazine)

Orchids in Their Native Habitat. (Copyright illustration of The Smithsonian Series)

below the level of nutrient solution to insure priming.

There are two ways to place orchids in the bench. One is to fill the bench with gravel and plant the orchids directly into it. This method has such definite disadvantages that it is not recommended. For one thing, the roots become so entangled that it is difficult to remove the plants. A better method is to pot the plants separately in gravel, and then plunge the pots into the gravel in the bench. Even so, the surface roots grow around into the gravel in the bench, but most of them are confined to the pot. With care, an individual plant may be removed from the bench for display purposes or for some other reason, and then returned to the bench.

The bench is flooded with nutrient solution about once a week. The plants can have a mist spray on bright days, but the mist must not be so heavy that it dilutes the nutrient solution.

The valve between the bench and the cistern must be left open at all times between floodings.

The nutrient solution is allowed to rise in the benches to a level one inch below the surface of the gravel, and then to drain out immediately. The flooding will take between fifteen minutes and one hour, depending on the size of the bench and capacity of the pump. Drainage will take a comparable length of time. The surface of the gravel is kept on the dry side to discourage growth of algae. Care of the plants as to ventilation, humidity, light, and temperature is the same as for orchids in general.

To insure the plants the right proportions of nutrients, and to eliminate waste products that collect in the re-used solution, the solution should be renewed every two weeks. At this time it would also be well to flush out the bench with plain water.

21 | *Orchid Ailments*

ORCHID health depends on three fundamentals—good inheritance, proper environment, and freedom from disease and injury. Enough has been said previously about inheritance to emphasize the importance of selecting strong, free-growing, promising plants, whether you acquire them as small seedlings or as mature plants. Environmental conditions that contribute to the health of the plant are the right amount of light, temperature within the proper day-night range, humidity coupled with good air circulation, water to suit the needs of the plants, and proper nutrition combined with root aeration. Deviations from the optimal in any of these conditions may cause variations from the normal, thrifty condition of the plant. Diseases are caused by invading viruses, bacteria, or fungi, and, although orchids are remarkably free from such attacks, they occur. Orchids are less vulnerable to pests than are most greenhouse crops, but prevention of insect injury is an absolute necessity.

■ AILMENTS ARISING FROM ENVIRONMENTAL CONDITIONS

Light. When the light is too strong, chlorophyll (the green pigment) is destroyed faster than it is made, and leaves become yellow, or even white in young seedlings. Yellowed leaves cannot make as much food as leaves that have the normal amount of chlorophyll. If the condition is not corrected, the older leaves may fall before they should. The general result is a retarded plant.

Sudden exposure to too strong light may burn localized areas. Naturally, the efficiency of a leaf is decreased by the presence of a burned area. The sudden exposure may result from removing too much shading in the fall, from not applying it soon enough in the spring, or by allowing strong light to focus on a plant through a clear area on the glass or through an open ventilator. Flowers are sensitive to the excessive heat produced by too much light, and become dry and thin before their time from its effects.

Insufficient light causes the plants to become a darker green than normal. Even though the dark green plants are handsome to the eye, they are not as healthy as when the foliage is a lighter shade. The plants are usually soft and succulent, susceptible to disease, and their growths do not mature and harden as they should. Flower production is cut down or inhibited entirely.

258

Temperature. Each kind of orchid has its own temperature requirements. At night temperatures too high for their kind, they will not flower. Growth is poor because food is used faster than it can be made. Often the leaves fall prematurely and death may result.

At temperatures below the specific requirement water and minerals are absorbed but slowly, and formation of chlorophyll is hindered. Yellow foliage and poor development result, and poor flowering is the logical sequel.

There is also an optimal difference between day and night temperatures. Too wide a gap, or not enough drop at night, retards growth.

Orchids can survive short spells of extremely hot weather if everything is done to aid them. The leaves absorb light with its associated heat, and their temperature is therefore usually warmer than the surrounding air. They have some protection from heat in their evaporation of water (transpiration), which acts as a cooling system. For Cattleyas, it has been demonstrated that burning occurs if the temperature of the leaves remains at 110° F. for a few hours, or at 120°-125° F. for shorter periods. This means that during hot spells when the greenhouse temperature soars above 100° F., the temperature of the leaves may reach the danger point and sudden burning may occur. I know of a case where every plant in a small greenhouse was burned black when it was accidentally left unattended on a hot day. During hot weather everything must be done to lower the temperatures of leaves. The plants should have cooling mists over the foliage, and proper attention to ventilation, shade and air circulation.

Burning due to strong light would actually seem to be a heat effect. Concentration of light on one area of a leaf raises the temperature of that area to the burning point.

Flowers are even more sensitive to heat than plants. Flowering plants should therefore be kept as cool as possible under conditions of hot weather to prevent premature fading.

For regions where hot summers are a rule, varieties should be chosen with care as to their particular temperature requirements.

Freezing kills plant tissues just as burning does. However the frozen areas become soft and watery, dirty yellow-green in color and then black. Frozen areas should be cut off and the cut surfaces be treated with Tersan or other fungicide to prevent infection of the wounds. Do not syringe until the cuts have dried and healed. If severe freezing leaves only a small portion of the plant intact, it should be treated as a potted division until it is actively growing again.

Humidity. Insufficient humidity in the air makes it difficult to maintain an even water supply to the plants. The potting medium dries out quickly, and the plants lose water rapidly through their foliage. This is especially critical for newly potted plants, whose root systems are temporarily non-functioning, and for young seedlings.

Excessive humidity is dangerous for it brings about susceptibility to certain diseases. Flowers may become spotted, either by simple engorgement of water or by fungus growths. *Botrytis* fungus causes pink or brown spots, and flowers may also become spotted with a sooty black mold. Plant parts may be attacked by various bacteria and fungi.

The danger of infection during the high relative humidity maintained for the purpose of cooling the plants in the daytime is lessened by good air movement. However, excessively high relative humidity (above seventy per cent) contributes to succulent growth which is more susceptible to infection than hard growth.

Watering. Enough has been said about the effects of overwatering on plants and flowers (see Chapters 4 and 20) but we might repeat here that overwatering is one thing to suspect when a plant is not making vigorous growth or when its older leaves are turning soft and yellow. Examine the potting medium and the roots. If the medium is broken down and is wet and mushy it will contain few if any active roots. Repotting is then in order.

Underwatering will cause shriveling of the leaves and pseudobulbs and new growths will be small. The roots may be thin and starved. If the medium is in good condition (and it probably is since it has been kept dry) simply step up the frequency of watering.

It may take more than a year to bring back the vigor of a plant that has been stunted by one of these conditions, but it is rewarding to see them improve.

Nutrition. Chapter 20 gives the symptoms of various nutritional deficiencies. It is not likely that plants potted in good osmunda will suffer any nutritional lack, provided they are potted firmly. Plants loosely potted will suffer from lack of minerals and perhaps water also. Some of the leaves will turn yellow and die. In bark, yellow leaves are a sign of lack of nitrogen (if it can be ascertained that they are not from root loss). The fertilizers prepared for use with bark contain a higher nitrogen concentration because of the inherent lack of sufficient nitrogen in bark.

Air relations. Industrial regions offer hazards to orchid growing, both by the production of smoke and haze which reduce the light available to the plants, and by the production of noxious fumes. The former is being reduced by modern methods of smoke control. The latter is not such a simple problem (see Sepal Wilt, below).

If you live where soot and grime collect on the plants, wash them off with a forceful spray of water at frequent intervals. Dirt collecting on the leaves may plug up the stomata (see drawing page 25) and cut down the working power of the leaf.

Artificial illuminating gas is disastrous to plant life. Even a small amount of the raw gas leaking into the greenhouse will quickly kill the plants. One grower lost a great many when the gas main in the street broke and the gas seeped through the earth into his orchid house. Artificial gas is not safe to use in the greenhouse, nor is gas that has the slightest amount of artificial gas mixed with it. On the other hand, absolutely pure natural gas is perfectly safe, as is bottled gas (butane), provided the heaters are vented.

■ SEPAL WILT AND PREMATURE AGING

When a flower fades normally, after having lasted its usual length of time, the sepals are the first parts to show signs of deterioration. Starting at the tips, they lose their waxy sheen, become thin and transparent, and finally become tissue-like. The rest of the flower follows suit soon afterward, sometimes remaining in good condition a few days longer than the sepals. Sometimes the aging process sets in prematurely, occasionally almost as soon as the flower opens. There are two types of premature aging, one caused by some failure in cultural, environmental, or inherited factors which prevent the flowers from attaining their normal vigor and substance, and another caused by actual poisoning by substances in the atmosphere. We shall take up the first under the heading "Short Flower Life" and the second under "Sepal Wilt."

Short flower life. Anything which interferes with the health of a plant can result in flowers that are thin in substance and which do not last the normal length of time. Poor potting, improper watering, poor nutrition, excessive temperatures, lack of humidity, insufficient light, root loss—any or all can debilitate a plant. Flowers produced on such plants may be thin from the time they open, never attaining the firm substance expected of them, or they may appear normal for a while but soon fade. Any kind of orchid may respond with poor flowers when the plants are not vigorous. Cattleyas seem to be the most sensitive to insufficient light, and this is most often the cause of their premature aging. They are also most sensitive to the causal agents of sepal wilt.

A plant brought into the house before the buds are open must be kept in a bright window until the flowers are fully mature, else they will be thin. Long spells of dull weather may cause Cattleya flowers to be less firm than they are normally, with the sepals becoming limp and transparent soon after the bud opens and the rest of the flower lasting only a short time. This condition may be confused with "sepal wilt," but it differs in the fact that the whole flower is thin or becomes thin soon after the sepals shrivel, while in true sepal wilt, the petals and lip are usually quite normal. Premature aging or short flower life in Cattleyas, due to insufficient light, occurs in regions with prolonged spells of dull weather. It is also a common complaint where too heavy shading is used at any season.

The sudden fading of a normal flower may result from pollination by a visiting insect. The petals usually fold together and turn papery. Notice whether there are pollinia on the stigma.

Removal or dislodgement of the anther causes premature aging of Cymbidium flowers, and possibly some other kinds. A jostling of the buds or open flowers, even by a strong stream of water, may be enough to jar loose the anther in its socket. The fading of one or two flowers on a stem is often a clue to this.

Excessive heat may cause premature fading of flowers throughout the greenhouse, either extreme day temperatures or inordinately high night temperatures. This is particularly likely to happen when the air is too dry in the presence of high temperatures. Too low night temperatures, which do not allow the full development of the flowers, may also be a cause.

When all possible factors are checked, and a plant in apparent good health consistently gives poor flowers year after year, the cause is probably its genetic makeup. Within any species, or in any group of hybrids, there are a few individuals that just do not have the ability to give good flowers. It is not worthwhile to keep such plants. Also, some plants are not good growers, in spite of all the care that you can give them, and because of lack of vigor they flower poorly. These, too, should be disposed of.

Sepal wilt. Sepal wilt, also called dry sepals, is a peculiar condition whose mysteries have required much experimentation and detective work to unravel. Cattleyas are affected most severely. However, the factors that cause sepal wilt in Cattleyas may also affect some other kinds in other ways, and may be doing damage not yet realized.

For Cattleyas, a typical sequence of events is this: In the midst of a period when flowers are opening in good condition, there comes an interval when some or all opening flowers have thin, dry sepals, brown at the tip. Then, just as suddenly, the interval is over, and flowers are again normal. In affected flowers the sepals wilt as soon as the bud opens. The rest of the flower usually gains its normal substance and lasts well, but the flower is, of course, ruined by the affected sepals. Often the sepals turn soft and leathery before the bud opens, and in many cases the bud is entirely prevented from opening. Observations during short periods of sepal wilt suggest that the causative factors act on the bud just as it is getting ready to open, because (1) flowers already open are not affected, and (2) buds that are still quite green subsequently open normally. The fact that not all flowers are affected, and that the degree of severity varies among affected plants, suggests that some Cattleyas are more resistant than others.

Experimental work has shown that ethylene gas will cause sepal wilt. Ethylene gas is used to ripen fruit that has been picked green for shipping. This is essentially an aging process. The gas is present in smog, and in fumes from incomplete combustion of hydrocarbons (coal, oil, gas, gasoline, etc.). Sepal wilt is especially prevalent during periods of smog, frequently occurs in greenhouses heated by open-flame non-vented gas heaters, and is more common in, or close to, industrial areas than in open country. It occurs when the wind brings fumes from factory areas, and is absent when the wind blows the fumes in another direction. It occurs under certain atmospheric conditions when the air hugs the ground and smoke and fumes are layered within it. It is not necessarily connected to light conditions. Growers who have moved their collections away from cities and industrial areas have found that they are more free from sepal wilt. The new techniques for controlling smoke have improved the situation in some areas.

The reason for the prevalence of sepal wilt among Cattleyas is that they are far more sensitive to ethylene gas than other orchids and, indeed, than most other plants. According to O. Wesley Davidson, Cattleyas just beginning to split their sepals are affected by one part of ethylene in 300,000,000 to 500,000,000 parts of air. Tomato plants, on the other hand, require as much as one part ethylene gas in 10,000,000 to 20,000,000 parts of air in order to cause their leaves to fold. Carnation flowers become "sleepy" in response to one part ethylene in 20,000,000 to 25,000,000 parts of air. Tomatoes and carnations are therefore not affected by the extremely minute amounts that cause sepal wilt in Cattleyas. It would be desirable to have some indicator plant that is more sensitive than Cattleyas, but so far we do not know of any.

Other orchids, which are not affected by the small concentration that injures Cattleya flowers, may be injured by stronger concentrations. Plants themselves may also be injured. We have had two experiences that have alerted us to these possibilities. Both instances were caused by the rusting through or disconnection of the vent pipe from natural gas heaters in our own greenhouses. Cymbidium plants near the break showed premature aging of the flowers. The flowers turned pink and faded (just as they do when the anthers are removed). Flowers that opened after the break was repaired showed no symptoms. In the other case, the Cattleya plants themselves were affected. On the plants near the break (where the fumes were strongest), the older leaves turned a bright orange and fell. For as long as a year afterward, leaves on these same plants continued to age prematurely, although the plants finally recovered. A report from Australia suggests that smog is the cause of a leaf-tip necrosis in Cymbidiums. We have heard that Cymbidiums, Cypripediums, and Odontoglossum flowers were injured at the New York International Flower Show a few years ago when trucks were used to clean the building and the fumes were retained in the building.

Gases other than ethylene may produce the same types of injuries. However, knowing that ethylene is at least one of the culprits removes some of the frustration we suffered in years past when we groped entirely in the dark. We know of nothing, yet, to prevent injury, except to vent all natural gas heaters and keep the plants in top condition. Plants that are not in the best of health may be more vulnerable to attack by the gas.

■ **MECHANICAL AND CHEMICAL INJURIES TO PLANTS**

Sharp bending of leaves, particularly the thick, brittle leaves of Cattleyas and others, will cause injury to the tissues. The leaves may show a split down the mid-rib, or the end of the leaf beyond the point where it was bent may die. Young leaves are particularly tender and are sometimes unconsciously broken when a plant is handled. They are also susceptible to bacterial and fungus infections, so if a leaf turns black investigate to see whether its death has been caused primarily by a break or by infection.

Insecticides not specifically recommended for orchids should not be used on them. Those recommended should be used exactly as directed on the label. Injury can be caused by insecticides not compatible with orchids, or by too strong concentrations even of those that are compatible. The injuries appear as burned or blistered spots on leaves. Flower buds may be killed, or blossoms be spotted.

■ **FREAKS**

Freak flowers or freak growths, called anomalies, occasionally occur; but for the most part they do not repeat themselves. Sometimes a flower has too few or too many parts, or the parts may be fused to each other. There have been reports of flowers having only two sepals, apparently a dorsal and a ventral sepal; of flowers having no lip or two lips, of flowers in which the lip has reverted to a petal in shape, of flowers in which petals have lip structure, of flowers in which the length of the lip is fused to the column or in which the sepals are fused for part of their length so that the bloom cannot open. Abnormal growths on plants have also been reported. For instance, a Cattleya can have a growth with no leaf or a flower stem apparently arising from the base of a pseudobulb instead of from the apex. Sometimes a leaf may be tubular, not opening flat; and sometimes a sheath seems to be part true leaf and part sheath.

Such anomalies are ordinarily accidents in development. They can occur on a plant that has till then given all normal flowers and which thereafter continues to give normal flowers. These are not caused by changes in the genetic makeup of the plant.

However, genetic changes can occur. They are very rare. If a plant gives deformed flowers from the start, the cause is in its genetic makeup. If one flowers normally at first and then starts giving, and continues to give, abnormal flowers, this indicates that some change has taken place in its genes.

Chromosomal aberrations, such as the loss of a chromosome or two, or aquisition of an extra one or two, may cause abnormal growth in a plant. Possession by the plant cells of an odd number of chromosomes (a number over or under an even multiple of the haploid number) is called aneuploidy. This condition may be the basis for some abnormalities.

■ PARASITIC DISEASES, BACTERIAL, FUNGAL, AND VIRUS

During the past ten years work on orchid diseases has been intensified. Much has been learned about the diseases, their diagnosis, and the organisms which cause them; and many agents for their control have been developed. Orchid growers are indebted to research workers in many countries, and in the United States particularly to Peter A. Ark for his work with bacterial and fungal diseases, and D. D. Jensen for his work with virus diseases.

In even the best managed greenhouse there is occasionally a diseased plant. Some diseases are mild, doing little damage and easy to control; some are more serious and resist control quite stubbornly but, with persistence, most

Fig. 139 A freak flower which has three equal petals and three anthers. This is a particularly interesting anomaly because it shows an apparent reversion to some possible ancestral type, a type in which the third petal had not been modified into a lip, nor the anthers reduced to a single one.

can be cured. A few come on suddenly and run rampant through a plant, at the same time exposing other plants dangerously. A grower must always be on the alert, ready with an effective fungicide to treat any suspicious spots, and observant of any spread of disease either in the plant in question or to its neighbors. If your experience with disease has been limited to an occasional incidence it is a compliment to your management. Maintainance of healthy growing conditions is in itself a method of disease control and prevention. The presence of a few diseased plants in a greenhouse where bad conditions exist can set off an epidemic, particularly when the elements conspire to spread infection, with long spells of cold, or warm, cloudy weather.

Bacteria, fungi, and viruses are ever present. Many that attack common garden crops will also attack orchids. Some species of these organisms are parasites on plant tissue and digest the cells for their own food. They enter the plant through wounds, even through such a small injury as an insect puncture, or through the stomata of the leaves. Bacteria reproduce in the plant tissue and come to the surface in minute, oozing droplets. They are spread from plant to plant by contact, contaminated hands or instruments, insects, and splashing water. A fungus usually grows with its cobweb-like body (mycelium) inside of a leaf, pseudobulb, etc., destroying the tissues as it spreads, the only part that appears on the surface being that which bears the spores, the reproductive cells. The spores are carried from plant to plant by the same means as bacteria. Viruses (which have characteristics of both living and non-living entities) reproduce only in living tissue, and travel very rapidly throughout the entire plant. Once infected, a plant contains the virus in all its parts. The infection can be spread to other plants by contaminated cutting tools and by aphids.

Bacterial and fungal diseases in their initial stages can be cured by the use of fungicides and, where necessary, by the removal of diseased parts plus treatment with fungicides. There are some bacterial and fungal diseases that typically advance so rapidly that they are rarely caught in time. As yet no cure has been found for virus diseases. Removal of a part that shows symptoms does not free the plant from the virus because it has traveled into every part. No chemical has been found which will kill the virus within the plant.

As the orchids themselves require certain conditions for favorable growth, so also do the bacteria and fungi. Many of the latter flourish when temperatures are low and humidity high, conditions that often plague European growers. So readily do diseases occur at such times that the earlier growers thought improper environment itself was the cause of disease. This idea prevailed until the last half of the nineteenth century, when it was demonstrated that plant infections were caused by bacteria and fungi, thriving and multiplying under these very conditions. Other pathogenic organisms thrive under conditions of warmer temperatures coupled with high humidity. Soft, succulent growth is particularly liable to infections.

Moisture is of the greatest significance in the spread of disease. In order for a fungus spore to germinate, or for bacteria to enter a plant, water must be present on rhizome, pseudobulb, leaf, or sheath. Hence good orchid culture calls for watering and syringing early enough in the day to allow the plants to dry off before night. Then, when temperatures are lower and humidity runs up to the saturation point, the plant offers dry surfaces to the potential enemy. Avoid crowding the plants on the bench, as this cuts down air circulation and allows moisture to remain for long periods.

Sanitation is important. Pathogenic organisms may be perpetuated on plant debris accumulated on or under the benches and may be spread from these sources by splashing water or by insects. Weeds, plant trimmings, old flowers, and all other debris must be cleared away. When treating a diseased plant any parts that are cut off should be burned or should be wrapped and disposed of with trash that is to be burned. Insect control is related to sanitation, since insects play a dual role in plant infection. They inflict wounds through which pathogenic organisms can enter, and they sometimes place in the wound organisms which they have picked up by contact with infected material. Aphids are particularly dangerous since certain species are known to be vectors of virus diseases.

When buying plants, choose those that appear to be disease-free. If you buy by mail, examine the plants carefully when they arrive before putting them with your other plants. If any have soft watery spots, or streaks or patterns of dead tissue in the leaves, reject them.

It is often difficult for an amateur to know what disease he is dealing with from the appearance of spots on his plants, particularly at the onset of the disease. In fact, for a long time it was difficult even for pathologists to do so. In the past few years pathologists have developed methods for culturing bacteria and fungi from tissues of diseased plants, inoculating the pure strains into healthy plants and observing the symptoms, and then recovering the organisms from the inoculated plants. Thus they have been able to study the symptoms produced by specific organisms and follow the course of the disease each causes.

Similarly, viruses have had to be isolated, purified, and inoculated into healthy plants. The virologists are now employing a new method for diagnosis, adopted from the field of immunology. Rabbits are injected with a pure strain of virus, to which they respond by forming antibodies. Juice from an infected plant is then added to a sample of serum taken from the rabbit blood. If the juice contains the specific virus with which the rabbit was inoculated, the antibodies will react with it. The descriptions of the various diseases, from their onset through the courses they generally follow, which the pathologists have now made available to us, are a great help to orchid growers.

Laymen are for the most part still not able to pin down each disease to its causative agent, but we can come a lot closer than we could a few years ago. Where a disease is quite specific to a certain kind of orchid, for example Miltonia scorch or Paphiopedilum crown rot, or when you have seen a certain type a number of times and have learned its course and how it responds to treatment, you become fairly confident in your diagnosing. The viruses are more elusive, although some are so characteristic that an amateur can recognize their patterns. Sometimes diseases may fool you, some little clue may escape you, or you may not notice the disease until it has gone beyond the beginning stages. As far as bacterial and fungal diseases are concerned, those which you cannot treat you will recognize quickly, and for those that can be cured any of a number of fungicides can be used.

The first steps in control are to isolate the diseased plants, cut down the humidity, dispense with syringing, and increase ventilation. This will not only reduce the spread of disease to healthy plants but will help to check its spread in infected ones. Then treat the infected plants. If additional plants in the greenhouse become infected and it appears that the disease is spreading, the whole greenhouse may be sprayed with a fungicide.

■ BACTERIAL AND FUNGAL DISEASES

Both bacterial and fungal diseases begin with water-soaked, semi-transparent spots. As the disease spreads a single spot may enlarge until it involves a whole leaf, sometimes spreading from there through the pseudobulb and into the rhizome, or a number of small spots may individually enlarge until they run together. Spots on leaves are easy to detect, but a diseased area on a pseudobulb may escape notice. If the side of a pseudobulb appears to cave in, or if the pseudobulb falls over, investigate to see whether there is an area softened by disease. Some diseases caused by soil-borne organisms may penetrate the plant by way of the roots, progressing to the rhizome and sometimes into the pseudobulbs. These are less obvious at their onset because their presence is not suspected until the leaves become soft and wrinkled, or the new lead turns black. In such cases it may be necessary to cut through the rhizome, starting at the older end of the plant, to determine whether the root loss and leaf wilt are caused by disease. If the tissue of the rhizome is clean and white, or cream-colored, it is healthy. If it has black or purple discoloration it is diseased. Before cutting into the rhizome, be sure that the root loss has not been caused by snails.

The list of effective fungicides is long, and new ones are being added to it rapidly. Among them are some with fairly long residual action; Bordeaux Mixture (copper sulfate and lime, an old remedy but still useful), Tersan, Ceresan, Arasan, Fermate, Parzate, Captan, Dithane, Zerlate, and Bioquin 1 (copper 8-quinolinolate). These are all valuable both as curative sprays and as preventive sprays where large numbers of plants require treating, but they may also be used to spray or sponge individual plants. Some are insoluble in water and are used in a suspension, some are combined with a sticker to make their application more permanent. Bordeaux Mixture may not be as effective as some of the newer fungicides, but if you are faced with the emergency treatment of a plant and cannot readily obtain one of the others, you can usually find Bordeaux Mixture at a local drug or garden store. It can be made into a thick slurry, even a paste, and be applied to wounds or diseased spots. Tersan may be used one teaspoon per gallon of water as a preventive spray, but for infected plants the solution should be one tablespoon per gallon. It may also be made into a slurry or a paste and applied to infected areas and to wounds.

Fungicides which have a shorter residual action but which are very effective are: mercuric chloride (corrosive sublimate), used only to sponge diseased spots on leaves, in a concentration of 1:1000 (it should not be al-

Fig. 140 Pythium black rot on Cattleya pseudobulbs. Left, the disease starting at the top of the pseudobulb. Right, spreading upward from the rhizome. (Courtesy of Peter A. Ark)

lowed to enter the pot); copper sulfate in a solution of 1:100,000, used as a drench; Natriphene (the sodium salt of o-hydroxydiphenyl) in a concentration of 1:2000, used as a spray or drench; and 8-quinolinol sulfate or 8-quinolinol benzoate (the active ingredient in Wilson's Anti-Damp and other preparations), used in a concentration of 1:2000 as a spray or drench. Those that can be used as drenches, in addition to being very effective, are nontoxic to plants; plants from community pot size to adults can be soaked in the solution for several hours at a time.

Not much work has been done as yet with antibiotics on orchids, and we cannot recommend any at this time. Growers should follow developments in this field for it may be that some will prove safe and useful.

Since diseases can be spread from plant to plant by cutting tools, these should be disinfected after they are used on a diseased plant and before they are used on another plant. The best method is to boil them or pass them through a flame. If a razor blade will do the cutting job at hand, a new one can be used for each plant and discarded afterward. An electric cautery tool, if one is available to you, is excellent.

Pythium black rot and damp-off. A water mold, *Pythium ultimum*, causes this disease which results in damp-off of community pot seedlings and which also attacks older plants. It requires free water in order to spread, and since community pots are kept damp and the plants are tender and close together, they are most vulnerable to this fungus. Prevention calls for watering the pots every month or so with 8-quinolinol sulfate or benzoate, or with Natriphene, or with copper sulfate 1:100,000. If a seedling in a pot shows evidence of infection by turning brown and transluscent, act quickly. Remove the infected seedling and soak the whole pot in 8-quinolinol benzoate for several hours. In older seedlings black spots on the basal portion or on the leaves quickly spread to involve the whole plant. Cut out diseased areas and soak as for community pots.

Older plants are usually infected through the roots and the disease spreads into the rhizome and thence into the pseudobulbs, but occasionally the route is reversed, starting with a leaf and spreading to the pseudobulbs and thence from one pseudobulb to another. High humidity and cool temperatures favor it. The streaked and blackened tissues sometimes become soft and limp, and exude water on pressure. As the leaves fall and the contents of the pseudobulbs become completely decayed, all that remains is a dried and husk-like remnant of the pseudobulbs. If the disease appears above the level of the rhizome of an adult plant, cut away the streaked and blackened tissue well down into healthy tissue, soak the whole plant, pot and all, for several hours in 8-quinolinol benzoate, and then let it dry out completely. Spray it with Tersan or Fermate, or one of the other long-lasting fungicides, and give water in the pot only (no syringing) for long enough to ascertain whether the disease is arrested. If the disease spreads upward through the rhizome (see illustration page 266), cut between the pseudobulbs until you find a healthy section of the plant. Save only this section and treat as above. If the disease continues to spread the plant may have to be discarded.

Collar rot or orchid wilt. This disease is caused by the fungus *Sclerotium rolfsii*, and affects many kinds of orchids, among them Cymbidium and Paphiopedilum. The base of the stem turns light yellow, later dark brown, and the infection spreads to the roots and up into the leaves. The white fungus growth can sometimes be seen on the stems. Later tiny, hard yellow bodies (sclerotia) are formed by the mycelium, which can live for a long time and serve to perpetuate the fungus. The disease thrives with temperatures of about eighty-five degrees and high humidity. Cut out the diseased portions and immerse the plant in one-tenth per cent Ceresan for fifteen minutes. Do not use a stronger solution else the plant may be damaged.

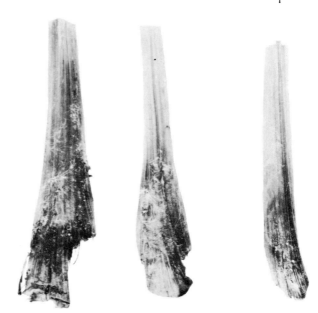

Fig. 141 *Sclerotium rolfsii* on the base of Cymbidium leaves. Note the white fungus growth and the small round sclerotia. (Courtesy of Peter A. Ark)

Heart rot. The fungus, *Phytophthera omnivora*, causes a serious rot that starts in the heart of the plant where the leaves join the stem, and spreads upward through the leaves. This fungus is related to the one that infects the potato, and which ruined the potato crop in Ireland in 1845, causing the famine that killed some 250,000 people. The *phytophthera omnivora* infection of orchids begins with the appearance of dark, sharply delimited lesions in the very heart of the plant. The infected area spreads rapidly, until within a few days the entire leaf is discolored and falls off. In severe cases the infection spreads from the heart to new leaves formed after the older ones have fallen. In milder instances, the infection may be confined to one of the older leaves, especially if the plant is kept dry. The disease spreads rapidly from plant to plant, injuring especially the highly susceptible Vandas and Phalaenopsis, but also infecting Cattleya and other genera. Young seedlings are very liable to infection. Moist, warm conditions favor its spread. Another species of fungus, *Phytophthera palmivora*, has been isolated from Dendrobium in Ceylon and Vanda and Cat-

Fig. 142 Cybidium tip burn caused by Botrytis fungus. (Courtesy of Peter A. Ark)

Cymbidium tip burn. *Botrytis* sp. causes the tips of the leaves to become spotted; as the spots coalesce the whole tip dries. Powdery masses of spores may be seen on dead leaf parts. Diseased tips should be cut off and the plant treated with Tersan or other fungicide.

Anthracnose or leaf spot. Many species of *Gleosporium* and *Colletotrichum* cause this disease in Cattleya, Pahpiopedilum, Epidendrum, Cymbidium, Vanda, Coelogyne, Laelia,

tleya in Java. Remove infected leaves or portions of leaves, in hopes of saving the growing point of the plant. Drench with Natriphene, or dip the plant (section above the roots) in Tersan and sprinkle Tersan powder into the heart section. If the growing tip of a Vanda is killed, cut the stem well below the tip area and hope for a healthy side shoot. In Dendrobium, or others, where the top or flowering section of the stem is killed, remove the stem to its healthy base. Repeat treatment with fungicide.

Fig. 143 Leaf spot caused by Gleosporium, on leaf of *Odontoglossum grande*. (Courtesy of Peter A. Ark)

Odontoglossum, Oncidium, Phalaenopsis, and others. The fungi are prevalent in most greenhouses and infection is favored by warm temperatures, excessive moisture, and insufficient light. Leaves develop circular or oval sunken spots, that are reddish brown at first, becoming dark brown or gray with age. As the spots dry, black fruiting bodies of the fungus form in the area and these can carry the disease to other plants. Infections are often quite mild, and may be limited by reducing the humidity. However, the whole greenhouse cannot be kept dry in order to control anthracnose, so the plants are best treated. Copper compounds are especially effective, swabbed on the spots, as are Bordeaux Mixture, mercuric chloride, Tersan and other fungicides. If the infection becomes more serious, and the spots enlarge and spread, entire leaves and occasionally a whole plant may be killed. Cut off the badly affected leaves, and repeat treatments with a fungicide until the spread is ended.

One species, *Gleosporium affine,* spreads rather rapidly through leaves of Oncidium, Odontoglossum and Dendrobium. As the infection progresses toward the base of the leaf the outer portion dies, becoming thin, dry, and light brown. Fruiting bodies of the fungus develop in concentric rings which may be circular or diamond shaped. One's first thought on seeing these is that they may represent a virus infection, but close examination will reveal that the rings are formed by tiny black bodies. If anthracnose is general throughout the greenhouse, spray with one of the long-acting fungicides described earlier.

Leaf blight. A water mold, *Pythium splendens,* causes leaf blight. The disease starts on a leaf, especially of Cattleya, as a round spot of chestnut brown color, often on the edge of the leaf, which enlarges rapidly and turns black. The area becomes thin. Cut out diseased portion well below infected area, and apply Tersan to the whole plant. Keep the plant parts dry and cut down on watering.

Leaf die-back. A fungus, *Glomerella cincta,* causes an infection which starts at the tip of the leaf and spreads toward the base, involving the whole width of the leaf. There is a marked line of distinction between the diseased and the healthy area. The infected area turns soft and brown; later it dries. Cut off the diseased area below the line of infection, and treat the cut edge and remaining part of the leaf with a fungicide such as Tersan. Many kinds of orchids are affected.

Flower speck and blight. *Botrytis cinerea* is a fungus that causes flower speck. It is especially prevalent under damp cool conditions, but can occur at other times. Light brown or pinkish specks appear on the flowers after they open. Infected flowers should be removed at once as their presence allows for the rapid spread of the disease. Old flowers can be a reservoir of infection. Reduce the humidity in the greenhouse and give good ventilation. If the nights are running too cool, raise the temperature somewhat. Flowers can also be infected with a sooty black mold under conditions of excessive humidity.

Fig. 144 Flower speck caused by *Botrytis cinerea* (Courtesy of Peter A. Ark)

Black sheaths. Green sheaths are sometimes attacked by one or another of the fungi described, especially under humid conditions and when water is left standing in the pocket between leaf and sheath. If the sheaths are treated in time and are allowed to remain dry the infection need not spread to the flower buds within. Cut off the sheath above the buds and spray the sheath and buds with mercuric chloride 1:1000 or drench with copper sulfate 1:100,000.

Rusts. Many kinds of orchids are subject to attacks by the rust fungus *Hemileia americana*, and possibly by some other species. The fungus produces powdery masses of yellow to yellow-orange spores, which are easily spread from plant to plant. Although plants are seldom killed they can be weakened so that they flower poorly or not at all. Treat with one of the copper-containing fungicides, or with Tersan or mercuric chloride.

Saprophytic fungi. These are not parasitic, that is, they do not attack living tissue. They live only on dead plant material, such as the dead sheathing leaves of stems, dead sheaths, or parts of leaves that have been killed by other organisms or have died naturally. They thrive under humid conditions where there is not sufficient air movement. Oddly enough,

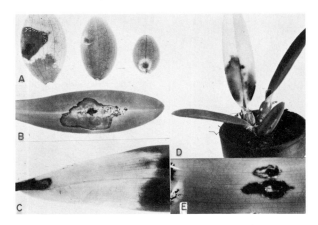

Fig. 145 Bacterial brown spot caused by *Phytomonas cattleyae*. A, B, C, on Phalaenopsis seedlings and full grown plants, D and E on *Cattleya trianaei*. (Courtesy of Peter A. Ark)

a single plant may show saprophytic fungi on the tissues clothing the stems or rhizomes when others around it are free. Perhaps it is too crowded by surrounding plants to allow the air to move as freely as it should, or the plant may have been kept too wet for a period, allowing the fungus to become established. Drying off the plant will stop the growth of the fungus, although the spots it caused will remain. While the saprophytic fungi are not a threat to the plant, they indicate a condition that should be corrected. Perhaps spacing the plants farther apart is all that is necessary.

Bacterial brown spot. This disease is caused by *Phytomonas cattleyae*, which enters the plant through wounds or through the stomata. While it attacks Cattleya and other species, it is particularly serious on Phalaenopsis and on community pot seedlings. It begins with a small water-soaked spot which is dirty green at first, turning brown and sometimes black. The spot enlarges rapidly. On Phalaenopsis the spot is blister-like and quickly spreads to the heart of the plant so that if it is not arrested it will kill the plant. Seedlings are also killed quickly. The infected tissues are soft and watery, often breaking open and exuding masses of bacteria which can then quickly spread the infection. On Cattleyas, older seedlings and mature plants, the disease does not travel so rapidly, except that a young lead can be quickly killed. Cut out all diseased areas as soon as the disease is detected. Soak community pots, young seedlings, and mature plants for several hours in 8-quinolinol benzoate or sulfate. As soon as the plant parts are dry, spray with Tersan, Fermate, or another long lasting fungicide. On mature plants the disease may be arrested by swabbing the spots when small with mercuric chloride 1:1000.

Miltonia scorch. Also called Bacterial tip burn and streak. This is found thus far only on Miltonia, and the organism has not yet been identified. It is a cool temperature disease and extremely infectious. It starts as water-soaked spots on the tip or margin of a

Fig. 146 Miltonia scorch. Also called bacterial tip burn and streak. Left, infection originating in pseudobulbs. Right, originating on leaves (Courtesy of Peter A. Ark).

leaf, often on newly developing leaves, and spreads to the pseudobulb. The pseudobulb becomes yellow to orange in color, and has areas that look eaten or burned away. They become tough and leathery. The diseased parts should be cut away, and the plant should be immersed in 8-quinolinol benzoate or sulfate for several hours.

Brown rot of Paphiopedilum. This disease is caused by the bacillus, *Erwinia cypripedii*, which apparently enters through wounds. (See illustration page 185.) It starts as a small chestnut-brown spot on a leaf, usually spreading in both directions so that it soon reaches the crown of the plant. It spreads through successive leaves until a whole growth is affected. Sometimes the growth is killed before the outer ends of the leaves have turned brown. It spreads so rapidly that it can travel through a plant of many leads killing the whole plant. If it is caught soon enough, however, the plant may be saved by cutting off leaves below the infection, cutting out whole growths by severing the rhizome if they have been infected to the base. The plant is then soaked for several hours in 8-quinolinol benzoate or sulfate. The soaking should be repeated two or three times at intervals of a few days, else the disease may start up again. After treatment try to keep the foliage dry, watering the pot carefully so as not to splash water on the leaves. In a group

of plants where this disease has once occurred, it will help prevent further attacks if they are sprayed with Tersan, Fermate or other fungicide every three months or so.

Bacterial soft rot. Incurable. This disease is caused by the bacillus, *Erwinia carotovora*. Cattleyas are most seriously affected, although a large number of other kinds are also attacked. The disease is rare, but it is so destructive and infectious that it is suggested that plants be destroyed immediately rather than be treated. The disease starts with a water-soaked dark green spot on the upper end of a leaf. It feels watery and breaks open at a slight touch. The inner tissues of the leaf are rapidly destroyed and the leaf becomes flaccid and wrinkled. The epidermis is so soft that it often breaks open, exuding its watery content and thus contaminating the bench and in fact the whole area surrounding the plant. A foul smell often accompanies the disease. After destroying the plant, thoroughly disinfect the area by drenching bench, post, and floor with mercuric chloride solution 1:1000. Treat neighboring plants with a fungicide.

Bacterial leaf rot. The bacillus *Erwinia chrysanthemi* has recently been found to be

Fig. 147 Bacterial soft rot. Incurable. Caused by *Erwinia carotovora*. The affected leaf shows wrinkling due to collapse of internal tissues. (Courtesy of D. P. Limber and B. A. Friedman)

the cause of leaf rot in a number of kinds of orchids in Hawaii. In Grammatophyllum diseased areas are water-soaked and brownish. In Dendrobium, the leaves are water-soaked and yellow. In Vanda the disease begins with translucent areas on the leaves, which become dark in color and finally black and sunken. Prevention includes spraying with Natriphene before and during wet weather, and control necessitates removal of the diseased areas and treatment with a fungicide.

■ VIRUS DISEASES

The study of virus diseases in orchids is a tremendous field; a great deal has been accomplished in the short ten or eleven years of work devoted to it. The study is complicated by many things. A certain virus may infect a number of different kinds of orchids, producing different symptoms in each, while different viruses may produce the same symptoms in a single host. In one host a virus may cause only mild symptoms, while in another host the same virus may produce a serious disease. Viruses have been isolated from many kinds of orchids. A goodly number of these have been inoculated into species other than those in which they were originally found in an effort to determine whether they are capable of infecting different kinds of plants. It has been found, for instance, that the virus causing severe color breaking in Cattleya flowers produces a bar-mottle pattern in Cymbidium leaves. The virus that produces Cymbidium necrotic ringspot infects Cattleya and Spathoglottis causing death of the new shoots. Cymbidium mosaic virus produces dead areas in the leaves of Cattleya. In order to separate just a few of the viruses and determine their action on just a few species, thousands upon thousands of separations of viruses, inoculations into healthy plants, and reverse inoculations from these back to members of the original host species have had to be performed.

Viruses are spread from plant to plant by means of infected cutting tools (sometimes infected in such an apparently harmless way as cutting flowers), and by insect vectors. Divisions of infected plants carry the virus with them. Plants known to be infected should be destroyed. This is a simple matter when the grower can recognize the symptoms, as in Cattleyas with color break of the flowers, and when, as Dr. Jensen says, the plant does so poorly that the grower gets rid of it, probably without even knowing that it has had a virus infection. But when the symptoms are obscure or mild enough to pass unnoticed or to be thought not significant, it is not such an easy matter. One cannot always throw away plants on a mere suspicion. If you suspect a plant of having a virus infection, and cannot be sure from descriptions or photographs, keep it somewhat separate from other plants and enlist the aid of some of the experienced growers you know. Not that they will be infallible, but they may have seen the same thing elsewhere or be able to tell you where to get help.

To disinfect tools, either flame or boil them. It may be that chemical sterilization of some sort will be found effective, so keep an eye out for such reports in the future.

VIRUS DISEASES IN CATTLEYA. Severe color break of flowers. The color of the flowers is irregularly mottled with light and dark areas and the flowers are often malformed. The mottling is evident as dark and light areas in the bud. Leaves formed after infection have a mottling of dark green raised areas, called mosaic mottle. Young growths often have a streaking of rosy color. The virus is transmitted by the green peach aphid, less often by tools. The same virus infects Cymbidium, producing **bar mottle** in the leaves, and it can also infect Oncidium.

Mild flower breaking. Less severe mottling of the flowers without malformation and milder symptoms in the leaves are caused by the **Odontoglossum ringspot virus.** Because the symptoms are mild, the disease is sometimes overlooked until valuable plants are attacked. Intergeneric hybrids of Cattleya are equally susceptible.

Symmetrical flower breaking. Dark pigment outlines the sepals and covers all but the

Fig. 148 Cattleya severe flower break virus symptoms in Cattleya and Cymbidium. From left to right: flower showing severe color break and some malformation; young Cattleya shoot showing rosy mottling; mature

Cattleya leaf with mosaic of dark green raised areas; two Cymbidium leaves with bar mottle caused by the Cattleya severe flower break virus. (Courtesy of D. D. Jensen)

median area of the petals in flowers that have previously been normal. The disease seems thus far limited to Cattleyas.

Leaf necrosis. Caused by the **Cymbidium mosaic virus.** The initial infection may kill some of the leaves, and it produces various pat-

terns of dead tissue in others. After the first shock to the plant, leaves formed subsequently may show only mild symptoms and be overlooked. Unless the disease is caught during the early stages, the plant may thus remain in the greenhouse as a reservoir of infection. Necrotic

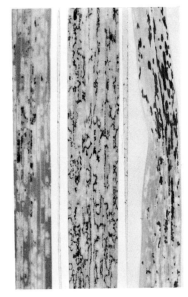

Fig. 149 Cymbidium mosaic virus affecting Cattleya and Cymbidium. The three Cattleya leaves at the left show respectively light brown pits on the under surface; streaks of black and yellow tissue; and necrotic rings

on the under surface. The three Cymbidium leaves at the right show various mosaic patterns of light and dark green tissue, with some black areas of dead tissue. (Courtesy of D. D. Jensen) areas may appear as brown sunken pits on the underside of the leaves, as alternate black and chlorotic streaks, or occasionally as rings of dead tissue on the underside.

Severe leaf necrosis. Caused by the **Cymbidium necrotic ringspot virus,** is deadly, although rather rare. New shoots as well as older leaves are killed, and death of the plant soon follows.

VIRUS DISEASES IN CYMBIDIUM.
Cymbidium mosaic. The most common virus disease in orchids. It is this virus with which Cym. Alexanderi 'Westonbirt' is infected, and all of the divisions of that original plant carry the virus. Since the virus is not transmitted through the seed, it is still possible to use this valuable hybrid (and others) as parents. The

Fig. 150 Necrotic ringspot virus of Cymbidium, the most severe virus disease of Cymbidium which also causes severe leaf necrosis in Cattleya. The first two Cymbidium leaves show necrotic rings and spots resulting from the original infection. The next two leaves, produced respectively several months and one year after the infection, show necrotic and chlorotic mottling. At the right is a young Cattleya leaf wih severe necrosis caused by the Cymbidium necrotic ringspot virus. (Courtesy of D. D. Jensen)

symptoms first appear as small elongated yellow (chlorotic) streaks on the younger leaves. As growth advances, the chlorotic streaks widen and elongate, and become more sharply defined, sometimes including in their width streaks of green tissue. Necrosis (death of tissues) does not usually occur on the young leaves, but older infected leaves frequently show black streaks and spots, often so severely as to cause the premature death of these leaves. This symptom gave rise to the original name of the disease "black streak." Sometimes the mottling that is present when the leaves are young become less conspicuous as the leaves become old. Plants with mild infection are not greatly affected as to growth and production of flowers, but badly infected plants grow and flower poorly. Viruses extracted from *Laelia anceps, Angraecum eburneum,* Epidendrum, Zygopetalum, and Oncidium caused identical symptoms in Cymbidium and may be the Cymbidium mosaic virus. This virus causes **leaf necrosis in Cattleya.**

Necrotic ringspot. The most severe virus disease in Cymbidiums. Instead of causing merely yellowed areas, it produces dead areas —in a pattern of rings, spots, and streaks— on old as well as young leaves. It frequently kills new growths and sometimes the whole plant. This is the virus that causes **severe necrosis in Cattleya** and Spathoglottis.

Diamond mottle. The **Odontoglossum ringspot virus** (which also causes **mild flower break in Cattleyas**) produces elongate chlorotic areas which are often diamond shaped. In older leaves, however, the areas may become necrotic and coalesce to form patterns called "hieroglyphic."

Bar mottle. Caused by the **severe flower-break virus of Cattleya.** Produces very pronounced intermittent lines of rectangular chlorotic areas. Some of the areas may later become necrotic.

VIRUS DISEASES IN ONDONTOGLOSSUM.
Ringspot. Affecting especially *Odontoglossum grande,* in which it produces concentric rings of necrotic tissue that may enclose some

normal green tissue. The rings may coalesce to form varied patterns. Symptoms are worse during the first few months of the disease, and many leaves may fall. After the initial shock wears off, the plant may show few symptoms, although it still carries the virus. The **Odontoglossum ringspot virus** causes **mild flower break in Cattleya** and **diamond mottle in Cymbidium.**

Streak. Irregular streaks and small rings, which are light green to yellow at first, later become reddish to black.

Mosaic. Leaves are stunted and have mosaic patterns of light and dark green areas.

VIRUS DISEASES IN SPATHOGLOTTIS. Diamond spot.

Chlorotic spots and streaks are followed by reddish-brown to black spots, necrotic rings, and diamond-shaped areas, with severely damaged leaves falling prematurely. H. H. Murakishi, searching for a plant that could be used as an indicator of virus in other orchids, especially those with mild or doubtful symptoms, found that Spathoglottis is extremely susceptible to infection by a variety of viruses in other genera. Viruses from eight genera—including Cattleya, Cymbidium, Dendrobium, Miltonia, Vanda, and others—were experimentally inoculated into healthy Spathoglottis seedlings. In almost every case, they produced necrotic ringspots and mosaic, the symptoms in Spathoglottis being almost identical regardless of the symptoms caused in the plants from which the viruses were taken. Two of the test viruses, recovered from infected Spathoglottis seedlings and inoculated back into the genus from which they were originally taken, reproduced the symptoms of the original disease.

VIRUS DISEASES IN OTHER ORCHIDS.

A **mosaic disease** occurs in *Dendrobium nobile*, consisting of chlorotic areas varying from small spots to large mottled areas, with occasional rings enclosing green tissue. A **mosaic with flower break** has been reported from Hawaii on *Dendrobium superbum*, and a **ringspot** on *Dendrobium phalaenopsis*, also from Hawaii.

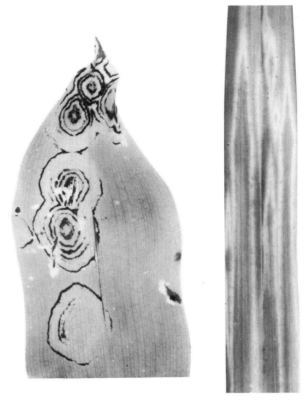

Fig. 151 Odontoglossum ringspot virus. Left *Odontoglossum grande* with concentric rings of necrotic tissue enclosing normal or light green tissue. Right, a Cymbidium leaf showing diamond mottle as a result of infection with the Odontoglossum ringspot virus. (Courtesy of D. D. Jensen)

Severe mosaic streaking occurs in *Oncidium varicosum* and *Oncidium concolor*, characterized by irregular chlorotic spots and streaks in the leaves. Apparently this is the same virus that causes **Cymbidium mosaic** and **Cattleya mild flower break.** An infection consisting of **stippled streaks** has been found in *Oncidium flexuosum* and a **light green mosaic mottle** in *Oncidium altissimum*.

Black streak is common in *Epidendrum O'Brianianum* hybrids. It starts with black sunken spots on the underside of the leaves, which show rosy rings on the upper surface. Later the dark areas extend into streaks or lines of spots. When inoculated into Cymbidium seedlings, the virus produces mosaic symptoms and may be the **Cymbidium mosaic virus.**

A disease called **"etch"** has been found in

a group of plants of *Laelia anceps* in California. Leaves show lines and partial rings of brown to necrotic tissue on the outer portions. Although half of the Cymbidium seedlings inoculated with the juice from these plants developed mosaic, the relationship between this and the true Cymbidium mosaic virus has not yet been established.

A striking infection was discovered in a group of *Stanhopea* plants imported into California. **Yellow spots and rings** form a sharp contrast to the green leaf tissue. Young leaves acquire the symptoms while small, and the symptoms increase with the age of the leaf.

Work is in progress on viruses in other genera. Instances of virus infection have shown up in Catasetum, *Dendrobium phalaenopsis, Lycaste aromatica, Miltonia roezlii,* and *Vanda boschii,* on which work is continuing. Viruses that produce known diseases in certain genera may be the cause of infections not yet realized, and others will undoubtedly be discovered.

■ PESTS

Many of the pests that attack orchids in their native habitats, and which used to come into this country with their hosts, are seldom seen in our greenhouses today. The U. S. Bureau of Entomology and Plant Quarantine bars them at our shores, and modern insecticides have pretty well eliminated those that had gained a foothold here. The pests which concern us now are for the most part kinds that live on garden plants and which invade our greenhouses.

A regular program for control of the various pests is easy to carry out and is better than waiting for populations to build up to high levels. It is difficult to get rid of a heavy infestation of any kind of pest, and a great deal of damage can be done by the pests in the meantime. A very small arsenal of weapons against pests will suffice. Two insecticides, DDT and Malathion, will take care of most insects, and these should both be kept on hand. A metaldehyde preparation is a necessity for control of snails and slugs. A miticide, preferably one that kills both types of mites prevalent

in orchids, such as Dimite, should also be on hand. To control ants, cockroaches, etc. one might also have chlordane. Where a regular program has not been practised, and insects have built up to large populations, it is necessary to treat the greenhouse several times at short intervals, perhaps three times ten days apart, with the specific chemical for the particular pests involved. Once the greenhouse has been cleaned up, a spraying every month or six weeks during warm weather, and every two months during cold weather, should keep things under control. In the meantime, be alert for local infestations, and treat these as needed.

We do not like to recommend chemicals that are extremely toxic to warm blooded animals including man. Such are the organic phosphates, with the exception of Malathion. Parathion was one of the first of these, and a number of deaths were reported from its use. TEPP is another very poisonous substance. As a matter of fact, Malathion does everything that these can do and more. When used with care, it is far safer. Nor can we at this time recommend any systemic treatment (in which the poison is taken up by the plants and kills insects feeding upon them). Those being tested are all extremely toxic to man, and not enough is yet known about their action on the plants. Since chemicals that are less poisonous to man are available, and will do just as good a job on the pests, we see no reason to risk using the more dangerous materials.

This does not mean that one should ever be careless with a pesticide. All are potentially dangerous to human beings, and should be treated with great respect. They should be kept locked away from the reach of children. They should always be used exactly according to directions. Concentrations that are too strong may injure the plants. Wear a long sleeved shirt and waterproof gloves while spraying, and change clothing immediately afterward. Wash all skin surfaces that have been exposed. While it is not necessary to wear a gas mask (as it was with Parathion) for any of the materials recommended here, it is wise to avoid breathing much of the fumes.

Spider mites. Called red spider or two-spotted mites, these are particularly troublesome on thin leaved orchids, and seem to have a special affinity for Cymbidium and Cycnoches. They suck the plant juice and leave tiny white scars on the undersurface of the leaves, where they prefer to live. The result is a fine stippling or silvering of the leaf surface. They are also injurious to the flowers. Their favorite point of attack on flowers is along the seams where the sepals come together in the bud, where they leave small transparent spots (See illustration page 40.) surrounding the punctured areas. One such spot is a blemish, but many spots actually ruin the flower. Sometimes as the sepals split apart, the red spiders enter the bud and cause enough damage to distort the flower. Red spiders are very small, one-fiftieth of an inch long, and protect themselves and their eggs with a fine web. They thrive under warm, dry conditions, and their populations can be reduced somewhat by frequent syringing. They belong to the genus Tetranychus. The most common is *Tetranychus telarius*, of which one form is bright red and another yellowish or greenish. We have found the best control to be Dimite, although Malation is also effective against them. Aramite, Chlorobenzilate, and Kelthane are also recommended.

False spider mites. These are extremely small, often difficult to detect without a hand lens. They are different from the spider mites in that they do not spin webs and they feed on both upper and lower surfaces of the leaves. They are the cause of damage to flowers but are often not seen upon them because of their minute size. The most common species are *Brevipalpus californicus*, the omnivorous mite; *Brevipalpus oncidii;* and *Tenuipalpus pacificus*, the Phalaenopsis mite. All will do damage to a number of orchids. Dimite is the best control, for they are not killed by Malathion, and Aramite is only partially effective against them. Kelthane has recently been reported effective.

Fungus mites. There are many kinds, but two we have seen are a small, colorless mite, about the size of red spiders but covered with long hairs, and a round dark brown mite which is hard and shiny with a little shield on each side over its legs. These may not do damage to plants, since they apparently feed on decaying organic matter, or on fungi and algae. They are seen only occasionally, but appear in tremendous numbers when they occur. Like Collembola (below), they are an eyesore, and if one is not forewarned about them they can be the cause of great concern. They may appear on an injured part of a plant, or on the new lead to which they are attracted by the honey it exudes, or on algae covering roots or pots. They look like a sprinkling of fine sand. Malathion will get rid of them.

Thrips. These are small chewing insects with narrow tapered bodies, which crawl about rapidly and hide at the slightest disturbance. They are about one-twenty-fifth of an inch long and can be yellow, gray, or black. Some species feed on leaves, on which they produce a fine silvery stippling. They can be particularly injurious to seedlings. Other species feed on flowers, and the little irregularly shaped scars are scattered over the flower surface. Evidence of their presence, if the insects themselves are not seen, is the tiny black dots of their excrement. Species of Anaphothrips, Taeniothrips, and others are common on orchids. DDT and Malathion are both effective against them.

Scale insects. There are two types of scales, the soft scales and the armored ones. The young stages of both are free moving, but as they mature they select sites, stick their proboscises into the plant tissue, and remain there. The soft scales have a waxy or rubbery covering, while the armored scales secrete a hard shell. The soft scales excrete a sweet substance on which a sooty black mold grows. Eggs or living young are produced in large numbers by the females, and as they emerge from under the bodies of the females, they crawl for a few days. Colonies of scales may cluster under the sheathing leaf of a pseudobulb or rhizome, or at the juncture of leaf and stem, or on the undersides of leaves.

The most common species of soft scale are the soft brown scale, *Coccus hesperidum;* the orchid soft scale, *Coccus pseudohesperidum,* which is less often seen than the former; the hemispherical scale, *Saissetia hemisphaerica;* and the black scale, *Saissetia oleae.* They vary from one-quarter to one-third of an inch long, being in general larger than the armored scales. Repeated spraying with Malathion will give eventual control. Dithio smoke fumigation is also reported to be good. Neither will kill all of the adults at first, but repetition will kill the crawling stages and eventually the adults.

Among the armored scales the most notorious is the Boisduval scale, *Diaspis boisduvalii.* The shells of the females are a grayish white, oval, somewhat like an oyster shell in appearance. They may occur so thickly as to form an encrustation on the plant. The males occur in cottony masses. They are about one-eighth of an inch long. Many other armored scales occur on orchids, and some of them inject a toxin into the plant in addition to injuring them by sucking the juice. The first good control of armored scales was by DDT in a xylol emulsion. This penetrates the armor and kills both adults and young. Within a few days after treatment the dead scales fall away from the plant, or can be easily brushed or washed off. A second, later treatment gets those that may have escaped the first time. Newer DDT preparations without xylol are not effective so quickly, although they are of wider general use. DDT and Malathion will both kill the young stages, but it will take several repetitions at weekly intervals to kill the adults and control successive hatches of young. Scrubbing badly infested plants with a DDT solution, described on page 50, is an effective way to handle scale on a few plants.

Unlike thrips, aphids, red spiders, etc.—which can enter the greenhouse from the garden—scale does not usually recur in greenhouses regularly treated with DDT and Malathion. It can however be brought in on newly acquired plants, especially if these are from collections not properly cared for.

Aphids. Soft-bodied, sucking insects of a number of species, some with wings and some without, can enter the greenhouse, and are particularly attracted to flower buds and open flowers. The females produce living young which take about a week to reach adult size. They may enter the greenhouse by way of the ventilators, or they can be brought in by ants. Their punctures spoil the looks of the flowers. They are particularly troublesome on sprays of small flowers, such as those of Oncidium and Epidendrum, where their presence may not be noticed at first because of the denseness of the flowers and the minuteness of their parts. They are more easily seen on large flower buds and flower parts, such as those of Cattleya and Cymbidium. The work of ants can be suspected when isolated infestations are found. The pale green peach aphid (*Myzus persicae*) is commonly found in the greenhouse, and because of its color is not as readily detected as the black bean aphid (*Aphis fabae*), which is another kind commonly found. The lantania aphid has been reported on orchids, but not as often. This is flat and black with a white fringe around its body. DDT will control some types of aphids, but Malathion gives better general control. Lindane (Benzene Hexachloride) is also effective.

Mealy bugs. A number of species of mealy bugs generally infest greenhouse plants and are reported to be a particular pest on Phalaenopsis. They are flat, segmented, whiskery bugs that are coated with wax. Some produce live young and others lay eggs in cottony sacs. The wax they secrete makes their control somewhat difficult, but Malathion used several times at three week intervals will control them.

Slugs and snails. Slugs are shell-less snails that slide along by means of a foot and lubricate their path with a trail of slime. Often the slime is the clue to their presence. They usually feed at night, and hide in the daytime under the plant parts or the rim of the pot. Young slugs may be only a quarter of an inch long, while adults may reach two inches. The snails that are particularly bothersome are a small, flat-coiled, brown-shelled kind, which reaches about a quarter of an inch in diameter. Both snails and slugs are equipped with a radula, a series of rasps on a moving band, with which they rasp away plant tissue. They prefer succulent parts such as root tips, young leaves and flower buds. See illustration page 40. One slug can literally mow down a pot of small seedlings in a night. Both slugs and snails lay eggs within the pot, usually near the bottom. Metaldehyde is the best control. It may be used in dust form, actually dusted on the plants and pots, and then watered into the pot, or it may be applied in liquid form. Either is better than pellets or meal containing arsenic, which cannot be put on the pots, but which must be used on the benches or floor. These are not satisfactory because they do not get the slugs or snails that live in the pots. Repeated treatments are necessary to rid the greenhouse of slugs and snails. They are very stubborn pests and the grower must be equally stubborn.

Ants. While they do not seem to damage plants, ants bring in aphids. The ants are attracted by the honey secreted by new leads and sheaths. They are killed by Malathion. Chlordane sprinkled on the ground under the benches will help in keeping them out of the greenhouse.

Cockroaches, sowbugs, millipedes. Sowbugs and millipedes are common in the soil and will invade the greenhouse. Cockroaches are prevalent in warm climates. All will feed on orchids. Chlordane sprinkled on the ground or watered into the ground will control the under-bench population, and DDT sprayed on plants and pots will kill them in the potting medium.

Collembola. These wingless insects are called springtails because they are equipped with a jumping apparatus on their tails. They are one-eighth of an inch long; may be grey, or black, or banded; and live in soil all over the world. Their presence in orchid houses was rarely noticed until DDT came into general use. They are resistant to DDT, and increase where it alone is used. Until the advent of Parathion and its successor Malathion, it was almost impossible to get rid of Collembola. They do little damage to the plants, except possibly to root tips when they are present in great numbers, but pots swarming with Collembola are an eyesore. A regular spray program that includes Malathion will keep them in control.

Black fly. Common in greenhouses, this little black fly thrives in over-wet soil or potting medium. Its tiny little white grubs (larvae) dwell in the soil, and the adults flutter up from the soil surface when disturbed. Apparently they do no damage to orchids but, like Collembola, they are a nuisance. DDT and Malathion will control them.

Cattleya fly, Dendrobium weevil, Dendrobium beetle. These are specific pests which used to plague orchid growers, and which still do where orchids are grown in the open in tropical areas. They are controlled by both DDT and Malathion and are now almost never seen in this country.

Other insects. Various beetles, leaf hoppers, grasshoppers, etc. occasionally enter the greenhouse, to say nothing of bees. A residue of DDT will kill some of them, and hand capturing or swatting will get rid of the rest.

Nematodes. There are many kinds of nematodes, called "eel worms," both soil- and water-dwelling, that are harmless to plants. But some are parasitic on plants, usually definitely associated with certain hosts or groups of hosts. The parasitic kinds are almost microscopic, ranging in length from one-sixty-fourth to one-quarter inch. Among the species that infest plants are some that cause root knots, some that cause root lesions, some that invade leaf and stem tissue, and some that attack flower buds. As far as we know, only two kinds have been found on orchids. These are a species that feeds on and kills the flower buds of terete Vandas in Hawaii and a root-lesion type recently found in Cymbidiums of some California areas. The Vanda bud nematodes are being controlled by picking off and burning all infested spikes. There is as yet no safe control for root lesion nematodes in orchids. These nematodes live in the root tissue and feed upon it. Areas which they destroy are then subject to invasion by fungi and bacteria. Infested plants show rotted and discolored roots, with the root system in general becoming much reduced. Soil intended for use in potting mixes can be sterilized to free it of nematodes, but chemicals which would kill the nematodes already present in the roots are so toxic that they will also kill the plant. It is to be hoped that in the near future some safe control will be developed. It is also to be hoped that instances of root lesion nematode infestation remain as rare as they apparently are at present.

22 | *Housing Your Orchids*

THE first advise to prospective greenhouse owners is to build a greenhouse large enough to hold an expanding hobby. A small greenhouse will look tremendous for a while, compared to the space ordinarily given to house plants. But it is legendary that orchid growers are never satisfied; they are always adding to their collections. Perhaps you will be interested in only one or two kinds at first, and feel you would be satisfied with but a few plants of each. Inevitably you will fall in love with another kind, and then another. You will buy a few seedlings of this and then a few of that. The seedlings will grow to maturity and the mature plants will need dividing. Soon your benches will be overflowing, and you will join in the plaint common to most amateurs, "Oh, for some more space!" We suggest that you drive the old car for a few years longer or take a less expensive vacation in order to build a fairly generous greenhouse.

There are other reasons for not building too small a greenhouse. A very small house is difficult to manage; its small volume of air heats up quickly and cools off quickly, creating a rapid fluctuation of temperature. It is difficult to work in. Large sprays of flowers become entangled with each other. Plants become crowded, causing unhealthy conditions and difficulties in handling.

A very minimum (and this will not hold a large number of plants) would be something in the neighborhood of eight by ten feet. This width would allow two side benches and a center walk. A twelve-foot width would give you two side benches and a center bench. A greenhouse twelve feet wide and fifteen or eighteen feet long is large enough to give space for growing a truly satisfying number of plants, and at the same time is not too large for a busy person to care for in his spare time. The cost of a greenhouse and its equipment does not double when its size is doubled; instead, the cost is about one and one-half or one and one-third. In other words, you can get twice the space for about a half or a third more in cost.

To obtain an idea of types and costs of greenhouses, send for catalogues from various greenhouse manufacturers. Visit some of the home greenhouses in your town. Talk to the owners and find out what faults lie in certain plans, and what good features, so that you can avoid the former and adopt the latter. Inquire about heater efficiency and notice whether certain installations would be satisfactory for orchids. Examine thoughtfully the relation between greenhouse shapes and the amount of bench space allowed.

Perhaps the most economical, from the point of view of space and efficient operation, are the types that have been in use for many years. There are some novelty styles that may appeal to some from the point of view of decorativeness, but before considering one of these be sure that it will give you what you need and want.

Fig. 152 Two types of attached greenhouse. Upper, attached by one end. In another situation this greenhouse could extend to a greater length. (Courtesy Aluminum Greenhouses, Inc.) Lower, a lean-to. Note louvered section at end for ventilation in addition to roof ventilator. (Courtesy Lord and Burnham)

A greenhouse may be a free-standing unit, or it may be attached to an existing building. In the latter case, it may be attached by one end, with its length running out from the building, or it may be a lean-to, attached along one side, with the wall of the building substituting for one side wall of the greenhouse. Less desirable for orchids, but still usable, is a breezeway, a glassed-in passageway between two buildings, the house and garage, for instance. A breezeway does not offer as good light, but if the kinds of orchids are chosen for the location, they should do well and give much pleasure.

In locating a greenhouse, the aim is to give it a spot where it will receive as much light as possible throughout the day. If you are planning a greenhouse along with a new home you can assure it a good spot, but it is a challenge sometimes to find an ideal spot in an already established yard. A free-standing type can be placed in any open spot, out of the shadow of the house or nearby buildings, and away from trees. If trees are present, pick a place that receives their shade for the fewest number of hours a day, and then plan to utilize the shade in place of artificial shade on the glass. A clear exposure from the south is important in the winter, because the sun swings to the south at that season. If the greenhouse is to be in a yard facing north, be sure that it stands where the house will not cast a shadow on it in the winter time. It is generally thought that a greenhouse should run from north to south to allow the sun to travel across it from east to west. Home owners are not always able to achieve this, and should be comforted to know that a greenhouse that runs east and west, or north-east and south-west will function very well.

A lean-to should preferably be located so that one side or one end receives light from the east and one side light from the south. A lean-to on the west side is difficult to manage in the summer, although an evaporative or refrigerative cooler may take care of the excessive heat that results from this location.

A place to do the potting and to store materials is a great convenience. The ideal situation (not achieved by all of us, by any means) is to have a potting shed attached to the north end of the greenhouse, as shown in Figure 153. If you have hot water heat for the greenhouse, the shed can also house the boiler. If the greenhouse is attached to the garage, or handy to it, perhaps part of the garage may be used for potting. Otherwise,

wood in a short time, actually seeming to be pushed off by moisture moving through the wood from within. Paint stays on the inside far longer than on the outside. A new latex outside paint is now on the market which we hope may work for greenhouses. Further experimentation with it and methods for application are necessary before it proves itself. But

Fig. 153 A free-standing greenhouse with attached work room. Note roller blinds for shading. (Courtesy of Lord and Burnham)

a potting bench may be incorporated in the greenhouse, at the north end so as not to take the best growing space.

■ MATERIALS AND EQUIPMENT

Aluminum is at present the preferred material for the framework of the greenhouse. It does not rust (as does its antecedent, steel) and need not be painted. The sash bars are narrow and admit more light. Wood is, however, still widely used for home greenhouses and is somewhat less expensive than aluminum. The upkeep of wood is more troublesome, both in labor and cost of paint. Cypress and redwood are chosen for greenhouse construction because they resist decay. Ordinary house paint tends to peel off the

you might watch the developments and take advantage of it if it proves satisfactory. We are trying this ourselves.

A number of glass substitutes—fiberglass and various polyester and polyethylene films— are being tried experimentally. Some growers like fiberglass very much from the point of view of light transmission and diffusion. (Use only white or a light yellowish color, not green or blue.) Problems sometimes arise from weathering of the fiberglass, and it may be necessary to clean it and coat it with special preparations every few years.

The plastic sheeting materials offer tempting savings in construction, but many products that have been put on the market have proved to have much shorter life than was originally

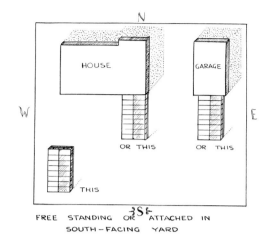

FREE STANDING OR ATTACHED IN
SOUTH-FACING YARD

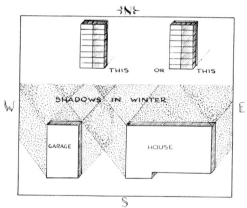

FREE STANDING IN NORTH-FACING YARD

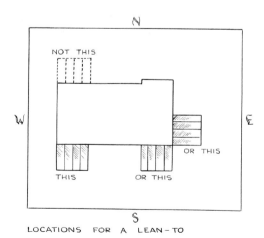

LOCATIONS FOR A LEAN-TO

expected of them, lasting only months instead of years in some cases. For permanent weatherproof construction for such valuable plants as orchids, it would seem wiser to use glass rather than any of the plastic films available at present.

In many home greenhouse styles, the manufacturers use large panes of double thick glass instead of the older system of many small panes in each section. Construction is made easier by this means. The glass is held in place by patented clips or bar caps, and the owner can easily replace a broken pane.

A masonry foundation is preferable to a wooden one, which will eventually rot out. The foundation walls should be set on a footing that goes below frost level, and may be of brick, stone, cinder block, or any similar material.

Assembling a prefabricated greenhouse is simple. The home owner and his family can put one up by following directions. They come complete with all parts and hardware. Before building the foundation, however, obtain specific details from the greenhouse company for its dimensions and any fittings necessary to hold the sill of the greenhouse. There are definite advantages in buying a complete product designed by greenhouse experts. If you do not want a package unit as offered, often you can buy what parts you wish from the manufacturer to fit a plan of your own. Many growers have built their own greenhouses, from new or used materials, with great success, and have possibly saved a good bit on the cost. A word of caution to the do-it-yourselfers—study standard greenhouse plans and construction first, so that you can come as close to a professional model as possible.

Walks should be at least two feet wide. Plants have a way of hanging out into the aisle if they are narrower than this. We feel that it is preferable to leave the ground under the benches bare. The damp earth helps keep

Fig. 154 Suggestions for locating a greenhouse, as to exposure and relationship to home.

the humidity up, and serves as a method of draining off excess water. If you prefer a solid concrete floor, there should be a floor drain and adequate slope to it. Otherwise, you will be wading in water much of the time.

Prefabricated benches are available. If you wish to build your own, you may make the frames either of wood (painted or treated with a preservative such as Cuprinol or Kopex, *never creosote*) or of pipe or concrete forms. Wooden bench legs should be set on bricks or concrete blocks to keep them from the wet floor. The bottom of the bench should allow free drainage, and free air movement up and through the pots. Such materials as hardware cloth (galvanized wire mesh), steel mesh, or

perforated transite are preferred, but wooden slats may also be used. Don't make the benches so high or so wide that you knock over plants in the front row in order to reach those in the back. Stepped benches can be used to give a little more room, provided that they do not cut off the light from plants on either side. A stepped bench is particularly useful on the wall side of a lean-to.

It is well to have both hot and cold water in the greenhouse and a mixing faucet, so that you can warm the water for use in the winter. An extra electrical outlet may come in handy for plugging in an emergency heater or some other piece of equipment.

The heating system is probably the item

Fig. 155 A greenhouse partitioned to give two sets of temperature conditions, in this case a cool section and an intermediate section. (Courtesy of Aluminum Greenhouses, Inc.)

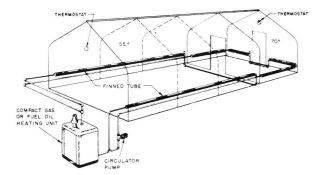

Fig. 156 Zone-controlled, automatic forced hot water heat, using finned tubing for circulation of water. The boiler can be fired either by gas or oil. The flow to each of the two sections is controlled separately. (Courtesy of Aluminum Greenhouses, Inc.)

of largest concern. In a very mild climate or where electricity is cheap, electrical heat may be feasible. An electric heater may be used to boost the temperature when a freak spell of cold weather hits your area. Otherwise, either warm air or hot water heat would be the choice. Hot water is perhaps ideal, but it is also the more expensive of the two. Before installing either, obtain information from a heating engineer as to the capacity of the heater or boiler, amount of pipe, etc., necessary for the size of your greenhouse and the temperature you wish to maintain. If you obtain this information from an expert not in your locality, be sure to give him data on the weather in your region, especially the extremes of cold that can be reached.

The smaller the greenhouse, the larger is the proportionate cost of a heating system for it. This is because certain items in the heating system cost the same whether they are for a large or a small unit. Also, a heater or a boiler increases in price relatively little for each increase in capacity. However, the basic cost is still higher than we could wish, and it would be desirable to have some ingenious thought applied to the problem.

A hot water system keeps a relatively even temperature. The pipes continue to radiate some heat after the controls shut off the flow. Finned tubing is more efficient than plain pipe,

and although it costs more per foot only about a fourth as much is required.

Warm air heaters are used by many orchid growers, fired either by gas or by oil. Both must be vented and be equipped with a thermostat and, for best performance, a blower. Gas heaters must have a safety shut-off valve. If gas is used, it must be 100 per cent natural gas or bottled gas. Artificial gas must never be burned in a greenhouse, nor must gas that has any artificial gas mixed with it. There has been a definite improvement in the types of warm air heaters offered for small greenhouses. Some models are made especially for greenhouses, and some are intended to be used in the home as room heaters or space heaters but are equally satisfactory for greenhouses. Some require a flue or chimney to carry out the fumes from combustion. Others are self-venting, designed to be set in the wall and having a sealed-off firing chamber that operates outside the greenhouse. It is possible to use hot air from the home if a duct system can be conveniently installed.

Cooling systems may be either evaporative or refrigerative, the former being in widest use. Both types come as self contained units, in a number of sizes. It would be best to obtain the advice of a local expert in air conditioning as to the size required for your greenhouse. It takes a larger unit to cool a greenhouse than it takes for a room of the same size. For most efficient cooling, an evaporative unit should take in air from outdoors. It is therefore best set in an opening in the wall, with the cabinet projecting outside and the opening from the blower flush with the wall. A ventilator at the opposite end should be opened a few inches to allow the air to move through the greenhouse. A cooling thermostat should be installed to operate the unit. This type, which blows cooled air into the greenhouse, is called a "positive pressure" system.

A pad and fan arrangement works on the same principle as an evaporative cooling unit, with the fan thermostatically controlled. An aspen pad is set in one wall. Above it is a perforated trough and below it a trough or pan. Water is conducted to the lower container by a small tube and its level is controlled by a float valve. A pump installed in the lower container moves the water through a tube to the upper trough, from which it trickles down through the pad, to be collected in the lower trough. A fan, placed either directly in front of the pad or in an opening at the opposite end of the greenhouse, pulls outside air through the moist pad. When the fan is directly in front of the pad, a ventilator should be open at the opposite end. This is another example of the "positive pressure" type. When the fan is in an opening at the opposite end, it pulls the air through the greenhouse and exhausts it, so that no ventilator need be open. This is called a "negative pressure" type. It is not quite as efficient as the former.

Shading the greenhouse can be achieved by several possible means. There are certain advantages and disadvantages in all kinds, but this is to be expected when you are trying to adjust the light through various seasons. White shading compound, sprayed or painted (with a paint roller on a long handle) is most widely used. Shading compounds may be obtained from greenhouse suppliers, and are used according to directions. In order to keep the white shading on our greenhouses through spring snows and summer hail we mix it with a small amount of linseed oil. This makes a more permanent paint than many growers would wish, and should probably be used only where it is desirable to have some remain on the glass through the winter, as in areas with very bright winter sun. Without linseed oil, the paint flakes off more readily, and may have to be renewed more often. The advantages of a white shading compound are its low cost and the fact that it can be applied thin or thick according to the season.

Slat shading is made in sections that can be screwed to the sash bars or fastened by brackets. The distance between the slats determines the percentage of outdoor light transmitted. During early spring and late fall perhaps a thin coat of white shading might be used, and the slat shading put up for the warmer months. Roller blinds are another type of slat shading. Their advantage is that they can be rolled up on dull days to give the plants as much light as possible. They are subject to damage by wind, however. Louvered aluminum shading is another form of slat shading, except that the louvers are extremely small and the light is finely broken. This is perhaps best used only on a side or end where the light is extremely strong.

Some growers like plastic screening, fiber mesh coated with plastic, which can be fastened either outside or inside the greenhouse. It comes in various grades designed to transmit different amounts of sunlight. The grower chooses the type suitable for his needs. Some growers make use of fiberglass panels as shading. For a bit of extra shade for individual groups of plants, cheesecloth is very satisfactory. It may be tacked up to wooden sash bars, or fastened to a framework of wood or wire, and can be used as thick or as thin as needed.

Automatic vent control is a great help to growers who must be away from home all day. Small motors, in series, are attached to the vent handles and are controlled by a thermostat. Where a cooling system is in use, automatic vent control is not necessary.

Fig. 157 Use of fiberglass in the roof, both for shade and for resistance to hail. (Additional shading may have to be used in many areas.) (Courtesy of Redfern's Prefab Greenhouse Mfg. Co.)

Humidifiers range from the simple spray nozzle placed in front of a fan (perhaps in front of the heater so that its blower distributes the moist air), to various kinds of mist-making apparatus. The latter are self-contained units which create a fine mist and blow it into the air. If the blower is strong enough, it will also help to circulate the air in the greenhouse.

One of the most important pieces of equipment for any greenhouse is a standard high-low temperature alarm, wired to ring a bell in the house when the greenhouse temperature reaches a dangerous level. It has a temperature dial and a hand that moves with the temperature. On each side is a set-hand which you set for the minimum and maximum desired temperatures. When the moving hand comes in contact with a set-hand it makes an electrical contact which rings the warning bell. The mechanism should be wired to batteries so as not to be affected by a power failure. The bell can be placed anywhere in the house where you can hear it easily.

■ ORCHIDS IN YOUR HOME

For all of the pleasure and ease in the possession of a greenhouse, there is nothing quite like having orchids in your home. Those who would experience the thrill of growing orchids, but for whom a greenhouse is out of the question, should certainly try a few, on a window sill, or in a case made especially for them. Growing orchids in the home is a somewhat different art from growing them in a greenhouse.* However, if you have a bright window, preferably east or south, that will allow them good light all day and direct light for part of each day, you can find kinds that will do well for you. In choosing a window for orchids, avoid one that becomes too hot for any plants, such as some west-facing bay windows or picture windows unfortunately are.

In a place where the night temperature cools off to 55° to 60° you can grow many of the intermediate kinds. Where the night temperature does not fall below 65° you had better try

* See Orchids As House Plants, Northen.

some of the warm kinds. The cool orchids are more difficult to grow in the home because, ordinarily, home temperatuers do not go as low as the needed 50°, but if you have a glassed in porch you might try some of these. We do not recommend the kinds that are most demanding of light, in any temperature group, for example, Vandas, some Dendrobiums, and Cymbidiums. Cattleyas and some others which are quite light-demanding, have a fairly wide light range, and in the home during the brightest hours of the day they may receive enough light (perhaps in the neighborhood of 2000 to 3000 foot candles when the sun is shining in the window) to enable them to grow and flower fairly well. They will probably not become the heavy, floriferous plants that they would be in a greenhouse, but will do well enough to give you great pleasure.

Some kinds will do better without the protection of a case—among them Cattleya, Epidendrum, Coelogyne, Lycaste, some of the small Oncidiums, and some botanicals—because they receive better light when directly in the window. If the leaves become too hot when the sun shines on them, pull a glass curtain or a piece of cheesecloth across the window and give them a mist spray over the foliage. The object is to give them all the light they can take because they do not have as many hours of it in the home as they would in a greenhouse. Water them when they need it, and give fertilizer a bit less frequently than you would for greenhouse plants. Do not let heat from a register blow on the plants. During warm summer nights the window can be left open to bring them the cooler, damper air. Watch for insects and control them as described earlier. Pests from other house plants can attack orchids, and it is well to keep these free from insects also.

The kinds that need the extra humidity of a case are Phalaenopsis, Paphiopedilums, Miltonias and some botanicals. In addition, these require less light than the Cattleya group and hence do not suffer from having the light cut down by the extra pane of glass between them and the window. The case should be tall enough to have a good volume of air, and should be equipped with a top and bottom ventilator and a door that opens wide for ease in working with the plants. In the bottom there should be a pan to hold water and to catch the drip from watering. Above the pan is set a grille on which to stand the pots. Depending on the temperature of the spot where the case is to be put, choose the kinds to be grown in it: Phalaenopsis and the mottle leaved Paphiopedilums if the temperature ranges between 60° and 65° or stays close to 65°; Miltonias and the plain leaved Paphiopedilums if it ranges between 55° and 60°.

Management of an orchid case follows pretty much the rules for managing a greenhouse. The sun shining in the window can heat up the case just as it does a greenhouse, and it may be necessary to draw a thickness of cheesecloth across the window during the hottest hours. At this time open the top and bottom ventilators and give the plants a mist spray. The case should be ventilated each day, even when the sun is not shining, and the plants may be given a mist spray once a day, allowing them to dry off by night. The air in the case should be kept fresh and buoyant, not stuffy or over-damp. Some of the troubles people have experienced with orchids in cases come from keeping the humidity too high; this causes black sheaths, spotted flowers, and rapid fading of flowers. Plants will dry out faster in the winter, with furnace heat, than in the summer, and this is true both of those in cases and out in rooms. Watering therefore has to be more frequent in the winter, though care against over-watering must always be exercised.

Flasks of seedlings or community pots will thrive in orchid cases. They may be grown in their own case, with shade across the window to subdue the light, or they may share one with larger plants, being placed behind them so as to be shaded. When the seedlings grow larger and need more light, adjustments will have to be made for them.

Fig. 158 An orchid case in the living room.

■ ORCHIDS IN YOUR GARDEN

Growers in such a fortunate climate as that of Hawaii, Florida, and parts of California can grow orchids in their gardens all year round, using them as an integral part of the landscaping. Those of us not so blessed in the matter of climate can at least have a few plants out-of-doors in the summer. In fact, in areas with quite hot summers, many kinds benefit from being moved outside; these include Cymbidiums especially, but also Cattleyas, Dendrobiums, Oncidiums and others.

In regions where orchids can be put outdoors for only part of the year, it is best to hang the pots or baskets on the lower limbs of tall trees, or to place them on a bench and build a lath or screen roof over them. Pots can sometimes be set in places where they will add to the decoration of a patio if the light conditions are right. Plants will dry out faster outside than in a greenhouse, so careful attention to watering is in order. Rain may do the job at times, but it cannot be depended upon

Fig. 159 Orchids in a Florida garden. The plants are naturalized on the tree or hung from the branches. In this group are Cattleyas, Phalaenopsis, Dendrobiums, Oncidiums, *Renanthera coccinea* and *Vanda coerulea*. (Courtesy of H. F. Loomis)

(Sometimes the rain overdoes it!) Guard the plants from the usual array of garden insects by spraying when needed. When moving greenhouse-tender plants outside, do not let them have too much sun at first. Some kinds can be hardened to take clear early morning and late evening sun, with some shade during the hot noon and afternoon hours.

Where orchids can be kept outside all year round, almost all of the greenhouse epiphytes can be naturalized on trees, where they will take root and grow just as they do in the wilds.

Plants that are potted in osmunda can be removed from the pot and the ball of fiber and roots can be firmly wired to a branch or to the trunk. For plants taken from bark, a chunk of fiber should be wired to the branch and the plant then wired in place upon it. The new growth should be next to the bark. As the roots grow, they extend out of the fiber and attach themselves to the tree. Another method is to fasten a half-pot or half a coconut husk to the branch and then settle the plant in the container with enough fiber to keep it firm. Plants naturalized in these ways must be watered regularly when there is not sufficient rain, and should be given frequent applications of fertilizer since they will not have so rich a source of nutrients as they would in jungle trees.

Some kinds can be grown in beds especially prepared for them. Terrestrials such as Phaius, Bletia, Calanthe and others need a well drained bed in which the soil has been replaced with the loose, fluffy type of compost you would use for them in pots. A mixture of sand, gravel or bark, leaf mold, and fibrous loam should be satisfactory. The bed must be located in a spot where the light will be right for the kinds you wish to grow in it.

Epiphytic or semi-epiphytic kinds can also be grown in beds, except that the bed should be raised eighteen to twenty-four inches to allow especially free drainage, somewhat after the manner of a rock garden. The lower foot of its depth is filled with very coarse gravel, and the upper eight to twelve inches with a mixture suitable for epiphytes, perhaps bark mixed with shredded tree fern or leaf mold. Vandas, reed-type Epidendrums, some Dendrobiums, Cyrtopodium, and some of the warmth-tolerant miniature Cymbidiums can then be planted in the bed. Tall plants should have some support, perhaps that furnished by a wall to which they can be trained or tied. Plants grouped in the same bed should, of course, have the same light requirements, and the bed should be located to receive the proper amount of sun and shade.

23 | *The Care and Use of Cut Flowers*

Even if at first you cannot bear to cut an orchid while it is still fresh, there will come a time when you will want some to wear, to use in a bouquet, to give to a friend, or even to sell. Because of their good keeping qualities, orchids make wonderful corsages that can be worn to one event after another. And because they are in demand commercially, most small growers can find a florist who will be glad to buy an occasional few. Thus an amateur can enjoy his flowers for a few days and then turn them into dollars for the support or expansion of his hobby.

The beauty of growing your own orchids lies in the possibility of having the plants to cherish and the flowers to enjoy in any number of ways.

■ MAKING CORSAGES

The larger orchids make attractive corsages when only one is used at a time. The smaller ones may be used in groups of two or three, or as a dainty spray if they are very tiny. A single large Cattleya is about as much as most women can wear without seeming to be overdressed, but for special occasions, two medium sized ones make an elegant corsage.

A single Cymbidium or Paphiopedilum makes a neat, tailored corsage that can be worn with a suit or other daytime attire and is no less lovely when worn with an evening gown. For more elaborate corsages, Cymbidiums and Paphiopedilum may be made up two or three together. Among the dozens of orchids described in this book, there are many that would make outstanding corsages, all the more desirable for being unusual. Imagine the comment of your friends if you appeared wearing a *Peristeria elata,* an *Oncidium splendidum,* or a *Diacrium bicornutum,* or their wonder at a few velvety Miltonias or lacy Odontoglossums, or sweetly rounded Phalaenopsis.

When you grow your own orchids, you can design the corsages according to your own whims and fancies.

The flowers should be cut only after they have been open forty-eight to seventy-two hours. Colored blooms should reach their richest hue, white ones should have lost all traces of their early green or creamy tinge. At the peak of perfection the fragrant ones will smell their sweetest. With a razor blade, cut the flower from the plant, leaving as long a stem as possible. Bring it into the house and, holding the stem under water, cut off a thin slice from the end. This prevents air bubbles from entering the cells, and enables the stem to take up water more efficiently. Then put the flower in water in a narrow necked vase so that the water does not touch the flower itself. Set it in a cool, shaded place until you are ready for it.

A tiny glass tube of water may be placed on the stem to keep the flower fresh while it is being worn. Special corsage tubes are made for this purpose. The stem is placed in it as far as it will go, being certain that the hole in the rubber cap is not so tight that it will pinch the stem, yet tight enough to prevent leakage of the water. In lieu of a tube, the stem may be wrapped in wet cotton and covered with polyethylene film. Stem and tube, or stem and cotton, will be covered with flora-tape or parafilm. Florists often eliminate the tube, but it insures a longer life to the corsage.

Corsage-making kits are available. They contain wires of various thicknesses, ribbons, pins, and the all-important flora-tape or parafilm for wrapping the stems. Since orchids come in so many colors and shades, no kit will always have the right ribbon for every flower. For an occasional corsage you may be able to find suitable ribbon at a notion counter, but if you intend to make many you should lay in a stock of assorted colors from a florist supply house.

The accompanying photographs give the step by step method for making a corsage. The brittle stem must be supported by wire. It is not necessary to puncture the stem of a large flower; the wire is simply laid along the stem and together they are wrapped with parafilm. If the flower is to go into a tube, the wire may be wound around the stem in a spiral manner first, and then the stem and tube can be wrapped together. To apply the parafilm, press the end to the stem just under the flower and wind it several times to give extra support. Then, turning the flower with one hand, draw the tape spirally along the stem pressing it tightly with your fingers. Continue until the wires are also wrapped to the end, as they can be formed into a decorative curl.

An orchid really needs no decoration, but most people feel that the addition of a bit of ribbon completes the dressing of the flower. A very simple bow of only two, possibly three or four, double loops of ribbon is enough. It is a shame to see an orchid so highly dressed that the ribbon is more conspicuous than the flower. The ribbon may blend with the tones of the flower, or perhaps a happy contrast in color may be found. The bow is made by forming the loops with your fingers and then gathering the ribbon in tightly with a fine wire. The ends of the wire serve to fasten the bow to the stem. Stretchy paper ribbon may be used in place of wire.

When a corsage is to be made of several small flowers, it is usually best to separate them and wrap each stem individually. Delicate stems are likely to break at the back of the flower and should have a wire looped over the column and dorsal sepal, then wound down the stem. The ends of the wire are allowed to extend longer than the stem, and then stem and wire are wrapped with flora-tape. The flowers are then arranged in whatever way you wish, each facing front, and the stems are wired together. After they have been joined, the individual flowers may be turned to give the most effective design. Perhaps a group of small flowers may be made to follow the neckline of a dress, or one flower may stand on the shoulder while the others descend in a graceful curve. There is no limit to what can be done with a spray corsage, and your own ingenuity will produce many lovely arrangements. A spray to be worn in the hair should be light as a feather and may be wired to a comb or a barette to make it secure. Any group of small orchids is more effective when each flower stands alone in airy grace. A jammed up bunch looks awkward and hides the beauty of the flowers.

A single flower is most attractive worn right side up, as it grows. When several blooms are used in a corsage, the central one should be right side up, and the others may be turned to make a tasteful design. When you put on the corsage, let the pin go through the ribbon, not through the stem.

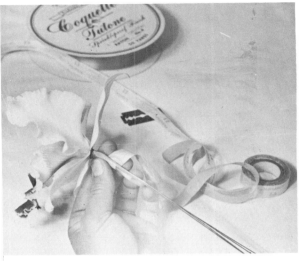

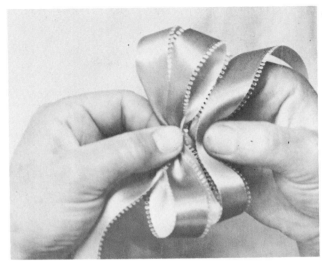

Fig. 160 Steps in making a corsage. Upper left, lay several strands of fine wire along the stem, allowing them to extend some distance beyond. Wrap the stem at its base and the upper ends of the wire snugly with several thicknesses of parafilm. Then spirally wrap the length of the wires. Upper right, florists have many ways of making a bow. One is to gather loops one by one, pinching in the center, and holding them firmly.

A fine wire or a light paper ribbon is then tied tightly around the pinched-in center portion. Lower left, the bow is snugged up under the lip and lower sepals and tied to the wrapped stem. Lower right, the finished corsage. The length of wrapped wire can be curled into a decorative coil. The ribbon chosen here matched the deep tones of the lip.

■ **KEEPING THE CORSAGE**

After you have worn your corsage, you will want to keep it fresh for another time. The flowers should be kept in a refrigerator, at a temperature not lower than forty-five degrees. Most kinds keep beautifully in an airtight container, without being placed in water. The whole corsage may be laid on a bed of wax paper in a large-mouthed jar with a tight lid. A good procedure is to put the jar in the refrigerator when you put on your orchid, so that it will be cool when you are ready for it. As you take off the lid to put the corsage in it, blow into the jar, so that a film of water vapor covers its sides. Then quickly lay the corsage on the shredded wax paper (to prevent contact with the cold glass), replace the lid, and return the jar to the refrigerator. The moisture retained in the jar is enough to keep the flower fresh for ten days to two weeks.

A bag of polyethylene film may keep the flower even longer. Put some shredded wax paper in the bag and lay the corsage on it. Then fold the end of the bag tightly and fasten it with a couple of paper clips. To avoid having the corsage crushed when things are moved around in the refrigerator, lay it in a small box. The life of many kinds of orchids can be extended after they are cut by keeping them in the refrigerator in polyethylene film. Flowers which you wish to use later for corsages or for other purposes can be cut and stored in this manner.

ORCHIDS AS DECORATIONS

A flowering plant commands attention, even in its red clay pot, and a plant set temporarily in a pretty jardiniere is an addition to any room. There is no danger to the flowers in moving them from the damp greenhouse into the living room. A flowering plant may even be transported to a hospital room for the pleasure of a sick friend.

But many orchid plants are stiff and ungraceful, and their flowers may be used in a more decorative manner if they are cut. A fine hand with flowers can turn out beautiful things. One orchid in a simple little vase is a spot of beauty for table or mantel. Grand, impressive arrangements using whole sprays of Cymbidiums with other flowers, low settings for a few Cattleyas, stunning combinations of Paphiopedilums with unusual foliage, arrangements of Oncidiums with Delphinium that are all blue and gold lace, and so on ad infinitum. The flowers used with orchids will have to be renewed from time to time, for the orchids will far outlast them in freshness. Never cut foliage from an orchid plant.

To keep the cut orchids for as long as possible, remove them to a cool place at night. And trim the stems from time to time, holding the tip under water as described above.

SELLING AND SHIPPING BLOOMS

Orchid flowers must be carefully packed in order to arrive at their destination in perfection. Whether you send a corsage to a faraway friend or blooms to a wholesaler in the next town, the same packing method is used. Shredded wax paper is obtainable at any wholesale florist house, or possibly from your local florist. This springy, non-absorbent stuff protects the flowers from jostling and keeps the flower parts from rubbing and bruising each other.

A few swatches of shredded wax paper are laid between sepals and petals and around the lip. The flower in its tube of water is then laid on a bed of shredded wax paper in a strong box. The tube must be fastened firmly to the bottom of the box so that the flower will not move from its position. Holes punched in the box on either side of the tube allow wire or a twistem to be tied around the tube, or it may be fastened down with Scotch tape. More shredded wax paper is tucked under the large parts of the flower, and a little put on top to keep them firm.

In moderate weather, the box need be wrapped in only one thickness of paper. But in cold weather, the box is wrapped in layer after layer of newspaper to insulate it. The insulation retains the inside warmth for an hour or two, possibly longer depending on the number of layers. Railway and Air Express are recommended as the best shipping methods, the extra expense being worth the care in handling. A label on the box stating that it contains cut flowers to be protected from heat and cold will insure its being properly cared for.

If you have only two or three cut flowers to market at a time you will do better to sell them to a local florist rather than to a wholesaler. The wholesaler buys flowers either on a commission basis, or outright at a price within the range of their market value. He must make a profit on them, above his cost of handling and bookkeeping. The trouble of opening your occasional small shipment, grading your flowers, and keeping track of their sale is really not a profitable venture for him, compared to what he can make on a shipment of a hundred blooms. Nor is it profitable for you to pay shipping expenses and the sales commission. If you have a steady supply of good quality flowers, and the wholesale florist can count on you for a certain number a week, then it becomes profitable for both of you.

The ups and downs of the market are sometimes disconcerting. Perhaps you ship a box of nice blooms, only to receive fifty cents apiece for them because your contribution arrived at the wholesale house at an inauspicious time. At another time, if orchids are scarce, you may receive three or four times that amount. In general good Cattleya flowers wholesale for between one and a-half and two and a-half dollars, depending on their size and quality. Poor samples sell for very little or are dumped.

In a town where there is not a wholesale florist, the retail florist must send away for his flowers and pay the packing and shipping charges. He may be very glad to buy orchids at home if he can thereby save some expense. Also, the convenience of having a grower nearby from whom he can get a flower at an hour's notice is a factor in your favor. However, if you wish to sell flowers consistently, you must always be certain of their quality and be willing to replace one that does not hold up. If the florist knows that what he gets from you is fresh and of good quality, and that the flowers will last well both for his customers and in his refrigerator, he will continue to buy from you. You must be somewhat dispassionate about pricing and selling flowers. There may be times when to oblige the florist you will have to cut something you had wanted to keep, or sell a fine one for less than its actual value. There will be other times when you have many you'd like to sell but for which there is no demand.

The average customer of the average florist is not a connoisseur of orchids. He may know one or two kinds, but he will ordinarily not want to pay a premium for a flower that, for instance, has particularly broad petals. To him an orchid corsage should be had for a standard price, and the florist, in order to make the sale, may have to let a fine flower go for less than it would be worth in a more discriminating market. However, if a discerning customer who knows his orchids wants something especially fine, you may be able to make a better sale. Thus unusually fine blooms, or ones of unusual coloring, may command a higher price if there is a demand for them at the moment.

You can encourage the use of less well known kinds by showing them to the florists, or by inviting them to come to your greenhouse. When we first began growing orchids, even the florists knew only those most commonly used. But now they often request something different for special occasions and encourage their more discriminating customers to let them send corsages of unusual flowers. Prices on the smaller orchids, where several must be used in a corsage, have to be governed by the number needed to make a fair showing. The florist can help you out here. People are learning that a gift of orchids brings more oh's and ah's from a patient and his friends, to say nothing of the doctors and nurses, than a large bouquet of the usual cut flowers. A Cattleya in a small vase, a stem of Cymbidiums or Phalaenopsis, two or three Paphiopedilums, a graceful little spray of Dendrobiums, Epidendrums, or Oncidiums, may be the center of attention in a roomful of flowers. Once the customer and the florist have received the plaudits from such a gift, they are sure to want to repeat it.

Over the months you can get great pleasure from your flowers, yet still sell some to make them help support themselves. Even the commercial growers are amateurs at heart and often have collections separate from the plants from which they make their living. For many of us, selling flowers helps us pay for new plants to add to our collections and enables us to have many more kinds than we could otherwise afford.

A | *Appendix*

Key to the tribes and genera of the orchid family (Orchidaceae). (Note: This key is reproduced from the *Standard Cyclopedia of Horticulture* with the kind permission of The Macmillan Company (copyright 1900 and 1914) and its author, Liberty Hyde Bailey, copyright 1928. A few notes have been added (given in parentheses) as explanation to those tribes not described in the text of this book.)

I. Summary of Tribes

A. Fertile stamens 2, with a broad shield-shaped sterile one (staminodium) . . . . 1. CYPRIPEDIUM TRIBE
AA. Fertile stamen 1, with no staminodium.
  B. Anther persistent; pollinia with basal appendages.
    C. The anther erect.
      D. Stigma flat, unappendaged . . . . 2. SERAPIAS TRIBE
      DD. Stigma with appendages . . . . 3. HABENARIA TRIBE
    CC. The anthers placed obliquely . . . . 4. SATYRIUM TRIBE
  BB. Anther usually readily deciduous; pollinia not appendaged or with terminal ones.
    C. Infl. terminal.
      D. Lf.-buds convolute.
        E. Lf.-blade not jointed to stalk.
          F. The anther commonly much exceeding the beak of the column which is not distinctly cut.
            G. Lip without hypochil, usually spurless.
              H. St. short, with only 1 or 2 lvs. . . . 5. POGONIA TRIBE
              HH. St. long, with many lvs. . . . . 6. VANILLA TRIBE
            GG. Lip with distinct hypochil, which is often spurred . . . . 7. CEPHALANTHERA TRIBE
          FF. The anther commonly about as long as the beak of the column which usually bears a sharp cut or groove.
            G. Pollinia waxy or powdery, not divided.
              H. Lip turned down . . . . 8. SPIRANTHES TRIBE
              HH. Lip turned up . . . . 9. CRANICHIS TRIBE
            GG. Pollinia divided into distinct masses . . 10. PHYSURUS TRIBE
        EE. Lf.-blade distinctly jointed to the petiole.
          F. Pollinia 8: st. slender: fls. usually with spurs or chins . . . . 11. THUNIA TRIBE
          FF. Pollinia 4: st. a short pseudobulb: fls. without spurs or chins . . . . 12. COELOGYNE TRIBE
      DD. Lf.-buds conduplicate.
        E. Sepals and petals about equally developed, the lip usually very conspicuous.
          F. Lvs. usually not jointed: column footless . . . 13. LIPARIS TRIBE

FF. Lvs. usually jointed.
    G. Nerves of lvs. 1.
        H. Pollinia 2-4, with very short stalks . . . .   14. POLYSTACHYA TRIBE
        HH. Pollinia 4-8, with distinct caudicles.
            I. Column-foot forming a chin with the lateral sepals or a short sac with the lip . . . . . .   15. PONERA TRIBE
            II. Column footless . . . .   16. CATTLEYA TRIBE
    GG. Nerves of lvs. several . . . .   17. SOBRALIA TRIBE
EE. Sepals much more developed than the petals and lip . . . .   18. PLEUROTHALLIS TRIBE
CC. Infl. lateral, or on separate shoot.
    D. Lf.-buds convolute.
        E. St. slender or gradually swollen.
            F. Pollinia with caudicles but without stalks . .   19. PHAIUS TRIBE
            FF. Pollinia without caudicles but with stalks.
                G. Lip jointed to column-foot or forming a spur with it . . . .   20. CYRTOPODIUM TRIBE
                GG. Lip not jointed, often with a distinct hypochil . . . .   21. CATASETUM TRIBE
        EE. St. a short distinct pseudobulb.
            F. Lip jointed to the column-foot.
                G. Callus-ridges lengthwise . . . .   22. LYCASTE TRIBE
                GG. Callus-ridges transverse . . . .   23. ZYGOPETALUM TRIBE
            FF. Lip continuous with column-foot . . . .   24. GONGORA TRIBE
    DD. Lf.-buds conduplicate.
        E. St. terminating its growth in 1 year.
            F. Lip movably jointed to foot of column.
                G. Lvs. not strap-shaped: pollinia unappendaged or with either caudicles or stipes, but not with both.
                    H. Flowering st. arising from near the apex of the slender st. or from the pseudobulb . . . .   25. DENDROBIUM TRIBE
                    HH. Flowering st. arising under the pseudobulb or at the base of the st.
                        I. Pollinia without appendages   26. BULBOPHYLLUM TRIBE
                        II. Pollinia with distinct stalks.
                            J. Pseudobulbs usually present: flowering st. arising lower than new growth . .   27. MAXILLARIA TRIBE
                            JJ. Pseudobulbs usually wanting: flowering st. arising higher than new growth.
                GG. Lvs. strap-shaped: pollinia with broad caudicles and stipes . . . .   28. HUNTLEYA TRIBE
            FF. Lip immovably united to foot of column.
                G. Fls. with spurs . . . .   29. CYMBIDIUM TRIBE
                GG. Fls. without spurs.
                  H. The fls. narrow, not open . . . . . .   30. IONOPSIS TRIBE
                  HH. The fls. wide open.
                      I. Lip enrolled around the column . . . .   31. ADA TRIBE
                      II. Lip not enrolled.
                        J. The lip united to column to the middle . . . .   32. TRICHOPILIA TRIBE
                        JJ. The lip united only to the base of the column . . . .   33. ASPASIA TRIBE
EE. St. increasing in length from year to year . . . . . .   34. ODONTOGLOSSUM TRIBE
                                35. AERIDES TRIBE

II. Key to the Tribes

1. Cypripedium Tribe (See text)

A. Fl. persistent, withering on the ovary: Lf.-buds convolute . . . .   1. *Cypripedium*
AA. Fl. soon deciduous: Lf.-buds conduplicate.
    B. Ovary 3-celled, the placentae central; mouth of lip with broad inturned margin . . . .   2. *Phragmopedilum*
    BB. Ovary 1-celled, the placentae parietal; mouth of lip usually with no broad inturned margins . . . . . .   3. *Paphiopedilum*

2. Serapias Tribe

(Terrestrial, North Temperate Zone, not showy. *Orchis* is the type genus of the orchid family.)
A. Lip spurred.
    B. Sepals free . . . .   4. *Orchis*
    BB. Sepals united into an arching hood . . . . . .   5. *Galeorchis*
AA. Lip spurless.
    B. Pollinia glands in a single sac . . . . . .   6. *Serapias*
    BB. Pollinia glands separate, in 2 distinct sacs . . . . . .   7. *Ophrys*

3. Habenaria Tribe

(Terrestrial, temperate and tropical regions, not showy but includes some of our finest native orchids.)
A. Lip adnate to column at base; stigma broad . . . . . .   8. *Cynorchis*
AA. Lip free; stigma slender . . . . . .   9. *Habenaria*

4. Satyrium Tribe

(Terrestrial, South Africa, pretty, but hard to grow.)
Dorsal sepal helmet-shaped . . . . . .   10. *Disa*

5. Pogonia Tribe

(Terrestrial, mostly North and South America. A few can be grown in gardens.)
A. Fls. on a scape with a terminal whorl of lf.-like bracts . . . . . .   11. *Isotria*
AA. Fls. on a leafy st.
    B. Lip crested . . . . . .   12. *Pogonia*
    BB. Lip not crested . . . . . .   13. *Triphora*

6. Vanilla Tribe (See text)

Sts. rooting at nodes . . . . . .   14. *Vanilla*

7. Cephalanthera Tribe

(Terrestrial, North Temperate Zone, of minor interest.)
A. Fls. with a chin; lip long . . . . . .   15. *Cephalanthera*
AA. Fls. chinless; lip round . . . . . .   16. *Epipactis*

8. Spiranthes Tribe

(Terrestrial, mostly tropical, but with a few native species adaptable to gardens.)
A. Dorsal sepal forming a hood with the petals.
    B. Infl. 1-sided; fls. without a chin . . . . . .   17. *Spiranthes*
    BB. Infl. not 1-sided; fls. with a chin . . . . . .   18. *Stenorrhynchus*
AA. Sepals and petals spreading . . . . . .   19. *Listera*

9. Cranichis Tribe

(Terrestrial, native to tropical America, of minor interest.)
Lip and petals inserted upon the elongated column . . . . . .   20. *Ponthieva*

10. Physurus Tribe

(Terrestrial, widely distributed in temperate and tropical Asia and America. Of interest for their variegated foliage. The flowers are insignificant, the whole plant having the shape of a plantain weed. *Goodyera* and *Physurus* are fairly well known.)

A. Lip with a distinct spur.
   B. Lvs. green: lip concave above the spur .... 21. *Physurus*
   BB. Lvs. usually variegated: lip with a long fimbriate claw .... 22. *Anoectochilus*
AA. Lip spurless or nearly so.
   B. Column straight; fls. symmetric.
      C. The lip not clawed .... 23. *Goodyera*
      CC. The lip clawed .... 24. *Dossinia*
   BB. Column twisted; fls. not symmetric.
      C. The column with 2 upright appendages in front .... 25. *Macodes*
      CC. The column without appendages .... 26. *Haemaria*

11. Thunia Tribe

(Terrestrial, Asia. *Thunia* and *Bletilla* are seen in collections, the latter adaptable to gardens in some regions.)

A. Fls. without chin.
   B. Sts. without basal pseudobulbs .... 27. *Thunia*
   BB. Sts. with basal pseudobulbs .... 28. *Bletilla*
AA. Fls. with a distinct chin, formed of lateral sepals and column-foot .... 29. *Trichosma*

12. Coelogyne Tribe (See text)

A. Base of lip with sac-like hollow.
   B. Column short, winged above, sepals flat .... 30. *Pholidota*
   BB. Column slender; sepals sac-like, concave .... 31. *Neogyne*
AA. Base of lip flat.
   B. Column slender, without horns.
      C. Lvs. and pseudobulbs perennial .... 32. *Coelogyne*
      CC. Lvs. and pseudobulbs annual .... 33. *Pleione*
   BB. Column short, with 2 horns .... 34. *Platyclinis*

13. Liparis Tribe

(Terrestrial, North Temperate Zone, many in North America. Best known is *Calypso*, one of our native orchids.)

A. Lvs. green: fls. without chin.
   B. Lip shoe-shaped .... 35. *Calypso*
   BB. Lip not shoe-shaped
      C. Column short; lip turned upward .... 36. *Microstylis*
      CC. Column slender; lip turned downward .... 37. *Liparis*
AA. Lvs. wanting: fls. with chin .... 38. *Corallorrhiza*

14. Polystachya Tribe

(Mostly epiphytic, tropical except for one rare North American species. Seldom grown.)

A. Lip spurred.
   B. Plant tuberous: spur slender .... 39. *Tipularia*
   BB. Plant not tuberous: spur funnel-shaped .... 40. *Galeandra*
AA. Lip not spurred.
   B. The lip 3-lobed.
      C. Column short; chin distinct .... 41. *Polystachya*
      CC. Column slender, curved; chin indistinct .... 42. *Ansellia*
   BB. The lip entire .... 43. *Neobenthamia*

15. Ponera Tribe

(Epiphytic, Central America, seldom grown.)

A. Lip normal.
   B. St. slender, leafy; no pseudobulbs; pollinia 4 .... 44. *Isochilus*
   BB. St. a pseudobulb: pollinia 8 .... 45. *Coelia*
AA. Lip forming a beaker-like cavity, with the column, or the former hollow at base.
   B. Young shoots at the apex of the old .... 46. *Hexisea*
   BB. Young shoots from base of old.
      C. Fls. in dense spikes; pollinia 8 .... 47. *Arpophyllum*
      CC. Fls. in short clusters; pollinia 4 .... 48. *Hartwegia*

16. Cattleya Tribe (See text)

A. Anther not toothed, nor in an excavation.
    B. Pollinia 4.
        C. Lip adnate to the column, at least at its base.
            D. Ovary produced into a hollow neck .... 49. *Broughtonia*
            DD. Ovary not so produced .... 50. *Epidendrum*
        CC. Lip free.
            D. The lip flat, with 2 elevations on upper side .... 51. *Diacrium*
            DD. The lip enrolled about column, with no elevations .... 52. *Cattleya*
    BB. Pollinia 5-7, some of them often abortive .... 53. *Laelio-cattleya*
    BBB. Pollinia 8.
        C. Stigma pitted upon the front of the column; anther inclined.
            D. Base of lip gradually merging into blade.
                E. Lip distinctly surrounding the column; sepals and petals
                     not wavy .... 54. *Laelia*
                EE. Lip not as above; sepals and petals distinctly wavy .... 55. *Schomburgkia*
            DD. Base of lip tightly encompassing column, suddenly broadened
                 into the broad blade .... 56. *Brassavola*
        CC. Stigma running up on 2 extensions of the column-apex; anther
             erect .... 57. *Sophronitis*
AA. Anther 2-toothed below, in an excavation in the column .... 58. *Leptotes*

17. Sobralia Tribe (See text)

A. St. many-lvd., not bulbous at base: lip not bearded .... 59. *Sobralia*
AA. St. 1- or 2-lvd., bulbous at base: lip bearded .... 60. *Calopogon*

18. Pleurothallis Tribe (See text)

A. Lip turned upward; lateral sepals united into a boat-shaped hood .... 61. *Scaphosepalum*
AA. Lip turned down.
    B. Sepals united .... 62. *Masdevallia*
    BB. Sepals free, or the lateral only united.
        C. Dorsal sepal and petals attenuated into a club-shaped apex ...... 63. *Restrepia*
        CC. Dorsal sepal and petals not as above .... 64. *Pleurothallis*

19. Phaius Tribe (See text)

A. Lvs. not articulated to petiole.
    B. Lip free, encompassing the column .... 65. *Phaius*
    BB. Lip adnate to column, the blade spreading .... 66. *Calanthe*
AA. Lvs. articulated to petiole.
    B. Sepals and petals spreading.
        C. Lip with its base tightly inclosing the column, the blade spreading 67. *Limatodes*
        CC. Lip not inclosing column.
            D. Fls. with distinct chin .... 68. *Chysis*
            DD. Fls. without chin.
                E. Pollinia 8.
                    F. Middle lobe of lip not clawed .... 69. *Bletia*
                    FF. Middle lobe of lip clawed .... 70. *Spathoglottis*
                EE. Pollinia 4 .... 71. *Aplectrum*
    BB. Sepals and petals erect .... 72. *Acanthophippium*

20. Cyrtopodium Tribe

(Both epiphytic and terrestrial, tropical, seldom grown.)
A. Fls. spurred or with sac-like base.
    B. Sepals narrower and less colored than petals .... 73. *Lissochilus*
    BB. Sepals and petals alike or nearly so .... 74. *Eulophia*
AA. Fls. not spurred nor saccate.
    B. Lip only inserted on column-foot .... 75. *Cyrtopodium*
    BB. Lip and lateral sepals inserted on column-foot.
        C. Chin distinct, rectangular .... 76. *Warrea*
        CC. Chin indistinct, round .... 77. *Eulophiella*

21. Catasetum Tribe (See text)

A. Fls. perfect; column twisted .... 78. *Mormodes*
AA. Fls. of 2 or 3 forms; column not twisted.
    B. Column stout, straight; fls. with antennae .... 79. *Catasetum*
    BB. Column slender, curved; fls. without antennae .... 80. *Cycnoches*

22. Lycaste Tribe (See text)

A. Pollinia upon a single stalk.
    B. Fls. globose .... 81. *Anguloa*
    BB. Fls. with spreading sepals and petals.
        C. Stalk of pollinia long and narrow; fls. 1 to few.
            D. Infl. of a single erect fl.; lip turned down .... 82. *Lycaste*
            DD. Infl. of 2 to few drooping fls.; lip turned upward .... 83. *Paphinia*
        CC. Stalk of pollinia short; fls. many .... 84. *Batemannia*
AA. Pollinia upon 2 separate stalks .... 85. *Bifrenaria*

23. Zygopetalum Tribe (See text)

A. Lip clawed distinctly .... 86. *Colax*
AA. Lip not distinctly clawed.
    B. The lip with horseshoe-shaped callus .... 87. *Zygopetalum*
    BB. The lip with few longitudinal lamellae .... 88. *Eriopsis*

24. Gongora Tribe (See text)

A. Lip turned downward.
    B. Fls. with sepals and petals erect or incurved.
        C. Hypochil separated from column by a strong stricture; no
            pleuridia .... 89. *Lacaena*
        CC. Hypochil united with column by a broad base: pleuridia present.
            D. Epichil movably attached to hypochil; pollinia with short stalk
                at most .... 90. *Peristeria*
            DD. Epichil immovably attached to hypochil; pollinia with
                elongated stalk .... 91. *Acineta*
    BB. Fls. with sepals and petals spreading or reflexed.
        C. Lateral sepals much larger than the dorsal sepal and petals ...... 92. *Coryanthes*
        CC. Sepals and petals nearly alike.
            D. Hypochil concave; epichil flat.
                E. Pollinia 2 .... 93. *Stanhopea*
                EE. Pollinia 4 .... 94. *Aganisia*
            DD. Hypochil not concave .... 95. *Houlletia*
AA. Lip turned upward .... 96. *Gongora*

25. Dendrobium Tribe (See text)

A. Sts. many-jointed; rhizome short.
    B. Lip without callus, or with lamellate or elevated lines .... 97. *Dendrobium*
    BB. Lip with basal callus; joints of st. long-filamentose .... 98. *Inobulbon*
AA. Sts. 1- or rarely 2-jointed; rhizome long-creeping .... 99. *Sarcopodium*

26. Bulbophyllum Tribe (See text)

A. Lateral sepals with their outer margins adhering, except at the free base. 100. *Cirrhopetalum*
AA. Lateral sepals free .... 101. *Bulbophyllum*

27. Maxillaria Tribe (See text)

A. Lip without claw, movable: lvs. normal .... 102. *Maxillaria*
AA. Lip clawed, or adnate to column-base: lvs. whip-shaped .... 103. *Scuticaria*

28. Huntleya Tribe

(Epiphytic, Central and South America. Similar to *Zygopetalum*.)
A. Pseudobulbs distinct .... 104. *Promenaea*
AA. Pseudobulbs wanting or rudimentary.
    B. Lip entire .... 105. *Chondrorrhyncha*

BB. Lip lobed.
 C. Callus of lip fringed . . . . 106. *Huntleya*
 CC. Callus not fringed.
  D. Column boat-shaped, concave . . . . 107. *Bollea*
  DD. Column slender, not concave.
   E. Claw very short: callus free in front and resting upon the
    lip . . . . 108. *Warscewiczella*
   EE. Claw distinct: callus not free in front . . . . 109. *Pescatorea*

29. Cymbidium Tribe (See text)

A. Lvs. many: sts. elongated . . . . 110. *Grammatophyllum*
AA. Lvs. few: sts. short.
 B. Sts. concealed by the lf.-sheaths.
  C. Pollinia pear-shaped, upon a quadrate stalk: st. not bulbous . . . . . 111. *Cyperorchis*
  CC. Pollinia round, upon a stalk much broader than high: st. bulbous 112. *Cymbidium*
 B. Sts. naked: lvs. only at its apex . . . . 113. *Grammangis*

30. Ionopsis Tribe (See text)

A. Sepals free . . . . 114. *Trichocentrum*
AA. Sepals, the lateral ones, united, at least below.
 B. The lip spurred . . . . 115. *Rodriguezia*
 BB. The sepals spurred.
  C. Spur short . . . . 116. *Ionopsis*
  CC. Spur long and slender . . . . 117. *Comparettia*

31. Ada Tribe (See text)

A. Lvs. flat.
 B. Sepals free . . . . 118. *Ada*
 BB. Lateral sepals united . . . . 119. *Mesospinidium*
AA. Lvs. cylindric . . . . 120. *Quekettia*

32. Trichopilia Tribe (See text)

Lip rolled around the column . . . . 121. *Trichopilia*

33. Aspasia Tribe (See text, with *Odontoglossum* Tribe)

A. Middle lobe of lip broad . . . . 122. *Aspasia*
AA. Middle lobe of lip narrow . . . . 123. *Cochlioda*

34. Odontoglossum Tribe (See text)

A. Lip surrounding column with 2 longitudinal calluses: blade reflexed . . . . 124. *Gomeza*
AA. Lip not as above.
 B. Base of lip parallel to column and sometimes adnate to it . . . . 125. *Odontoglossum*
 BB. Lip spreading from base of column.
  C. Lateral sepals united entirely; lip like dorsal sepal . . . . 126. *Palumbina*
  CC. Lateral sepals free or only partly united; lip unlike dorsal sepal.
   D. Sepals and petals long and much attenuated; lip entire or
    fiddle-shaped . . . . 127. *Brassia*
   DD. Sepals and petals not much attenuated.
    E. The lip entire, flat, broad . . . . 128. *Miltonia*
    EE. The lip mostly 3-lobed, with warts or a cushion at base 129. *Oncidium*

35. Aerides Tribe (See text)

A. Lip movably jointed to column.
 B. Middle lobe of spurless lip flat . . . . 130. *Renanthera*
 BB. Middle lobe of spurred lip compressed . . . . 131. *Arachnanthe*
AA. Lip immovably united with column.
 B. Spurless.
  C. Column without a foot.
   D. Summit of lip laterally compressed . . . . 132. *Vandopsis*
   DD. Summit of lip not compressed . . . . 133. *Luisia*
  CC. Column with a foot, the lateral sepals attached to it . . . . 134. *Phalaenopsis*

BB. Spurred.
  C. Column without a foot.
    D. Pollinia upon a single stalk.
      E. Spur appendaged.
        F. With a longitudinal septum .... 135. *Sarcanthus*
        FF. With the mouth covered with a plate .... 136. *Cleisostoma*
      EE. Spur not appendaged.
        F. Stalk of the pollinia filiform.
          G. Fls. firm; lip turned downward .... 137. *Saccolabium*
          GG. Fls. fragile; lip turned upward .... 138. *Acampe*
        FF. Stalk of the pollinia broadened upward or through-out.
          G. Spur short and broad .... 139. *Vanda*
          GG. Spur long and slender .... 140. *Angraecum*
    DD. Pollinia on 2 separate stalks, or these united by the gland.
      E. Stalks membranous, the pollinia attached to the face.
        F. Plants leafy: lip entire .... 141. *Macroplectrum*
        FF. Plants without lvs.: lip 3-lobed .... 142. *Polyrrhiza*
      EE. Stalks slender.
        F. Column bent toward the dorsal sepal .... 143. *Listrostachys*
        FF. Column straight .... 144. *Mystacidium*
  CC. Column with a foot, the lateral sepals attached to it.
    D. Spur curved upward against the lip-blade .... 145. *Aerides*
    DD. Spur straight or reflexed.
      E. Lip 3-lobed .... 146. *Camarotis*
      EE. Lip entire .... 147. *Rhynchostylis*

B | *Appendix* SOURCES OF PLANTS AND SUPPLIES

Compiled from advertisements. This list is for your convenience in sending for lists and catalogues. No endorsement of the companies is implied, and we take no responsibility for transactions between them and our readers.

ORCHID PLANTS (In addition to these there may be local growers who can furnish plants.)

L. Sherman Adams Co., Wellesley 81, Mass.

Aina Okika, Wallace H. Otaguro, 741 S. Queen St., Honolulu 13, Hawaii

Alberts and Merkel Bros., Inc., P. O. Box 77, Rte. 6, S. Jacksonville, Fla.

Armacost and Royston, Inc., West Los Angeles, Calif.

Armstrong and Brown, Clint McDade, Tunbridge Wells, Kent, England

Ashcroft Orchids, 19062 Ballinger Way, Seattle 55, Wash.

Robert Bean Orchid Nursery, 10136 Foothills Blvd., San Fernando, Calif.

Biddy-John's Orchids, 3201 El Prado Blvd., Tampa 9, Fla.

Black and Flory, Ltd., Slough, Bucks, England

Bonniewood Orchids, Inc., 14248 Des Moines Way, Seattle 88, Wash.

B. O. Bracey and Co., 2363 S. E. Mesa Drive, Santa Ana, Calif.

Bluegrass Orchids, Winchester Rd., R. F. D. 4, Lexington, Ky.

Charlesworth and Co., Ltd., Haywards Heath, Sussex, England

Clarelen Orchids, Fox Bluffs on Lake Mendota, Madison, Wis.

Crestwood Gardens, 420 Fairmount Rd., Signal Mountain, Tenn.

Creve Coeur Orchids, 12 Graeser Acres, Creve Coeur 41, Mo.

Del Ora Orchids, 7700 Miller Dr., Miami 55, Fla.

Dorset Orchids, Plush, Dorset, England

Dos Pueblos Orchid Co., P. O. Box 158, Goleta, Calif.

H. A. Dunn, P. O. Box 1077, Balboa, Canal Zone

Fennell Orchid Co., Homestead, Fla.

Field's Orchids, 196 N. W. 91st St., Miami 50, Fla.

Fuchs Orchids, Box 113, Naranja, Fla.

T. Fukumura, 863 Kilauea St., Kahului, Maui, Hawaii

John Germaske Orchids, 3355 N. W. 46th St., Miami, Fla.

Gold Point Orchids, Odie M. Helton, Hixon, Tenn.

R. H. Gore Orchids, Box 211, Ft. Lauderdale, Fla.

Etta Gray Orchids, 1639 N. Martel Ave., Hollywood 46, Calif.

Greenhouse Hawaii, John K. Noa, 3394 Waialae Ave., Honolulu 16, Hawaii

Gubler Orchids, 9441 E. Broadway, Temple City, Calif.

Herb Hager Orchids, P. O. Box 544, Santa Cruz, Calif.

Gordon M. Hoyt, Orchids, Seattle Heights, Wash.

Hand Grown Orchids, Rte. 8, Box 606, Houston, Texas

Hilo Vanda Nursery, Dr. H. Nishimura, 10-11 Young Bldg., Hilo, Hawaii

Hirose Nurseries, P. O. Box 51, Hilo, Hawaii

Margaret Ilgenfritz, Orchids, Monroe, Mich.

Ilsley Orchids, P. O. Box 46695, West Branch, Los Angeles, Calif.

Yoshito Inouye, 98 Kawananakoa Pl., Honolulu 17, Hawaii

H. Iwanaga, 5398 Papai St., Honolulu 16, Hawaii

Jones and Scully, Inc., 2154 N. W. 33d Ave., Miami 35, Fla.

Patrick O. Kawamoto, 3142 E. Manoa Rd., Honolulu 14, Hawaii

T. Kazamura Orchid Nursery, 145 N. Judd St., Honolulu, Hawaii

A. J. Keeling and Sons, Westgate Hill, Bradford, Yorks, England

Kiesewetter's Orchid Gardens, Albertson, Long Island, N. Y.

Wm. Kirch Orchids, Ltd., 732 Kapahulu Ave., Honolulu 16, Hawaii

Oscar M. Kirsch, 2869 Oahu Ave., Honolulu 14, Hawaii

Kodama Orchid Nursery, Ltd., 1039 Kamehameha Rd., Honolulu, Hawaii

Kushima Nursery, 91-770 Pohokupuna Rd., Ewa Beach, Hawaii

Lager and Hurrell, 426 Morris Ave., Summit, N. J.

Marcel Lecoufle, 1 Rue de l'Eglise, Boissy-St. Leger (S & O), France

Lines Orchids, Taft Highway, Signal Mountain, Tenn.

Stuart Low Co., Jarvisbrook (Crowborough), Sussex, England

Joseph A. Manda and Son, 737 Northfield Ave., W. Orange, N. J.

Mansell and Hatcher, Ltd., Rawdon, Leeds, Yorks, England

M. Mayamoto Orchids, 617 Libby St., Honolulu 17, Hawaii

McBean's Orchids Ltd., Cooksbridge, Sussex, England

Mrs. Lester McCoy Orchids, 3735 Diamond Head Rd., Honolulu, Hawaii

Rod McLellan Co., 1471 El Camino Real, S. San Francisco, Calif.

Morgan's Orchids, 7031 S. W. 82nd Ave., Miami 43, Fla.

Muse's Orchids, 3187 S. W. 26th St., Miami, Fla.

Dr. and Mrs. Yoshio Nagano, 261 Eifukucho, Suginami, Tokyo, Japan

Nelson Nurseries, 1975 Opa Locka Blvd., Miami, Fla.

Nakagawa Orchid Nursery, 128 Aalapuna St., Hilo, Hawaii

T. Ogawa Orchids, 1454 Kilauea Ave., Hilo, Hawaii

Orchid Company of Altadena, 560 W. Woodbury Rd., Altadena, Calif.

Orchid Imports, 11802 Huston St., N. Hollywood, Calif.

Orchid Ranch, 3486 N. W. 25th St., Miami 42, Fla.

Orchidário Brasil, Ltd,. P. O. Box 339, Petropolis, Estada Do Rio, Brazil

Orchideario Catarinense, P. O. Box 1, Corupa, Santa Catarina, Brazil

Osprey Adventurer Inc., P. O. Box 36-385, Miami 56, Fla.

T. Ota Orchid Nursery, 266 Kilohana St., Hilo, Hawaii

H. Otake Orchid Nursery, 45-270-A Puaae Rd., Kaneohe, Oahu, Hawaii

Palolo Orchid Garden, 3901 La-I Rd., Honolulu, Hawaii

H. Patterson and Sons, Bergenfield, N. J.

Joseph R. Redlinger, Orchids, 9236 S. W. 57th Ave., Miami 56, Fla.

Rivermont Orchids, Signal Mountain, Tenn.

Riverview Orchids, Inc., E. Liverpool, Ohio

Daniel Ryerson, P. O. Box 805, Homestead, Fla.

David Sanders Orchids Ltd., Selsfield, East Grinstead, Sussex, England

Santa Barbara Orchid Estate, 1250 Orchid Dr., Goleta, Calif.

Shaffer's Tropical Gardens, Inc., 1220 41st Ave., Santa Cruz, Calif.

Sherman Orchid Gardens, Glendora, Calif.

Shimamoto Orchid Nursery, 271 Momi Lane, Wailuku, Maui, Hawaii

Earl J. Small Orchids, Inc., 6901 49th St., North, St. Petersburg, Fla.

Snyder Bros. Orchids, 120 Parkside Rd., Plainfield, N. J.

Sterling Orchids, Inc., 2107 Cedar Lane, Knoxville 18, Tenn.

Fred A. Stewart, Inc., 8606 E. Las Tunas Dr., San Gabriel, Calif.

Takakura Orchids, 221 Baldwin Ave., Paia, Maui, Hawaii

Thornton's Orchids, 3200 N. Military Trail, W. Palm Beach, Fla.

Toy's Orchids, 4548 Alondra Blvd., Gardena, Calif.

Tradewinds Orchids, Inc., 12800 S. W. 77th Ave., Miami, Fla.

Vallemar Gardens, Coast Highway 1, Pacifica, Calif.

Maurice Vacherot, 31 Rue de Valenton, Boissy-St. Leger (S & O), France

Vacherot and Lecoufle, "La Tuilerie," Boissy-St. Leger (S & O), France

J. Milton Warne, 260 Jack Lane, Honolulu, Hawaii

E. C. Wilcox, Cypripediums, 1336 N. Michillinda Ave., Arcadia, Calif.

Wilcox's Orchids, 898 N. W. 45th Ave., Miami, Fla.

Wilkin's Orchid Nursery, RR 1, Box 258, Homestead, Fla.

Wilson's Orchids, 490 Beverly Ave., San Leandro, Calif.

SUPPLIES (Insecticides, potting materials, greenhouse equipment, labels, orchid tubes, shredded wax paper, etc. In addition to these supply companies, many orchid plant dealers also furnish supplies.)

Nui Nursery, 5846 Kalanianaole Highway, Honolulu 16, Hawaii

McHutchison and Co., 695-B Grand Ave., Ridgefield, N. J.

Reinfrank and Hudson, 5414 Sierra Vista Ave., Los Angeles 38, Calif.

Wrightwood Floral Co., 1420 Wrightwood Ave., Houston 9, Texas

AGAR AND AGAR-NUTRIENT MIXTURE for seed germination.

Daniel M. Hill, 605 E. Granada St., Ontario, Calif.

Difco Laboratories, Detroit 1, Mich.

Princeton Phytochemicals, Inc., Box 7, Princeton Junction, N. J.

C | *Appendix* ORCHID LITERATURE

Many kinds of books on orchids are listed below. Some are descriptive of the orchids of particular areas, and are of special interest to those who have a wide variety of kinds in their collections. Others are on culture. Some are old, some are new. Those written before our time, and especially those on culture in other countries, employ terms and describe methods that are strange to us. Nevertheless we can learn much from them. Any grower who is seriously interested in orchids will be well rewarded by reading a few of the old books. Not only will he come to know more about his plants through learning something of their history and their handling in other eras, but he will come to feel a kinship with the growers who nurtured the plants and learned their ways, and who handed on this rich heritage to us. Books that are out of print can often be obtained in used condition through dealers in old books, and some, of course, are rare and quite expensive. They may also be obtained for short periods through the Inter-library Loan Service for a fee that covers handling, postage, and insurance.

American Orchid Society. *Handbook on Judging and Exhibition.* 1960. 3d edition. American Orchid Society, Inc., Botanical Museum of Harvard Univ., Cambridge 38, Mass.

Ames, Blanche. *Drawings of Florida Orchids,* with explanatory notes by Oakes Ames. 1959. 2nd edition. Botanical Museum of Harvard Univ., Cambridge.

Ames, Oakes. *Orchids in Retrospect.* 1948. 172 pages. Botanical Museum of Harvard Univ., Cambridge.

———. *An Enumeration of the Orchids of the U. S. and Canada.* 1924. Boston.

———, and Donovan S. Correll. *Orchids of Guatemala.* 1952-1953. Two vols, 726 pages. Fieldiana: Botany, Vol. 26, Nos. 1 and 2. Chicago Natural History Museum, Chicago, Illinois.

Bailey, Liberty Hyde. *Standard Cyclopedia of Horticulture.* Popular edition. 1935. 3 vols., 3639 pages. The Macmillan Co., New York.

Boyle, Frederick. *The Culture of Greenhouse Orchids, Old System and New.* 1902. London.

Boyle, Louis M. *Growing Cymbidium Orchids and Other Flowers.* 1953. 520 pages. El Rancho Rinconada, Ojai, Calif.

———. *Cymbidium Orchids For You.* 1950. El Rancho Rinconada, Ojai, Calif.

Bruhl, Paul. *A Guide to the Orchids of Sikkim.* 1926. Thacker, Spink and Co., Calcutta and Simla, India.

Burberry, H. A. *The Amateur Orchid Cultivator's Guide Book.* 1899. 3d edition. Liverpool, England.

Burgeff, Hans. *Die Samenkeimung die Orchideen.* 1936. Jena.

Constantin, Julien. *Atlas en Couleur des Orchidées Cultivées.* 1000 orchids in color. circa 1915. Paris.

———. *La Vie des Orchidées.* 1917. 185 pages. Paris.

Correll, Donovan S. *Native Orchids of North America, North of Mexico.* 1950. 400 pages. Chronica Botanica. Now published by The Ronald Press Co., 15 East 26th St., New York.

Cox, J. M. *Cultural Table of Orchidaceous Plants.* 1946. Sydney, Australia.

Curtis, Charles H. *Orchids for Everyone.* 1910. London.

———. *Orchids.* 1950. 274 pages. Putnam and Co., Ltd., 42 Great Russell St., London.

Darwin, Charles. *On the Fertilization of Orchids by Insects.* 1889. New York.

Davis, Reg. S., and Mona Lisa Steiner. *Philippine Orchids.* 1952. 270 pages. The William Frederick Press, 313 W. 38th St., New York.

Dunsterville, G. C. K., and Leslie A. Garay. *Venezuelan Orchids Illustrated.* Vol. 1. 1959. Andre Deutsch, London.

Duval, L. *Les Cattleya: Traité de culture practique.* 1907. Paris.

———. *Les Odontoglossum.* 1900. Paris.

———. *Les Orchidées.* 1905. Paris.

Fawcett, W., and A. B. Rendle. *Flora of Jamaica:* Vol. 1, *Orchids.* British Museum, London.

Fennell, T. A., Jr. *Orchids for Home and Garden.* 1956. Revised 1959. 160 pages. Rinehart and Co., Inc., New York.

Eigeldinger, O. *Orchids for Everyone.* 1957. 144

pages. John Gifford Ltd., 125 Charing Rd., London, W. C. 2.

Ghose, B. N. *Beautiful Indian Orchids*. 1959. 155 pages. G. Ghose and Co., Town-End, Darjeeling, Indian Union.

Gilbert, P. A. *The Charm of Growing Orchids*. 1952. 2nd edition. Shepherd Press, Sydney, Australia.

————. *Orchids: Their Culture and Classification*. 1951. 252 pages. Shepherd Press, Sydney, Australia.

Graf, Alfred Byrd. 1957. *Exotica*. 644 pages, 4000 illustrations. Roehrs Co., Rutherford, New Jersey.

Gratiot, J. *Les Orchidées, Leur Culture*. 1934. Paris.

Handcock, Ralph, and Margaret Smith. *You, Too, Can Grow Orchids*. circa 1955. 60 pages. Daymark's Book Arcade, Ltd., Sydney, Australia.

Harrison, C. Alwyn. *Commercial Orchid Growing*. 1914. London.

————. *Orchids for Amateurs*. 1911. London.

Hawkes, Alex D. *Orchids: Their Botany and Culture*. 1961. 297 pages. Harper and Bros., New York.

Hernandez, Mariano O. *Orquideas Colombianas*. 1958. 305 pages. Bilingual text. Publicaciones Tecnicas Ltda., Bogota, Colombia.

Heohne, F. C. *Flora Brasilica: Orchidaceae*. 1940-43. In parts, incomplete. Instituto de Botanica, Sao Paulo, Brazil.

Hogg, Bruce. *Orchids: Their Culture*. 1957. 139 pages. Cassell and Co., Ltd., Melbourne and Sydney, Australia.

————. *Orchids for Everybody*. 1946. Abbotsford, N. S. W.

Holttum, R. E. *A Revised Flora of Malaya*. Vol. 1, *Orchids of Malaya*. 1953. Government Printing Office, Singapore, Malaya.

Hooker, Sir Joseph Dalton. *Century of Orchidaceous Plants*. 1851.

————. *Himalayan Journals*. 1854.

————. *Flora of India*. 1855.

————. *Century of Indian Plants*. 1895.

————, and George Bentham. *Genera Plantarum*. An important contribution to plant classification. 1862-83.

Hurst, Charles C. *Experiments in Genetics*. 1925. Cambridge University Press, Cambridge, England.

————. *Mechanism of Creative Evolution*. 1932. Cambridge University Press, Cambridge, England.

Jackson, B. D. *A Glossary of Botanical Terms*. 1928. 4th edition. Reprinted, 1948. Duckworth and Co., London.

Kupper, Walter. *Orchidées*. Translated from German to French. Circa 1955. 100 color plates. Service d'Images Silva, Zurich, Switzerland.

Kränzlin, F. *Beiträge zu Orchideenflora Sudamerikas*. 1911. Uppsala and Stockholm.

Lawrence, W. J. C. *Practical Plant Breeding*. 1951. Revised 3d edition. 166 pages. George Allen and Unwin, Ltd., London.

Lecoufle, Marcel, and Henri Rose. *Orchids*. 1957. 112 pages. English edition. Crosby and Lockwood and Son, Ltd., 26 Old Brompton Road, S. W. 7, London.

Leon, Hermano. *Flora de Cuba*, Part 1 (pp. 341-404) *Orchids*. 1946. Havana, Cuba.

Logan, Harry B., and Lloyd C. Cosper. *Orchids Are Easy to Grow*. 1949. 312 pages. Ziff-Davis Publishing Co., Chicago.

McLeish, John, and Brian Snoad. *Looking at Chromosomes*. 1957. 87 pages. Macmillan and Co., Ltd., London.

Millican, Albert. *Travels and Adventures of an Orchid Hunter*. 1891. London.

Morris, F., and E. Eames. *Our Wild Orchids*. 1929. New York.

Moulen, Fred. *Orchids in Australia*. 1958. 148 pages, 100 colored figures. Australia Edita Pty. Ltd, Sydney, Australia.

Nicholls, W. H. *Orchids of Australia*. Vol. 1, Parts I to IV. 1951-58. Georgia House, Melbourne, Australia.

Nicolai, W. *Orchideen*. 1939. Frankfurt (Oder).

Noble, Mary. *You Can Grow Orchids*. 1954. Revised 1960. 152 pages. Published by author, 3003 Riverside Ave., Jacksonville, Fla.

————. *Florida Orchids*. 1952. 88 pages. State Dept. of Agriculture, Tallahassee, Fla.

Northen, Rebecca T. *Orchids as House Plants*. 1955. 122 pages. D. Van Nostrand Co., Princeton, New Jersey.

O'Brian, James. *Orchids*. 1890. London.

Oregon Orchid Society. *Your First Orchids and How to Grow Them*. 1955. Revised edition, 1961. 80 pages. Oregon Orchid Society, 1916 S. W. Madison, Portland, Oregon.

Orchid Digest Corporation. *Whys and Wherefores of Orchid Culture*. 1960. Selections from the Orchid Digest, 911 Claire Ave., Corcoran, Calif.

Osorio, L. F. *Colombian Orchids*. 1941. Medellin, Colombia.

Piers, Frank. *Orchids of East Africa*. 1959. 148 pages. Kenya, East Africa.

Reusch, Glad, and Mary Noble. *Corsage Craft*. 1951. 148 pages. D. Van Nostrand Co., Princeton, New Jersey.

Richter, Walter. *Die Shönsten aber Sind Orchideen*. 1958. 280 pages. 64 color plates. Neumann Verlag, Dr. Schmincke-Allee 19, Radebeul 1, Germany.

Riehl, Matthias. *Grosse Liebe zu Orchideen*. 1958. 112 pages. Falken-Verlag Erich Sicher, Schellendorffstrasse 29, Berlin-Dahlem, Germany.

Rittershausen, R. R. C. *Successful Orchid Culture*. 1953. 136 pages. London. Printed in New York by Transatlantic Arts., Inc.

Rolfe, R. A., and C. C. Hurst. *The Orchid Stud Book*. 1909. List and discussion of hybrids to that date. Kew Herbarium, London.

Rotor, Gavino B. *Daylength and Temperature in Relation to Growth and Flowering of Orchids*. 1952. Cornell Experiment Station Bulletin #885, Cornell University, Ithaca, New York.

Rupp, H. M. R. *Orchids of New South Wales*. 1943. National Herbarium, Sydney, Australia.

Sander, David. *Orchids and Their Cultivation*. 1956. Revised edition of earlier book by the Sanders of St. Albans. Blandford Press, London.

Sanders, (C. R., F. K., and L. L.). *Sanders' Orchid Guide*. 1927. Revised edition.

Sanders. *Complete List of Orchid Hybrids.* Compilation of hybrids to 1946, in first volume. Addenda: three volumes, 1946-48, 1949-51, 1952-54. *One Table List of Orchid Hybrids,* 1946-1960. England. Available from American Orchid Society, Inc., Botanical Museum of Harvard Univ., Cambridge, Mass.

Sanders, Fred. *Reichenbachia.* 1888-1894. 4 vols. Plates are now collectors' items.

Schlechter, Rudolph. *Die Orchideen.* 1927. 2nd edition. Berlin.

Schweinfurth, Charles. *Orchids of Peru.* 1958-1961. Fieldiana: Botany, Vol. 30, Nos. 1, 2, 3, 4. 1005 pages. Chicago Natural History Museum, Chicago, Illinois.

Seidenfaden, Gunnar, and Tem Smitinand. *The Orchids of Thailand.* 1959. Two parts of six or seven projected. The Siam Society, Bangkok, Thailand. Order from Munksgaard, 6 Norregade, Copenhagen K., Denmark.

Thomale, Hans. *Die Orchideen.* 1954. 189 pages. Eugen Ulmer, Ludwigsburg, Germany.

University of California. *The U. C. System for Producing Healthy Container-Grown Plants.* 1957. Manual #23. Agricultural Publications, Grinnell Hall, Univ. of California, Berkeley 4, Calif.

Vacherot, Maurice. *Charme et Diversité des Orchidées.* 1957. 68 pages. Paris, France.

———. *Les Orchidées.* 1954. 270 pages. Librairie J. B. Baillière et Fils, 19 rue Hautefeuille, Paris, France.

Veitch and Sons, *Manual of Orchidaceous Plants.* 1887. 2 vols. London.

Veitch, James. *Hortus Veitchii.* 1906. London.

Warner, Robert, and B. S. Williams. *Orchid Album.* 11 vols. 1881-1896. England.

Watkins, John V. *ABC of Orchid Growing.* 1948. 3d edition, 1956. 190 pages. Prentice-Hall, Inc., Englewood Cliffs, New Jersey.

Watson, W., and H. J. Chapman. *Orchids: Their Culture and Management.* 1903. Revised edition. London.

White, E. A. *American Orchid Culture.* 1927. Revised 1942. A. P. DeLaMare Co., Inc., New York.

Williams, B. S. *The Orchid Grower's Manual.* 7th edition revised by Henry Williams. 1894. Reprinted, 1960. Wheldon and Wesley, Ltd., Codicote, Hitchin, England.

Williams, Louis O. *The Orchidaceae of Mexico.* 1952. Four parts, as Vol. 2 of "Cieba." Escuela Agricola Panamericanes, Tegucigalpa, Honduras.

———, and Paul H. Allen. *Flora of Panama: Orchidaceae.* 1946-49. Annals of the Missouri Botanical Garden, St. Louis, Mo.

Willoughby, Adelaide. *Orchids and How To Grow Them.* 1950. 135 pages. Oxford University Press, New York.

Withner, Carl L. *The Orchids: A Scientific Survey.* 1959. 648 pages. The Ronald Press Co., 15 East 26th St., New York.

Wright, J. C. *Cymbidium Hybrids and Awards.* List from 1860 to 1957. 1958. Cymbidium Society, Inc., 7820 Pearle St., Paramount, Calif.

Wright, N. Pelham. *Orquideas de Mexico.* 1958. 120 pages. Bi-lingual text. La Prensa Médica Mexicana, Copilco-Universidad, Mexico 20, D. F.

ORCHID SOCIETIES AND THEIR PUBLICATIONS

It is of benefit to an amateur to belong to an orchid society, a group of growers with whom he can exchange information and share mutual interests, either on a person to person basis or through the pages of a publication. Most of the larger societies publish a periodical which is included with membership fees. In addition to news about orchids and growers, methods and problems, the periodicals offer the advertisements of dealers from whom the amateur can obtain plants and supplies.

American Orchid Society Bulletin. American Orchid Society Inc., Botanical Museum of Harvard University, Cambridge 38, Mass. $7.00, 12 issues a year.

The Orchid Digest. The Orchid Digest Corporation, 911 Claire Ave., Corcoran, Calif. $6.00, 10 issues a year.

The Florida Orchidist. South Florida Orchid Society, Inc., 4 La Gorce Circle, Miami Beach, Fla. $3.00, 6 issues a year.

Na Pua Okika o Hawaii Nei. Honolulu Orchid Society, Inc., 1410 Fort St., Honolulu 17, Hawaii. $4.00, 4 issues a year.

Bulletin of the Pacific Orchid Society of Hawaii. Pacific Orchid Society of Hawaii, P. O. Box 1091, Honolulu 8, Hawaii. $3.00, 4 issues a year.

Cymbidium Society News. The Cymbidium Society of America, Inc., 1820 Pearle St., Paramount, Calif. $8.00, 9 issues a year.

Orchid Society of Southern California Review. Orchid Society of Southern California, 618 North Crescent Drive, Beverly Hills, Calif. $3.00, 12 issues a year.

Oregon Orchid Society Bulletin. Oregon Orchid Society, 1916 S. W. Madison, Portland 5, Oregon. $2.00, 11 mimeographed issues a year.

Bulletin of the National Capitol Orchid Society. National Capitol Orchid Society, Inc., 3604 Thornapple St., Chevy Chase 25, Maryland. $1.00, 4 mimeographed issues a year.

The Orchid Review. The Orchid Review Ltd., 247 Three Bridges Road, Crawley, Sussex, England. About $7.00, 12 issues a year.

Australian Orchid Review. Shepherd and Newman Pty. Ltd., Yurong St., Sydney, Australia. $3.50, 4 issues a year.

New Zealand Orchid Review. The New Zealand Orchid Society, 108 Campbell Rd., Greenlane, New Zealand. £1/6, 4 issues a year.

Philippine Orchid Review. National Museum, Herron and Taft Ave., Manilla, R. P. $3.00, 3 issues a year.

PROCEEDINGS OF WORLD ORCHID
CONFERENCES

Containing all of the papers presented.

Proceedings of the Second World Orchid Conference. 1958. Harvard Univ. Printing Office, Cambridge, Mass. Can be procured from American Orchid Society.

Proceedings of the Third World Orchid Conference. 1960. The Royal Horticultural Society, Vincent Square, London, S. W. 1.

Index

The bold numbers indicate pages on which illustrations appear.